£81-

New Trends and Approaches in Electrochemical Technology

KODANSHA

VCH

Exclusive sales rights for
Japan, Taiwan, Hong Kong, Republic of Korea and People's Republic of China:
  Kodansha Ltd., 12-21, Otowa 2-chome, Bunkyo-ku, Tokyo 112-01 (Japan)
Distribution for
Switzerland: VCH Verlags AG, P. O. Box, CH-4020 Basel (Switzerland)
Great Britain and Ireland: VCH Publishers(UK), Ltd., 8 Wellington Court, Wellington Street, Cambridge,
  CB1 1HZ (Great Britain)
USA and Canada: VCH Publishers, Suite 909, 220 East 23rd Street, New York, NY 10010-4606 (USA)
for all other countries: VCH Verlagsgesellschaft, P. O. Box 101161, D-6940 Weinheim (Federal Republic
  of Germany)

ISBN3-527-28574-1   VCH Verlagsgesellschaft
ISBN1-56081-781-X   VCH Publishers
ISBN4-06-206137-6   Kodansha Ltd.

New Trends and Approaches in Electrochemical Technology

Edited by
Noboru Masuko, Tetsuya Osaka
and Yasuhiro Fukunaka

KODANSHA

Tokyo

VCH

Weinheim · New York
Basel · Cambridge

Noboru Masuko
Professor
Institute of Industrial
Science, University of
Tokyo, Tokyo 106

Tetsuya Osaka
Professor
Department of Applied
Chemistry, Waseda
University, Tokyo 160

Yasuhiro Fukunaka
Research associate
Department of Metallurgy,
Kyoto University,
Kyoto 606

Library of Congress Cataloging-in-Publication Data

New trends and approaches in electrochemical technology/edited by
 Noboru Masuko, Tetsuya Osaka, and Yasuhiro Fukunaka.
     p.   cm.
   Includes index.
   ISBN 1-56081-781-X : $120.00 (est.)
     1, Electrochemistry, Industrial.   I. Masuko, Noboru, 1935— ,
 II. Osaka, Tetsuya, 1945— .   III. Fukunaka, Yasuhiro, 1944— .
 TP257. N49   1993
 660'.297—dc20   92-46440
                                                       CIP

Die Deutsche Bibliothek-CIP-Einheitsaufnahme

New trends and approaches in electrochemical technology/ed.
by Noboru Masuko...–Tokyo: Kodansha; Weinheim; New
York; Cambridge; Basel: VCH, 1993
   ISBN 3-527-28574-1 (VCH, Weinheim...)
   ISBN 1-56081-781-X (VCH, New York...)
   ISBN 4-06-206137-6 (Kodansha)
NE: Masuko, Noboru [Hrsg.]

A CIP catalogue record for this book is available from the British Library.

Published jointly by
Kodansha Ltd., Tokyo (Japan),
VCH Verlagsgesellschaft mbH, Weinheim (FRG) and
VCH Publishers Inc., New York, NY (USA)

Printed in Japan

Editorial Board

List of Contributors*

Asaki, Z.   (215)
Dept. of Metallurgy, Kyoto University, Sakyo-ku, Kyoto 606, Japan

Collins, R.W.   (115)
Materials Research Laboratory and Department of Physics, The Pennsylvania State University, University Park, PA 16802, U.S.A.

Fukunaka, Y.   (215)
Dept. of Metallurgy, Kyoto University, Sakyo-ku, Kyoto 606, Japan

Fujishima, A.   (167)
Department of Synthetic Chemistry, Faculty of Engineering, The University of Tokyo, Bunkyo-ku, Tokyo 113, Japan

Homma, T.   (13)
Department of Applied Chemistry, Waseda University, Shinjuku-ku, Tokyo 169, Japan

Imafuku, M.   (247)
Advanced Materials & Technology Reseach Laboratories, Nippon Steel Corporation, Nakaharaku, Kawasaki 211, Japan

Itaya, K.   (181)
Department of Engineering Science, Faculty of Engineering, Tohoku University, Sendai 980, Japan

Ito, S.   (247)
Steel Research Laboratories, Nippon Steel Corporation Shintomi, Futtsu, Chiba 299-12, Japan

Ito, W.   (247)
Superconductivity Research Laboratories, Kohtoh-ku, Tokyo 135, Japan

Lien, M.   (77)
Corrosion Research Center, Department of Chemical Engineering and Materials Science, University of Minnesota, Minneapolis, MN 55455, U.S.A.

Martin, S.J.   (151)
Microsensor Department 1315, Sandia National Laboratories, Albuquerque, NM 87185, U.S.A.

Masuko, N.   (3)
Institute of Industrial Science, University of Tokyo, Minato-ku, Tokyo 106, Japan

Matz, R.   (235)
Siemens AG, München, Germany

McLarnon, F.   (215)
Energy & Environment Division, Lawrence Berkeley Laboratory, Berkeley, CA 94720, U.S.A.

* Numbers in parentheses refer to the page on which a contributor's paper begins.

Muller, R.H.   (195)
Materials Sciences Division, Lawrence Berkeley Laboratory and Department of Chemical Engineering, University of California, Berkeley, CA 94720, U.S.A.

Nakahara, S.   (39)
AT&T Bell Laboratories, Murray Hill, New Jersey 07974 U.S.A.

Okinaka, Y.   (39)
AT&T Bell Laboratories, Murray Hill, New Jersey 07974, U.S.A.

Osaka, T.   (13)
Department of Applied Chemistry, Waseda University, Shinjuku-ku, Tokyo 169, Japan

Pfuhl, G.   (235)
Freie Universitaet Berlin, Takustrasse 3, 1000 Berlin 33, Germany

Plieth, W.   (235)
Freie Universitaet Berlin, Takustrasse 3, 1000 Berlin 33, Germany

Ricco, A.J.   (151)
Microsensor Department 1315, Sandia National Laboratories, Albuquerque, NM 87185, U.S.A.

Sadoway, Donald R.   (65)
Department of Materials Science and Engineering, Massachusetts Institute of Technology, Cambridge, Massachusetts 02139-4307, U.S.A.

Shimada, H.   (247)
Advanced Materials & Technology Research Laboratories, Nippon Steel Corporation, Nakahara-ku, Kawasaki 211, Japan

Smyrl, W.H.   (77)
Corrosion Research Center, Department of Chemical Engineering and Materials Science, University of Minnesota, Minneapolis, MN 55455, U.S.A.

Tsuda, T.   (3)
Surface Coating Technology Section, Sumitomo Metal Industries Ltd., Minato, Wakayama 640, Japan

Yoshihara, S.   (167)
Department of Applied Chemistry, Faculty of Engineering, Utsunomiya University, Ishii-cho, Utsunomiya, Tochigi 321, Japan

Contents

Contents

Preface

Over the past few decades, the electronics industry has gone through a very rapid evolution towards microscale surface finishing, where high-tailored surface finishing including film formation, etching and ion implantation plays an important role.

Electrochemists and electrochemical engineers have developed many new processes and techniques, including plating and etching with photo-mask technology which permits micron and sub-micron dimensions, plating with extremely tight thickness and composition control, and plating with tightly controlled agitation and current distribution. Nowadays some of the most advanced techniques include electroless plating of a cobalt alloy with a very thin and homogeneous thickness for high-density magnetic disks, electroplating of a permalloy alloy with high compositional control in narrow places for the thin-film magnetic recording head and electroless plating of copper with very reliable connectors for more than 60 multi-layer boards. The demands of the electronics industry thus present a tremendous challenge to electrochemists and electrochemical engineers worldwide.

The International Symposium on Electrochemical Technology in Electronics held in October 1987 in Honolulu, Hawaii, as a part of the 172nd meeting of the Electrochemical Society Inc. was cosponsored by the Electrochemical Society of Japan and the Japan Society of Applied Physics. In September 1989, symposia on Electronic Materials in Electrochemical Technology and Electrochemical Processing for Tailored Materials were held in Kyoto, Japan, as part of the 40th International Society of Electrochemistry (ISE) Meeting. Some of the coorganizers of these symposia decided to publish review books on this field to stimulate further high-tailored research in electrochemical technology.

Hence, the editors selected various topics from these three symposia as the basis for this volume. We hope the topics discussed will contribute to the development of a higher level of electrochemical processing and create new areas of research and development.

January 12, 1993

Noboru Masuko
Tetsuya Osaka
Yasuhiro Fukunaka

I

**New Trends in
Electrochemical Technology**

1

Future Perspectives in Electrochemical Processing and Technology

Noboru MASUKO*[1] and Tetsuaki TSUDA*[2]

*[1] *Institute of Industrial Science, University of Tokyo, 7-22-1 Roppongi, Minato-ku, Tokyo 106, Japan*
*[2] *Surface Coating Technology Section, Sumitomo Metal Industries Ltd., 1850 Minato, Wakayama 640, Japan*

1.1 Introduction

While the subject of thin film growth on tailored materials is not new, its fundamental basis has not been fully established. It is possible to trace work back to AD 752–757 in Japan, when ancient craftsmen applied a gold-amalgam process to a large bronze statue 15 meters high, to plate a uniform gold layer of 5 micrometers thickness. Today, sophisticated wet processes are applied to advanced fabrication of micron size devices. For instance, magnetic thin film heads are fabricated utilizing micro-pattern electroplating technology through polymeric mask (see photo). Nevertheless, the development on electrodeposition processes still seems to remain as a state-of-art technology, and the theory of electrodeposition tends to limp behind the art to some extent. Further progress in basic understanding of electrodeposition processes will be essential for process optimization and, more importantly, for creative designs of innovative electrochemical systems, despite the wide variety of electrodeposition processes and the complicated chemistry involved.

In this short overview, the two key factors affecting the microscopic morphology, on a scale (microns) comparable to the thickness of solid phases on a substrate, of electro-deposited layers are discussed. Morphology of electrodeposit is influenced by various process variables, e.g. substrate materials, current density or cathode potential, electrolyte temperature, concentration of metal ion (*i.e.* major discharged species), other cations, anions, complexing ligands, inhibitors and pH, agitation of electrolyte which occasionally is not well-defined quantitatively, etc. From a phenomenological point of view, the electrodeposit becomes noncoherent, spongy, dendritic and/or powdery in general in the specific current density range, namely, at or below the exchange current density i_0 and at or above the mass-transfer limiting current density i_L. Compact deposits are obtained in a certain current density range in between i_0 and i_L, to the contrary. It should be noted that the aim of this overview is to provide a framework of ideas, in view of both kinetic and mass transfer parameters, which can be used to visualize various industrial electro-deposition processes in perspective.

1.2 Electrodeposition Process

1.2.1 Kinetic and Transport Aspects of Electrodeposition

A relation between flux of electrodeposited species $N_{(j)}$ and partial current density $i_{(j)}$ is represented in Faraday's law equation for each species j:

3

4

5×10^2cm

(a) The gold plated statue of Buddha in Nara

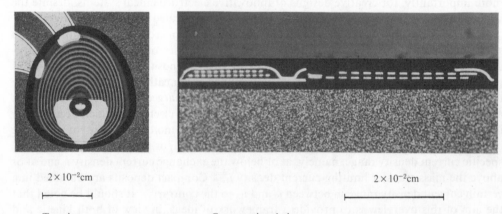

2×10^{-2}cm 2×10^{-2}cm

Top view   Cross-sectional view
(b) Electroplated Cu inductive coils and Ni-Fe (permalloy)
Plated pole pieces of magnetic thin film heads

Photo 1. Tailored materials manufactured by wet-processes in ancient and modern Japan.

$$N_{(j)} = i_{(j)}/Z_j F \tag{1.1}$$

where Z_j is the number of electrons transferred in the cathodic reaction, and F is the Faraday constant.   The average growth rate normal to the substrate of electrodeposited layer in the presence of simultaneous side reactions, such as hydrogen co-evolution, is then given by,

$$R_g = i \varepsilon_F M / ZF\rho \tag{1.2}$$

where R_g denotes the growth rate, i the total plating current density, ε_F plating current efficiency, M molecular weight, ρ the density of electrodeposited metal, and Z the number of electrons consumed or released in an electrochemical reaction.

Thin boundary layer approximation leads to the separation of the electrodeposition process into two parts.   Firstly, the description of the kinetics very close to the cathode in the reaction layer (of the order of 1–10 nm), and secondly the description of the mass transfer of ionic species through the diffusion boundary layer from the bulk of solution to just outside the reaction layer.

Electrodeposition rate may be expressed by the Tafel equation in case $|\beta ZF\eta/RT| \gg 1$

$$i = i_0 \exp\left[-\beta ZF\eta/RT\right] \tag{1.3}$$

or in the rate constant form, assuming first-order rate process,

$$k_R = k_R^0 \exp\left[-\beta ZF\eta/RT\right] \tag{1.4}$$

$$N_{(j)} = k_R C_S \tag{1.5}$$

where i_0 stands for exchange current density, β transfer coefficients, η surface overpotential, R gas constant, T absolute temperature, k_R heterogeneous rate constant, k_R^0 value of k_R at $\eta = 0$, C_S denotes the concentration of metallic ions just outside the double layer.

General equation for the mass transfer of species j in a dilute electrolyte[1] may be written as a summation of the electric migration term, diffusion term and convection term.

$$\tilde{N}_{(j)} = -Z_j U_j FC_j \nabla\Phi - D_j \nabla C_j + C_j \tilde{V} \tag{1.6}$$

Here, the subscript j designates species j, $\tilde{N}_{(j)}$ vector flux of species j, U the mobility, Z the ionic charge, C the concentration, d the diffusion coefficient, and $\tilde{V}$ the fluid velocity vector.   Influence of the ionic migration can be neglected in the presence of excess supporting electrolyte, thus Eq. (1.6) reduces to the convective-diffusion case.[2]   By introducing mass transfer coefficient k_M, the flux being transported through the diffusion layer δ_D towards the outside of the double layer is then

$$N_{(j)} = k_M (C_\infty - C_S) \tag{1.7}$$

and

$$k_M = D_j / \delta_D \tag{1.8}$$

where, C_∞ is the bulk concentration of metallic ions to be electrodeposited.   Substitution of Eqs. (1.7) and (1.8) to Eq. (1.5) gives,

$$C_S = \frac{C_\infty}{1 + (k_R/k_M)} \tag{1.9}$$

$$N_{(j)} = C_\infty \left(\frac{1}{k_R} + \frac{1}{k_M}\right)^{-1} \tag{1.10}$$

Limiting current density can be obtained when $C_S = 0$, for Eq. (1.7), and combining Eq. (1.1),

$$N_L = k_M C_\infty \tag{1.11}$$

or

$$i_L = ZFDC_\infty / \delta_D \tag{1.12}$$

The degree of electrodeposition uniformity is characterized by the Wagner number, which represents the ratio of the electrochemical reaction to the Ohmic resistances.

$$W = \frac{\kappa}{L} \cdot \frac{d\eta}{di} \tag{1.13}$$

or

$$W = \frac{\kappa RT}{Li\beta ZF} \quad \text{for Tafel polarization} \tag{1.14}$$

Here, κ is the conductivity of electrolyte, and L is the characteristic length dimension. The larger the Wagner number, the more negligible the primary current distribution. For microscopic topography of electrodeposits in the length order of microns, where $L \ll 1$, microscopic current distribution would be nearly independent of ohmic potential differences in the electrolyte, corresponding to very large W.

1.2.2   Electrocrystallization of Metal

The driving force of electrocrystallization[3] may be written as,

$$\triangle \mu = kT \ln (1 + \sigma) \tag{1.15}$$

where k is the Boltzmann constant and σ is the supersaturation expressed by

$$\sigma = \exp\left[-\frac{ZF\eta}{RT}\right] - 1 \tag{1.16}$$

On a parallel with the vapor deposition of metals, growth rate R_g and nucleation rate would be increased as supersaturation is increased. Unfortunately, there is so far no comprehensive model of electrocrystallization, relating atomistic scale processes to microscopic morphological development, due to the complexity arising from the presence of metal-solution double layer, adsorbed molecules or ions, desolvation of charged species, etc. As a first approximation, surface overpotential η in Eq. (1.3) may be associated with supersaturation σ in Eq. (1.16), although η is not divided into charge-transfer and crystallization overpotentials as individually defined by Vetter.[4] Thus, we may expect enhanced nucleation and growth, increasing surface overpotential η, which is also an increasing function of the fraction i/i_0, and vice versa.

According to Fischer's classification of polycrystalline deposits,[5] it is known that morphology of electrodeposit varies with surface overpotential η, in the following order:

$$\text{FI} \rightarrow \text{BR} \rightarrow \text{FT} \rightarrow \text{UD} \rightarrow \text{D or P}$$

where FI is "field oriented isolated crystal type," BR is "basis oriented reproduction type," FT is "field oriented texture type," UD is" unoriented dispersion type," and D or P is "dendritic and/or powdery crystal type."

Ibl[6] pointed out that instability of surface roughness could occur for a diffusion-controlled process due to difference in the diffusion boundary layer thickness between peak and recess. Namely, i_{peak} will be greater than i_{recess}, because δ_{peak} is smaller than δ_{recess}, resulting in evolution of dendritic growth at peaks. Popov et al.[7-9] studied the spongy deposit formation, which is caused by mass-transfer limitations under conditions of low nucleation rate (e.g. low overpotential η and small i_L). Pavlovic et al.[29] interpreted copper dendrite formation in terms of the ratio i_L/i_0. Typically, metals with high exchange current

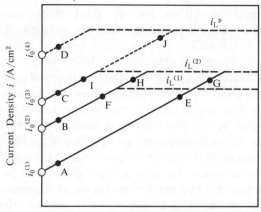

Fig. 1.1 Schematic diagram of operational windows for various electroplating systems.

	Exchange current density		Limiting current density	Process variables window
case I	$[i_0^{(1)}$	,	$i_L^{(1)}]$	Line A–E
case II	$[i_0^{(1)}$	,	$i_L^{(2)}]$	Line A–G
case III	$[i_0^{(2)}$	,	$i_L^{(1)}]$	Line B–F
case IV	$[i_0^{(2)}$	,	$i_L^{(2)}]$	Line B–H
case V	$[i_0^{(3)}$	,	$i_L^{(2)}]$	Line C–I
case VI	$[i_0^{(3)}$	,	$i_L^{p}]$	Line C–I for i
				C–J for η

densities, such as silver or aluminum in chloroaluminate melt, form nodular, dendritic and/ or powdery deposits during electrodeposition more readily than the metals with low exchange current densities, such as nickel or iron.

Along the lines of Winand's diagram,[10] Fig. 1.1 illustrates the conceptual basis for the optimal range of process variables (i, η) to obtain compact deposits, for a given electrodeposition process characterized in terms of the kinetic parameter i_0 and the mass transfer-related parameter i_L. Coherent deposit is obtained when $i_0 < i < i_L$. Ideally, i should be much higher than i_0, and it is also recommended that i not exceed about half of i_L. Wider operational windows are achieved by lowering i_0 and/or increasing i_L values, which can be easily seen by comparing cases I, II, III and IV. Organic additives, such as thiourea, poly acrylamides, polyethylene glycol, etc., are often introduced in the electrolyte in very minute amounts to inhibit the kinetics of electrodeposition by adsorption mechanism in practice. For metal deposition with high exchange current densities close to limiting current densities, such as seen in case V, application of pulse plating may offer the possibility of higher overpotential deposition, as in case VI, for tailoring the quality of deposits.

1.3　Hydrodynamic Effects

As described in the previous section, electrodeposition process is a multi-successive process, involving mass transfer and kinetic reaction at the cathode surface. Mass transfer depends greatly on convection, which is governed by the fluid velocity field in the system.

Well-defined hydrodynamic conditions are of great importance for describing electrodeposition processes. Take a particular case, for example, unstirred, so-called stagnant cells. It is likely for natural convection to be predominant. For a forced convection system, it is indispensable to appropriately define the characteristic length L of a given system, which is occasionally missing from the experimental conditions, in addition to the representative fluid velocity V. Two physical properties, kinematic viscosity ν and diffusion coefficient D are necessary to characterize the mass transfer in electrolytes.

If the actual fluid velocity field is difficult to calculate by solving the Navier-Stokes equation (e.g. many electrodeposition processes are operated in the turbulent flow regime) or even costly and time-consuming to measure in detail due to the complexity of practical electroplating systems, the transport behavior of the system can be described by an empirical function of dimensionless number through the use of dimensional analysis. The three most common dimensionless numbers associated with mass transfer are the Reynolds number Re, the Schmidt number Sc and the Sherwood number Sh:

$$Re = VL/\nu \tag{1.17}$$
$$Sc = \nu/D \tag{1.18}$$
$$Sh = k_M L/D \tag{1.19}$$

For a pipe flow through a rectangular channel with sides a and b, characteristic length L is equal to the hydraulic diameter d_H.

$$d_H = 2ab/(a+b) \tag{1.20}$$

A dimensionless correlation equation can be written in the following form.

$$Sh = A\ Re^p Sc^q \tag{1.21}$$

A large number of mass-transfer correlations are already established and tabulated. Limiting current is measured, utilizing fast Red-Ox couple such as $Fe(CN)_6^{3-}/Fe(CN)_6^{4-}$ system[24] or copper electrodeposition from acidic dilute $CuSO_4$ solution,[26] or using codeposition of tracer ion.[30] k_M is given by Eq. (1.21), and combining the previous equations (1.8) and (1.12), values for δ_D and i_L are obtained for pertinent industrial electrodeposition processes.

Figure 1.2 indicates the significant variations in Re of various hydrodynamic systems in nature and in man-made industrial products. It is interesting to note that an almost linear positive correlation between L and V is discernible, except for the water-jet cutting technology where extreme pressure on the order of 10^3–10^4 (kgf/cm^2) is applied. Re varies considerably, from creeping flow where viscous stresses dominate as in the case of motion of Coliform bacillus and / or the flow in a blood capillary, to huge Re values where inertial stresses are predominant as in the case of the motion of whales and/or the flow inside penstocks at a hydraulic power station. Re for most of the electrodeposition processes appears in the range from 10^2 to 10^5, and a weak negative correlation between L and V is seen, presumably due to the limitations associated with volumetric flow rates.

Unwin and Compton[31] suggested that electrochemical behaviors of a particular process at different electrode systems may be interrelated by simply interchanging the diffusion layer thickness of a rotating disc electrode with the average diffusion layer thickness of a channel electrode assuming first-order kinetics. Along the lines of Unwin, operational windows for various electrodeposition processes with different geometry and hydrodynamic systems are exhibited in Fig. 1.3 in view of estimated δ_D values. In each electroplating system, it is reasonable to expect that the upper limit of operating current

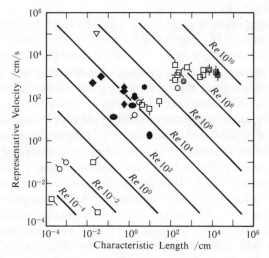

Fig. 1.2 Reynolds number of various hydrodynamic systems.

Moving Bodies: ⊡ Nuclear-powered Submarine[11]; ☐ Torpedo[11]; ☐ whale[13]; ☐ Swordfish[12]; ⊟ Dolphin[12]; ☐ Trout[13]; ☐-Dragonfly nymph (aquatic insect)[14]; ☐ Paramecium[15]; ☐ Coliform bacillus[16]; ☐ Amoeba[17]

Fluid Motion : ▽ Supersonic water-jet cutting[18]; ○ Circulating cooling water pipe for thermal power station[19]; ◎ Penstocks for hydraulic power station[20]; ○ Aorta[21]; ○ vena cava[21]; ○ blood capillary[21]

Electroplating System: ◆ Laser-enhanced jet plating[22,23]; ◆ Impinging jet plating[24]; ◆ Wall-jet plating[25]; ● Paddle-cell plating[26]; ● Continuous steel-strip plating[27]; ● Fountain-cell plating[28]

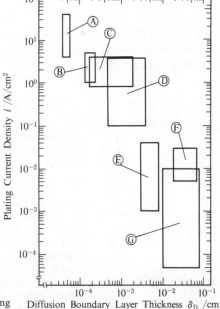

Region - Ⓐ Laser-Enhanced Jet-Plating
Region - Ⓑ Mechanical Brush Plating
Region - Ⓒ Impinging Jet Plating
Region - Ⓓ Continuous Strip Plating
Region - Ⓔ Paddle Cell Plating
Region - Ⓕ Electrolytic Copper Winning and Refining
Region - Ⓖ Electroless Plating

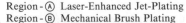

Fig. 1.3 Relation between the rates of electrodeposition and the estimated diffusion boundary layer thickness in a variety of electroplating methods and systems.

density is closely related to its i_L.

Various electroplating systems in Fig. 1.3 will be briefly featured. Extremely high current density operation can be achieved by focusing a laser beam on the localized plating region with an impinging electrolyte jet.[22,23,32] Mechanical abrasion during electroplating, the so-called Norton process and Dalic process, also results in very high current density operation.[33] The impinging jet electroplating is commonly used to enhance mass transfer noticeably, utilizing the uniformly accessible center region or the wall jet peripheral region.[24,25,34] Care should be taken with regard to the distribution of local mass transfer coefficients in the case of multi-jet application.[35] Intermediate current densities were applied in conventional continuous strip electroplating cells; modern plating cells with fluid injection, in contrast, achieved very high current density nearly identical to that of the impinging jet plating system.[27,36,37] High precision plating cells with reciprocating paddles have been extensively used to deposit uniform permalloy composition on pole tips of magnetic thin film heads.[26,38] Electrolytic copper refining and winning are operated with turbulent natural convection.[39] Electroless plating proceeds slowly by the mixed potential mechanism and natural convection mostly dominates the ion transport.[40] Forced convection can be superposed on natural convection, in the case of Ni-P electroless plating of high-density computer hard disks, by rotating the disks immersed in electrolyte.[41]

1.4   Concluding Remarks

Unique capabilities of electrochemical processing technology could meet the desired requirements on the frontier of tailored materials more effectively and precisely if we could further extend our basic understanding of the electrodeposition processes. It is sufficient in this context to stress the crucial role of the two process parameters, namely, i_0 and i_L, controlling the deposit quality. Compact deposit is formed when operational plating current density i is applied within a specific range between i_0 and i_L. Diversified i_L values of various electroplating systems with different geometry and hydrodynamics may be well organized in light of δ_D.

Nomenclature

A	a dimensionless constant
a	a side length of rectangular cross-section (cm)
b	a side length of rectangular cross-section (cm)
C_∞	concentration in bulk of solution (mol/cm^3)
C_S	concentration just outside the double layer (mol/cm^3)
C_j	concentration of species j (mol/cm^3)
D	diffusion coefficient (cm^2/s)
D_j	diffusion coefficient of species j (cm^2/s)
d_H	hydraulic diameter (cm)
F	Faraday's constant, 96487 (C/1mol electrons)
i	current density (A/cm^2)
$i_{(j)}$	partial current density of species j (A/cm^2)
i_{peak}	current density flowing to a peak (A/cm^2)
i_{recess}	current density flowing to a recess (A/cm^2)
i_0	exchange current density (A/cm^2)
i_L	mass transfer-limiting current density (A/cm^2)

j	subscript for chemical species j
k	Boltzmann constant, 1.381×10^{-23} (J/mol K)
k_M	mass transfer coefficient (cm/s)
k_R	heterogeneous rate constant (cm/s)
k_R^0	standard rate constant (cm/s)
L	characteristic length (cm)
M	molecular or atomic weight (g/mol)
$N_{(j)}$	molar flux of chemical species j (mol/cm^2 s)
$\tilde{N}_{(j)}$	molar flux vector of species j (mol/cm^2 s)
N_L	molar flux at limiting current (mol/cm^2 s)
p	a numeric power
q	a numeric power
R	gas constant, 8.314 (J/mol K)
R_g	normal growth rate (cm/s)
T	absolute temperature (K)
U_j	mobility of species j (cm^2 mol/JS)
V	electrolyte velocity (cm/s)
$\tilde{V}$	fluid velocity vector
Z	number of electrons transferred
Z_j	ionic charge of species j
Re	Reynolds number, VL/ν
Sc	Schmidt number, ν/D
Sh	Sherwood number, $k_M L/D$
W	Wagner number
β	cathodic transfer coefficient
δ_D	thickness of diffusion layer (cm)
δ_{peak}	diffusion layer thickness at a peak (cm)
δ_{recess}	diffusion layer thickness at a recess (cm)
ε_F	plating current efficiency, $0 \le \varepsilon_F \le 1$
η	surface overpotential (V)
κ	electrolyte conductivity (Ω^{-1} cm^{-1})
$\triangle \mu$	change in chemical potential (J/mol)
ν	kinematic viscosity (cm^2/s)
ρ	density (g/cm^3)
σ	supersaturation
Φ	potential in solution (V)

REFERENCES

1. J. Newman, *Electrochemical System,* Prentice-Hall (1973).
2. V.G. Levich, *Physicochemical Hydrodynamics,* Prentice-Hall (1962).
3. J.O'M. Bockris and A. Damjanovic, in: *Modern Aspects of Electrochemistry, No. 3,* Chapter 4, Butterworths (1964).
4. K.J. Vetter, *Electrochemical Kinetics,* Academic Press, (1967).
5. H. Fischer, *Electrolytische Abscheidung und Elektrokristallisation von Metallen,* Springer Verlag (1954).
6. N. IbI, in: *Advances in Electrochemistry and Electrochemical Engineering,* Vol. 2, Chapter 3, John Wiley & Sons (1962).
7. K.I. Popov and N.V. Krstajic, *J. Appl. Electrochem.,* **6**, 775 (1983).
8. K.I. Popov, N.V. Krstajic and S.R. Popov, *J. Appl. Electrochem.,* **15**, 151 (1985).
9. K.I. Popov, N.V. Krstajic, S.R. Popov and A.I. Cekerevac, *J. Appl. Electrochem.,* **16**, 771 (1986).
10. R. Winand, *J. Appl. Electrochem.,* **21**, 377 (1991).
11. Yomiuri Shinbunsha (ed.), *Advanced Weapons — Nuclear-Powered Submarines,* Vol. 2, Yomiuri Shinbunsha Press (1986).
12. Japanese Hydrodynamics Soc. (ed.) in: *Handbook of Hydrodynamics,* p. 761, Maruzen (1987).
13. R. Bainbridge, *J. Exp. Biol.,* **37**, 129 (1960).
14. W. Nachtigall, *The Physiology of Insecta,* Vol. 3, p. 381, Academic Press (1974).

15. K. Tawada and H. Miyamoto, *J. Protozool.,* **20**, 289 (1973).
16. K. Maeda, J. Shioi, Y. Imae and F. Ohsawa, *J. Bacteriol.,* **127**, 1030 (1976).
17. *Dictionary of Biology,* 3rd. ed., Iwanami Shoten (1989).
18. S. Matsui *et al., Kawasaki Juko Giho,* **108**, 51 (1991) (in Japanese).
19. *Mitsubishi Juko Giho,* **27**, (5), 480 (1990) (in Japanese).
20. *Mitsubishi Juko Giho,* **27**, (5), 432 (1990) (in Japanese).
21. R.L. Whitmore, in: *Rheology of the Circulation,* p. 18, Pergamon Press (1968).
22. C. Bocking, *Trans. IMF,* **66**, 50 (1988).
23. M.H. Gelchinski, L.T. Romankiw, D.R. Vigliotti and R.J. von Gutfeld, *J. Electrochem. Soc.,* **132**, 2575 (1985).
24. M. Kawasaki, S. Mizumoto and H. Nawafune, *Kinzoku-Hyomengijyutsu* (Metal Surface Finishing-Japan), **33** (6), 299 (1982) (in Japanese).
25. G.R. Schaer and T. Wada, *Plating and Surface Finishing,* **68**, 52 (1981).
26. D.E. Rice, D. Sundstrom, M.F. McEachern, L.A. Klumb and J.B. Talbot, *J. Electrochem. Soc.,* **135**, 2777 (1988).
27. T. Tsuda, A. Shibuya, M. Nishihara, K. Yamada, M. Katoh and K. Yanagi, *Tetsu-to-Hagane,* **72**, 946 (1986) (in Japanese).
28. E.S. Figuli, in: *The Western Electric Engineer,* **18**, (1), 18 (1974).
29. M.G. Pavlovic, S. Kindlova and I. Rousar, *Electrochim Acta,* **37**, 23 (1992).
30. H.M. Wang, S.F. Chen, T.J. O'Keefe, M. Degrez and R. Winand, *J. Appl. Electrochem.,* **19**, 174 (1989).
31. P.R. Unwin and R.G. Compton, *J. Electroanal. Chem.,* **245**, 287 (1988).
32. R.J. von Gutfeld, R.E. Acosta and L.T. Romankiw, *IBM J. Res. Develop.,* **26**, 136 (1982).
33. S. Eisner, *Plating,* **58**, 993 (1971).
34. D.T. Chin and C.H. Tsang, *J. Electrochem. Soc.,* **125**, 1461 (1978).
35. J.O. Nanzer and F. Coeuret, *J. Appl. Electrochem.,* **14**, 627 (1984).
36. T. Tsuda, A. Shibuya, M. Nishihara, F. Terasaki, K. Yamada, M. Katoh and K. Yanagi, *Proc. AES 71st Annual Technical Conference,* C7 (1984).
37. E. Nagel Soepenberg and B.K. Paramanathan, *Proc. Interfinish '88,* p. 179.
38. D.T. Schwartz, B.G. Higgins, P. Stroeve and D. Borowski, *J. Electrochem. Soc.,* **134**, 1639 (1987).
39. R.D. Pehlke, *Unit Processes of Extractive Metallurgy,* Elsevier Publishing Co., (1973).
40. M. Suzuki, N. Sato, K. Kanno and Y. Sato, *J. Electrochem. Soc.,* **129**, 2183 (1982).
41. T. Otaka, K. Araki, T. Nakamura, F. Matsui, M. Saito and S. Hashimoto, *Kinzoku Hyomen Gijyutsu* (Metal Surface Finishing-Japan), **38**, 554 (1987) (in Japanese).

2

High Density Magnetic Recording Media Prepared by Electroless-Plating Method

Tetsuya Osaka and Takayuki Homma

Department of Applied Chemistry, Waseda University, 4-1 Ohkubo 3-chome, Shinjuku-ku, Tokyo 169, Japan

2.1 Introduction

Since first reported in 1957,[1] magnetic disk drives have been the major data storage devices for computer systems, featuring large capacity, high accessability and high reliability.   The recording density of media is constantly increasing; it started with 2 kbits/inch^2 (100 BPI, 20 TPI),[2] and now media with an areal density of 100 Mbits/inch^2 (40–50 kBPI, 2 kTPI) have come into practical use.   Prototype systems of the order of Gbits/inch^2 have been announced.*

The achievement of such extremely high areal recording density is due to constant improvement and innovation of key technology: materials for media and heads, actuation, signal processing, etc.[6]   The recording media, for example, were first realized with iron oxide particles coated with organic binder.   As the demand for higher recording density grows they have been almost superseded by thin metal films which enable the achievement of higher density.   Thin film media were first tried in systems in the 1970s and realized for digital computer systems in 1981.   This film heads were introduced in 1979.

Thin film media are required to be as thin as several tens of nm and even thinner to achieve higher recording density.   Electroless-plating technique, as well as sputtering, has been applied to the fabrication of such media, featuring producibility and capability for uniform formation on substrates.

This article reviews the electroless-plated media for high density magnetic recording, especially those for the perpendicular magnetic recording system, the next generation of ultra-high density recording.

2.2 Magnetic Recording and Technology

When a magnetic field is applied to ferromagnetic materials such as Fe, Co, Ni and their alloys, they are magnetized along the direction of the applied field and retain magnetization after removal of the field.   In order to reduce this residual magnetization, M_r, to zero, the reverse field equal to coercivity, H_c, is required.   In other words, M_r indicates the "strength" of the magnet induced by an external field after the removal of the field, and the

---

* Areal densities of prototype systems were 1 Gbits/inch^2 (135-158 kBPI, 6.4-7.5 kTPI) by IBM in 1990[3] and 2 Gbits/inch^2 (120 kBPI, 17 kTPI) by Hitachi in 1991,[4] both for the longitudinal recording system.   For perpendicular recording system, the possibility of 1 Gbits/inch^2 recording (73 kBPI and 17 kTPI, or 100 kBPI and 10 kTPI) has been suggested by Fujitsu in 1991.[5]

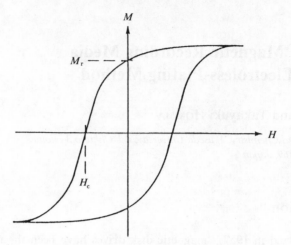

Fig. 2.1 Representative *MH* loop for a ferromagnetic material.

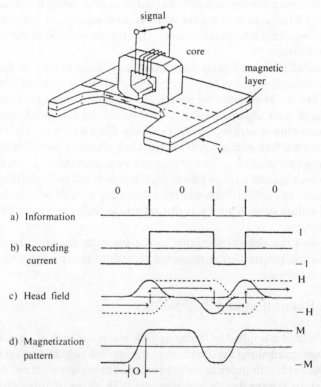

Fig. 2.2 A model for digital recording.[10]

H_c expresses the degree to which the magnet keeps its magnetization against the "demagnetizing" field.   The curve plotting the magnetization, M, against the applied field, H, is called hysteresis (or *MH*) loop.   Fig. 2.1 shows a representative *MH* loop of ferromagnetic material.   The physics of ferromagnetic materials is described in the literature.[7]

Magnetic recording,[8] first proposed by Smith in 1888 and experimentally confirmed by Poulsen in 1893,[9] is the most successful application of the hysteresis phenomenon of ferromagnetic materials.   Fig. 2.2 is an illustration of digital magnetic recording where the information, transduced into the change in electrical signal, is applied to a magnetic head, a kind of electromagnet, then transduced into the medium through a magnetic field.   As the head scans the recording medium, such as tape and disk consisting of ferromagnetic material, the information is finally stored in the medium as a change in magnitude and direction of residual magnetization.   The information is reproduced by reversing the process.

The combination of a ring-type magnetic head with high efficiency and a longitudinally magnetized medium has been the "standard" of magnetic recording systems, and continues to achieve higher recording density.   However, as will be described below, this system has a limit in achieving further higher recording density.   To overcome this limit, the perpendicular recording system, which utilizes the medium magnetized along a direction perpendicular to the film, was proposed by Iwasaki et al.[11] and is currently under investigation by a number of researchers.

2.3   Electroless-Plated Media for Longitudinal Recording

2.3.1   History of Electroless-Plated Longitudinal Media
Metal electroless deposition was found by Brenner and Riddell in 1946.[12]   The application of electroless Co film to magnetic recording media was first proposed by Fisher et al. in 1962[13] and a large number of studies were done during the 1960s, focusing on the correlation between plating conditions and film properties.[14-27]   At the same time, electrodeposited Co films were also studied extensively.[28-35]   However, electroless-plating processes are advantageous for mass production of large-scale thin film since no external power supply is required, enabling films to be deposited uniformly regardless of substrate shape.

The plated films were applied to magnetic drums and analog disks in the 1970s and to the high density storage system of PATTY by NTT in 1981.[36]   Electroless CoNiP media, as well as sputtered γ-Fe_2O_3 media, were utilized.   Subsequently, various plated disk systems have been shipped and precision production technology established.[37]

The key technologies for achieving the high reliability production of electroless-plated media are: 1) plating bath chemistry,[38] 2) substrate preparation,[39] 3) overcoating and lubrication,[40,41] and 4) process control.[42]   The development of electroless-plated media is reviewed in the literature.[43-51]

2.3.2   Higher Recording Density
In the longitudinal recording, the recorded bits of magnetization vector are opposite each neighbor, and there appears a "transition area" between these domains of opposite magnetization.   In order to achieve high recording density, decreasing the width of the transition area and increasing S/N ratio, i.e., increasing the output voltage and decreasing media noise, are required.   The width of transition area, x, and the output voltage, E, are expressed as follows[52,53]:

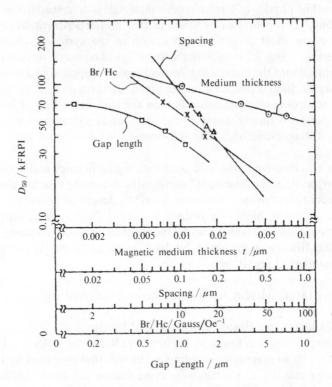

Fig. 2.3 Effects of head/disk parameters on D_{50} values.[54]

$$x \propto (M_r \delta / H_c)^{1/2}, \quad E \propto (M_r \delta H_c)^{1/2}$$

where δ is the medium thickness.   They depend on various parameters of both medium and head and their combinations.

The effect of these parameters on the D_{50} values of plated media was experimentally confirmed by Tanaka et al.[54]   Fig. 2.3 summarizes the results, indicating that increasing H_c and decreasing medium thickness, head gap length and head-medium spacing are significant in achieving higher recording density.   To achieve maximum results, the process parameters described above must be improved.

At the same time, in order to decrease medium noise, the isolation of each crystallite of the medium i.e., each domain, is essential, because the main source of noise in such media arises from the zig-zag domain patterns in the magnetization transition regions caused by the exchange coupling of the domains.[55,56]   It is known that in electroless-plated films the codeposition of the elements which are barely soluble in the matrix causes segregation, resulting in fine-particularization of the film microstructure.   In this approach, it was found that the addition of Zn to the Co alloy system is very effective for obtaining such a fine-particulated structure, resulting in lower noise ratio and higher H_c.[57-60]

The thickness of practical media is typically 50 nm, thus the conditions of substrate surface and initial deposition are extremely important in such media.[61-64]   The effect of substrate surface conditions on the deposited media was investigated and an attempt at controlling the medium properties was made by varying the pretreatment process of the substrate surface.[63]

Most rigid disk surfaces are circumferentially texturized, mainly to reduce the contact area between head and disk.　Recently such texturizing was found to induce magnetic anisotropy of the films along the circumferential direction.[65-70]　Such a texturizing effect is distinguishable in sputtering media, but a similar effect on electroless-plated media is also reported: the grains deposited along the texturized direction,[68] resulting in decreased media noise,[69] and in a 5-10% increase in output voltage.[70]

2.4　Electroless-Plated Media for Perpendicular Recording

2.4.1　Perpendicular Magnetic Recording System

As described above, higher recording density can be achieved by decreasing medium thickness and by increasing H_c in the case of the longitudinal recording system.　However, the former also decreases the total magnetization of the medium and the latter causes saturation of the recording head.　Moreover, it was observed that the reproduced voltage in the higher recording density region decreases rapidly with an increase in recording current.[71]　Iwasaki et al. confirmed that such a decrease in reproduced voltage is due to the formation of a circular mode of magnetization.[72]　They also found that such a circular mode of magnetization could be transformed to a perpendicular mode, recovering the reproduced voltage, and finally, they proposed a perpendicular recording system[11] (see Fig. 2.4).　Since that time, a number of researchers have worked to achieve this recording system.[73-75]

The perpendicular recording is free from the effect of the demagnetizing field, H_d, which forms the transition area in longitudinal media; thus the recording method is suitable for achieving ultra-high recording density, as has been confirmed both theoretically and experimentally.[75]　The demerits of the system are the requirements of very narrow spacing

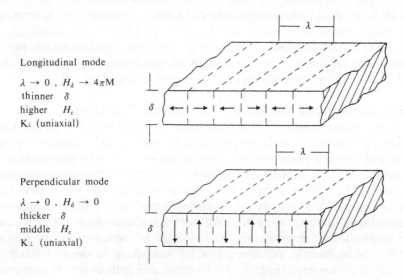

Longitudinal mode

$\lambda \rightarrow 0$, $H_d \rightarrow 4\pi M$
thinner　δ
higher　H_c
$K_\perp$ (uniaxial)

Perpendicular mode

$\lambda \rightarrow 0$, $H_d \rightarrow 0$
thicker　δ
middle　H_c
$K_\perp$ (uniaxial)

Fig. 2.4 Features of fundamental magnetization modes.[73]

and lower output voltage.   However, the latter can be avoided by applying a soft magnetic underlayer due to the formation of horseshoe mode magnetization in combination with a single-pole type (SPT) head.[76,77]

2.4.2   Perpendicular Magnetic Recording Media

In the perpendicular magnetic recording system, the medium must possess a perpendicular magnetic anisotropy, *i.e.,* the medium must be easily magnetized along the direction perpendicular to the film plane.   In order to achieve perpendicular magnetic anisotropy, magnetocrystalline anisotropy and micro-shape anisotropy are utilized.   The former and the latter anisotropies are, for example, caused by the uniaxial anisotropy of Co hcp ferromagnetic crystal and the compositional gradient of segregated structure, respectively.

Some media such as Ba ferrite[78] media achieve perpendicular anisotropy mainly by magnetocrystalline anisotropy, while others achieve it by shape anisotropy, e.g., FeTi[79] and partially oxidized Fe films.[80]   The media for perpendicular recording are reviewed in the literature.[81]   Cobalt-chromium films, the most conventional for perpendicular magnetic recording media, achieve perpendicular anisotropy by the aid of both magnetocrystalline and shape anisotropies.[82,83]   They consist of fine columnar structures of *c*-axis perpendicularly oriented hcp crystallite, and have a segregated microstructure,[84-88] which causes the isolation of ferromagnetic crystallites.   Magnetocrystalline and shape anisotropies are produced by such structures.

Much of the research on media is performed by dry processes such as sputtering and evaporation.   Media prepared by wet processes such as coating, electroplating or electroless-plating are also being investigated.

Before the perpendicular recording was proposed, some efforts were made to use a vertical magnetization mode for magnetic recording, using electrochemically deposited media such as electrodeposited CoNiP[89] and Co-electrodeposited alumite films.[90-92]   The electrochemically deposited medium for the perpendicular recording was first proposed by Chen, using electrodeposited Co film with a "cellular-like" columnar structure.[93,94] Horkans *et al.* proposed electrodeposited CoMnP as a medium.[95]   Electroless-plated media were first proposed by Osaka and Kasai[96,97] and have been investigated by their group, as will be described below.   Takano *et al.* also investigated electroless-plated media for perpendicular recording.[98,99]   Some of the literature also reviews electrochemically deposited films for perpendicular magnetic recording media.[100-108]

2.4.3   Electroless-Plated Media for Perpendicular Recording

The research on electroless-plated perpendicular magnetic recording media started with CoWP films,[96,97] with the *c*-axis perpendicularly oriented hcp structure.   The crystal orientation and magnetic properties were continuously improved by adding other elements such as Mn to the alloy systems, and CoMnP, CoNiMnP films were developed.[109-111] Codeposition of Mn induced strong *c*-axis orientation of hcp Co, which resulted in large anisotropy energy, H_k, and coercivity, H_c, although the Mn content in deposits was very small in these films.   By employing the CoNiMnP rigid disk medium, it was first confirmed that the perpendicular magnetic recording could be achieved by electroless-plated media.[109-111]   Subsequently, the element of Re was added to the CoNiMnP, and the CoNiReMnP films were developed.[112-117]   Codeposition of Re lowers M_s and thus reduces the demagnetizing field $4\pi M_s$ without destroying the crystal structure of the *c*-axis

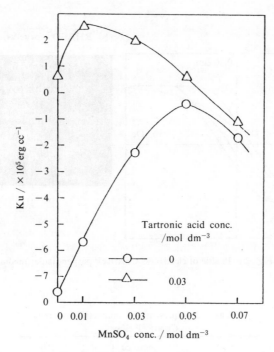

Fig. 2.5 Effect of $MnSO_4$ concentration on Ku value of Co alloy films at 0 or 0.03 mol dm^{-3} tartronic acid concentration.

TABLE 2.1 Basic bath composition and operating conditions of CoNiReP films

Chemical		Concentration (mol·dm^{-3})
$NaH_2PO_2 \cdot H_2O$	(sodium hypophosphite)	0.20
$(NH_4)_2SO_4$	(ammonium sulfate)	0.50
$CH_2(COONa)_2 \cdot H_2O$	(sodium malonate)	0.75
$C_2H_2(OH)_2(COONa)_2 \cdot 2H_2O$	(sodium tartrate)	0.20
$CH(OH)(COOH)_2$	(tartronic acid)	0.05
$CoSO_4 \cdot 7H_2O$	(cobalt sulfate)	0.06
$NiSO_4 \cdot 6H_2O$	(nickel sulfate)	0.08
NH_4ReO_4	(ammonium perrhenate)	0.003

Bath temperature	80°C
pH (adjusted with NH_4OH)	8.7

perpendicularly oriented hcp crystallite. The codeposition mechanism of Mn and Re has not been clarified yet; however, it has been suggested that the complextant plays an important role in controlling the codeposition of Mn or Re and the film properties.[118] Addition of tartronic acid as a mixed-complextant causes perpendicular orientation of the c-axis of hcp Co instead of Mn codeposition, as shown in Fig. 2.5. Thus, CoNiReP films without Mn addition were developed and demonstrated excellent properties.[119-125] The representative bath composition and operating conditions of the CoNiReP films are shown in Table 2.1.

a) MH loops.   b) RHEED patterns.

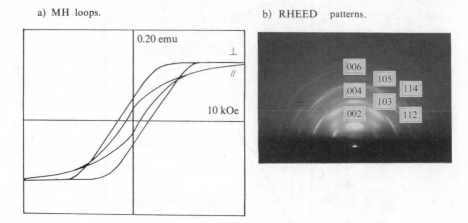

Fig. 2.6 Profile of electroless CoNiReP perpendicular media.

TABLE 2.2 Representative magnetic properties
of CoNiReP films

M_s	[emu cc^{-1}]	250
H_k	[kOe]	5.2
$H_{c(\perp)}$	[kOe]	1.3
$H_{c(/\!/)}$	[kOe]	0.6
Ku	[$\times 10^5$ erg cc^{-1}]	2.5

Figure 2.6 and Table 2.2 show a representative profile of the CoNiReP films. The perpendicular MH loop shows good squareness, and the RHEED pattern indicates that the film consists of hcp structure of perpendicularly oriented c-axis. The film shows positive anisotropy energy, K_u, indicating that the film has perpendicular magnetic anisotropy. It was also clarified that the magnetic properties of the CoNiReP film could be widely controlled by various factors, such as plating bath factors,[122,123] catalyzing processes[125] and underlayer conditions.[126,127]

Rigid and flexible media have been fabricated using the CoNiReP films. It was found that the addition of a very thin underlayer is effective for improving the medium properties.[128] An electroless NiP underlayer improves the crystallinity of the CoNiReP recording layer, as shown in Fig. 2.7. The electroless NiWP underlayer with quasi-soft magnetic properties, deposited from the bath shown in Table 2.3, also improves the crystal properties of the CoNiReP layer, resulting in excellent characteristics.[127] The recording characteristics of the media are described further on.

Based on the CoNiReP, further work was carried out to simplify the bath systems and alloy systems. Using this approach, various perpendicular anisotropy films were obtained,[119-132] and the CoNiP ternary alloy films for perpendicular magnetic recording media were obtained. Detailed characteristics of the CoNiP media are described below.

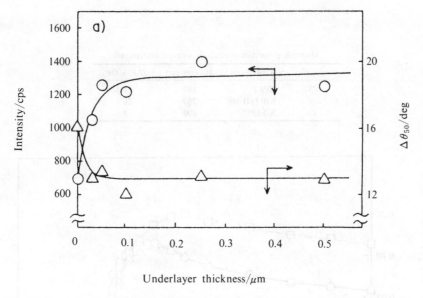

Fig. 2.7 Dependence of NiP (pH6) underlayer thickness on $I_{(002)}$ of electroless CoNiReP film.

TABLE 2.3 Basic bath composition and operating conditions of NiWP films

Chemical		Concentration (mol·dm^{-3})
NaH$_2$PO$_2$·H$_2$O	(sodium hypophosphite)	0.066
(NH$_4$)$_2$SO$_4$	(ammonium sulfate)	0.227
C$_3$H$_4$(OH)(COONa)$_3$·2H$_2$O	(trisodium citrate)	0.068
NiSO$_4$·6H$_2$O	(nickel sulfate)	0.027
Na$_2$WO$_4$·2H$_2$O	(sodium tangustate)	0.106

Bath temperature	90°C
pH (adjusted with NH$_4$OH)	9.0

2.5 Recording and Microstructural Characteristics of Electroless CoNiReP Perpendicular Media

2.5.1 Recording Characteristics

The recording characteristics of electroless-plated perpendicular media were investigated in combination with various underlayers, using ring-type heads. The recording characteristics of CoNiReP perpendicular media are seriously influenced by underlayer conditions; two kinds of effects of underlayers on the recording characteristics have been confirmed,[126,128] as seen in Fig. 2.8, where the CoNiReP media are measured with three underlayers: quasi-soft magnetic NiP (pH 10) and NiWP layers and soft magnetic NiFeP layer. One is the so-designated "double-layered (DL) effect," which enhances reproduced voltage due to the soft magnetic characteristics of the underlayer (seen in the medium with

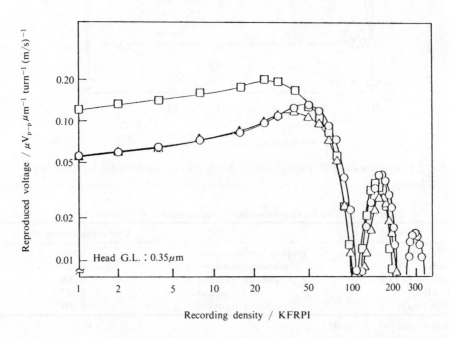

Magnetic properties of electroless-plated underlayers

	Underlayer	M_s/emu cc^{-1}	$H_c(/\!/)$/Oe
—○—,	NiWP	180	16
—△—,	NiP (pH 10)	200	20
—□—,	NiFeP	400	8

Fig. 2.8 Dependence of reproduced voltage on recording density for various double-layered media.

the NiFeP underlayer). The other is "underlayer (UL) effect," which improves the crystallinity of the recording layer deposited on the underlayer (seen in the medium with the NiWP underlayer).

The electroless NiWP underlayer,[99,133] in particular, provides both effects for the CoNiReP recording layer, resulting in excellent recording characteristics (D_{50}=172 kFRPI) for flexible disk media with a Sendust head,[127] as shown in Fig. 2.9. The rigid disk media also demonstrated high potentials: the D_{50} value of 134 kFRPI was achieved with CoNiReP/NiFeP DL media using a MIG (metal-in-gap) head.[131] Enhancement of reproduced voltage has also been reported with a very thin quasi-soft magnetic underlayer whose coercivity is 50 Oe or more.[126,127] Such a phenomenon was also reported in the case of CoCr[134] and FeCoO[135] composite media with quasi-soft magnetic underlayers.

Recently another enhancement effect of the reproduced voltage was reported. It appears with DL media whose underlayer coercivity is even higher than the "quasi-soft

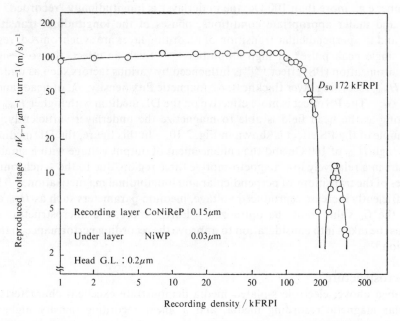

Fig. 2.9 Dependence of reproduced voltage on recording density for CoNiReP/NiWP double-layered medium.

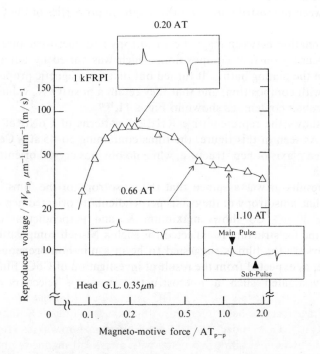

Fig. 2.10 Dependence of reproduced voltage on MMF for CoNiReP/NiFeP double-layered medium at 1 kFRPI and schematic models of waveform at various MMF.

magnetic" one, e.g., more than 100 Oe; the underlayer is longitudinally "recorded" by the head-field, and under appropriate conditions, phases of the longitudinal transition of underlayer and the perpendicular transition of recording layer are synchronized, resulting in a sharp single peak pulse* of high amplitude.[136]   Such an effect, the so-designated "phase synchronization (PS) effect,[136]" is influenced by various factors such as underlayer coercivity, $H_{c(u)}$, recording layer thickness, δ_p, magnetic flux density, B_s, of head, and head gap length, G_L.   The PS effect is more effective on the DL medium with higher $H_{c(u)}$ and δ_p values as long as the head field is able to magnetize the underlayer sufficiently.[137]   A typical example of the PS effect is shown in Fig. 2.10.   In this figure, the DL medium has a relatively high $H_{c(u)}$ of 160 Oe and the enhancement of output voltage with a single peak pulse appears in a relatively low magneto-motive force region, due to the synchronization of the phases of the transitions of perpendicular and longitudinal magnetization.   Thus, in order to sufficiently increase reproduced voltage, medium parameters such as $H_{c(u)}$ and δ_p, which suit the G_L value, must be optimized.   Furthermore, the microstructure of the medium must be taken into consideration to improve the recording performance in the high density region.[138]

2.5.2   Microstructure

As described above, electroless-plated media demonstrate excellent characteristics as perpendicular magnetic recording media, and a linear recording density higher than 300 kBPI has been achieved.[127]   In such a high recording density state, the magnetic properties of the media are directly influenced by their microstructures.   In this section, correlation between microstructures and the magnetic properties of the CoNiReP films is described.

First, the correlation between magnetic anisotropy and microstructure of the films was investigated, focusing on film composition, which was varied by adjusting the $CoSO_4$ concentration in the plating bath.   It turned out that the magnetic properties of the films change widely with composition, and that they retain a positive K_u value in the region of about 25–35% cobalt content, as shown in Fig. 2.11.[139]

Figure 2.12 shows the representative RHEED patterns of CoNiReP of various film composition.   As seen in this figure, the films containing 30–45 at% Co have a perpendicularly oriented c-axis of hcp structure, while no obvious crystal orientation is observed in the other area.

From these results, it was assumed that the anisotropy of the films is mainly due to magnetocrystalline anisotropy of the c-axis perpendicularly oriented hcp crystallite.   The film containing 30 at% Co shows maximum K_u and perpendicular coercivity, $H_{c(\perp)}$, values.   Since the fcc structure is expected for such a Ni-rich composition in the case of bulk CoNi alloys,[140] the film is suggested to be in a non-homogeneous condition, e.g. segregated state, as expected from the result of investigation of CoCr films.[84–88]

Next we investigated such a microstructure using a selective chemical-etching

---

* Usually a di-pulse shaped waveform is observed for the reproduced signal of perpendicular recording in combination with a ring-type head.[73]

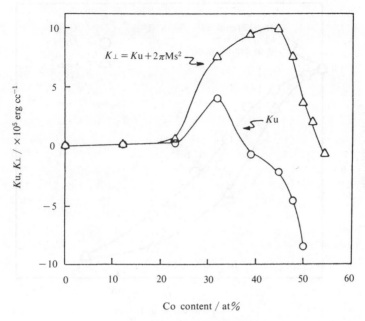

Fig. 2.11. Effect of Co content on Ku and $K_\perp$ of CoNiReP films.

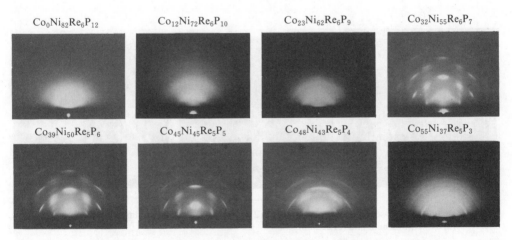

Fig. 2.12 Effect of Co content on RHEED patterns of CoNiReP films.   The composition of the films are shown
in at%.

method.[141]   Specimen films were immersed in $CH_3OH–HNO_3$–aqueous etchant at room
temperature.   The results of compositional analysis of the etched CoNiReP film indicated
that among four elements, Co was preferentially dissolved with the etching treatment.   Fig.
2.13 shows the changing behavior in M_s and the XRD peak intensity of Co(002) plane,
$I_{(002)}$, of the etched films as a function of the residual film weight, w.   Both values decrease

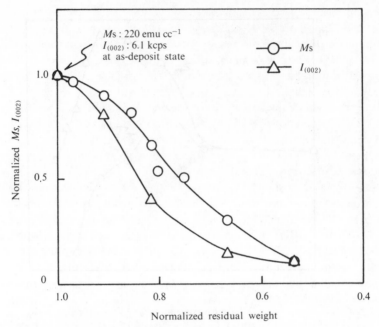

Fig. 2.13 Change in Ms and $I_{(002)}$ of the chemically-etched $Co_{32}Ni_{55}Re_6P_7$ film.

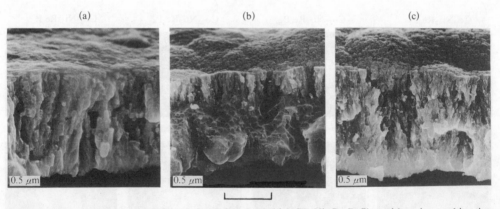

Fig. 2.14 Change in cross-sectional morphology of the 2 µm thick $Co_{32}Ni_{55}Re_6P_7$ films with various etching time;
(a) 0 min, (b) 5 min, and (c) 20 min.

with a decrease in w value to about one-tenth when w value is reduced to about one-half.   These results suggest that the Co-rich ferromagnetic region with high crystallinity is preferentially dissolved with the etching treatment.

Figure 2.14 shows the change in surface and cross-sectional morphology of the chemically-etched 2-µm thick film observed by high-resolution SEM.   As shown in Figs. 2.14(b) and 2.14(c), the rough structures with some 20-nm size grains are revealed with progression of the etching process.   Also, in the TEM bright field images of the 50-nm thick films, bright stripes of several nm width appeared on the inside of the grains with progression of the etching process.[141]   These are considered to be traces of the Co-rich segregated region described above, and such parts are isolated with the nonmagnetic region which is not dissolved with the treatment.   It is assumed that such structures produce the magnetic properties suitable for the perpendicular magnetic recording medium, *i.e.*, rotational mechanism of magnetization reversal and perpendicular magnetic anisotropy.[139]

It is important to evaluate the heat-change behavior of such film in the nonequilibrium state, because device fabrication processes usually have various heat-treatment.   Also, it is possible to predict the microstructure of the as-deposited films by analyzing their heat-change behavior.   From this point of view, the effect of heat treatment on magnetic and structural properties of electroless-plated CoNiReP films was investigated to clarify the microstructure of the as-deposited films as well as to evaluate their thermal stability.[142]

Due to the difference in composition, magnetic properties of the films were found to differ with heat treatment.   The films with high crystallinity showed larger changes in magnetic properties.   The $Co_{32}Ni_{55}Re_6P_7$ (at%) film with the largest perpendicular magnetic anisotropy retained its positive anisotropy energy with treatment up to 500°C, as shown in Fig. 2.15.   The *c*-axis perpendicularly oriented hcp structure of this film was also maintained with treatment up to 500°C.   However, heat treatment at 600°C altered the crystal structure of the films to the fcc structure without crystal orientation, causing a sharp

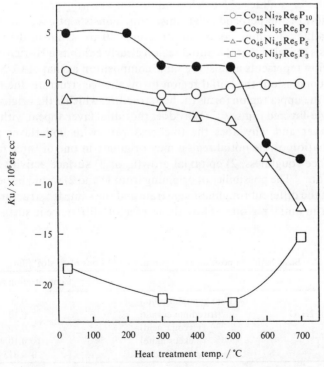

Fig. 2.15 Effect of heat-treatment temperature on *Ku* values of CoNiReP films of varied composition; $Co_{12}Ni_{72}Re_6P_{10}$, (A), $Co_{32}Ni_{55}Re_6P_7$, (B), $Co_{45}Ni_{45}Re_5P_5$, (C), and $Co_{55}Ni_{37}Re_5P_3$, (D).

change in the magnetic properties of the films.　Since the formation of Ni_3P compound was also detected with treatment higher than $500\,^\circ C$, it is assumed that in the as-deposited films the c-axis perpendicularly oriented hcp crystallites with high crystallinity segregate in the amorphous NiP phase.

2.6　Recent Topics of Electroless-Plated Media

2.6.1　CoNiReP/NiMoP Double-Layered Media

As described above, the authors extensively investigated the recording characteristics of electroless CoNiReP perpendicular recording media, especially in combination with various electroless-plated underlayers.　In these studies, we found that the double-layered (DL) medium with an electroless NiMoP underlayer[143-145] (almost nonmagnetic) demonstrated further larger reproduced voltage than that of the DL medium with amorphous electroless NiP underlayer (nonmagnetic) which is conventionally used for rigid disk substrates.[146-148]　The analysis of their magnetic properties clarified that the CoNiReP film on the NiMoP underlayer, deposited in the bath shown in Table 2.4, has a low H_c region at its initial deposition stage, as shown in Fig. 2.16.[146]　Such an initial region acted as a quasi-soft magnetic underlayer, enhancing the reproduced voltage.　Moreover, the thickness of such a initial region was found to be controllable by varying the Na_2MoO_4 concentration in the plating bath for the NiMoP underlayer film, as shown in Fig. 2.17.

Microstructural analysis of the media[149] indicated that the initial region consists of randomly oriented fcc crystallites of Ni-rich composition, showing granular condition, and that the upper region of the perpendicular anisotropy consists of c-axis perpendicularly oriented hcp crystallites, forming columnar structures 20 to 30 nm in diameter.　Also, precise EDX analysis revealed that the initial region clearly exhibits a Ni-rich composition, while the upper region represents almost the same composition as that of CoNiReP single-layered films.　In conclusion, the initial region forms the fcc structure due to its Ni-rich composition, while the upper region forms the hcp structure, which is the original crystalline structure of the single-layered films.[139]　Why does the initial layer appear with the addition of NiMoP underlayer and why does the thickness vary with underlayer plating conditions?　The formation of the initial region may originate in one of three factors of the underlayer: 1) surface roughness, 2) epitaxial growth, or 3) surface activity for Co alloy electroless-deposition.　The possibility of origining from 1) and 2) would be negative when it is considered that the different roughness substrate and the same fcc structure underlayer never produce such an initial region.　Thus, the last factor, difference in surface activity, is

TABLE 2.4　Basic bath composition and operating conditions of NiMoP films

Chemical		Concentration (mol·dm⁻³)
$NaH_2PO_2 \cdot H_2O$	(sodium hypophosphite)	0.20
$C_3H_4(OH)(COONa)_3 \cdot 2H_2O$	(trisodium citrate)	0.10
$HOCH_2COOH$	(glycollic acid)	0.20
$NiSO_4 \cdot 6H_2O$	(nickel sulfate)	0.10
$Na_2MoO_4 \cdot 2H_2O$	(sodium molybdate)	0–0.015

Bath temperature　　　　$80\,^\circ C$
pH (adjusted with NH_4OH)　9.2

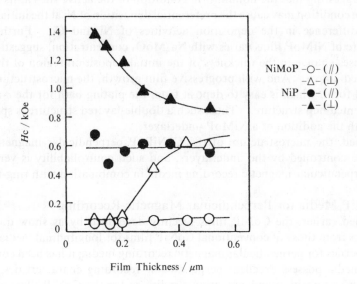

Fig. 2.16 Effect of film thickness on H_c of CoNiReP/NiP and CoNiReP/NiMoP double-layered media.

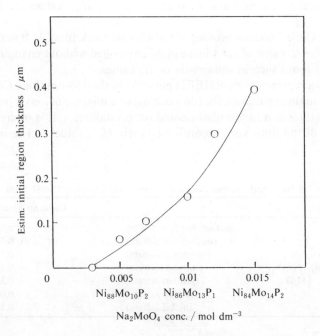

Fig. 2.17 Effect of Na$_2$MoO$_4$ concentration in NiMoP bath on the initial region thickness of the CoNiReP layer.

the most likely to produce the initial region described.

NiMoP films have a segregated structure consisting of fine crystallites and amorphous regions,[145] suggesting that the nonuniform condition of the active sites at its surface, and such a surface condition may cause the preferential deposition of Ni at the initial deposition, due to the difference in the deposition activities of Ni and Co.   Furthermore, the microstructure of NiMoP films varies with Na_2MoO_4 concentration, suggesting that such variation causes change in the thickness of the initial deposition region of the CoNiReP layer described above.   And with progressive film growth, the microstructures return to their original form, which is easy to deposit from the plating bath for the c-axis perpendicularly oriented hcp structure.   Thus, such a double-layered structure is spontaneously produced with the addition of a NiMoP underlayer.

As described, the microstructure of the CoNiReP perpendicular magnetic recording media can be controlled by the underlayers, and such controllability is very useful for designing perpendicular magnetic recording media in combination with ring-type heads.

2.6.2   CoNiP Media for Perpendicular Magnetic Recording

As described earlier, the CoNiP films recently developed by us show quite different characteristics from those of conventional CoNiP films for longitudinal media and exhibit suitable properties for perpendicular magnetic recording media; it has been confirmed that the CoNiP media possess excellent perpendicular recording characteristics.[132]   Representative bath composition and operating conditions for the CoNiP films are shown in Table 2.5.   The H_c of the CoNiP films can be controlled widely up to 1500 Oe only by adjusting some plating bath factors.[150]   In order to clarify such features of the films, the microstructure of electroless CoNiP films with various $H_{c(\perp)}$ values was investigated, focusing on three representative films, A, B and C, whose $H_{c(\perp)}$ values are 500, 1000 and 1500, respectively.[151]

Figure 2.18 and Table 2.6 show profiles of the 150-nm thick films A, B and C.   As seen in Fig. 2.18, only the H_c value of the films can be controlled without changing the general features of the MH loops such as squareness or H_k values.

Figure 2.19 shows representative RHEED patterns of the 150-nm thick CoNiP films A, B and C.   As seen in these patterns, the films consist of a mixture of c-axis perpendicularly oriented hcp crystallites and randomly oriented fcc crystallites.   It is interesting that the crystal conditions of the films vary according to their $H_{c(\perp)}$ values.   The increase in the

TABLE 2.5 Basic bath composition and operating conditions of CoNiP films

Chemical		Concentration $(mol \cdot dm^{-3})$
$NaH_2PO_2 \cdot H_2O$	(sodium hypophosphite)	0.20
$(NH_4)_2SO_4$	(ammonium sulfate)	0.50
$CH_2(COONa)_2 \cdot H_2O$	(sodium malonate)	0.75
$C_2H_2(OH)_2(COONa)_2 \cdot 2H_2O$	(sodium tartrate)	0.20
$C_2H_3OH(COONa)_2 \cdot \frac{1}{2}H_2O$	(sodium malate)	0.375
$CoSO_4 \cdot 7H_2O$	(cobalt sulfate)	0.06
$NiSO_4 \cdot 6H_2O$	(nickel sulfate)	0.168

Bath temperature   80° C
pH (adjusted with NH_4OH)   9.5

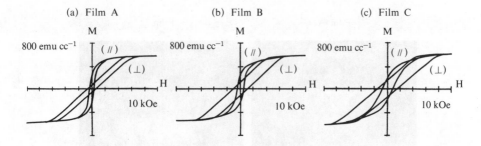

Fig. 2.18 Profile of CoNiP films A, B and C.

TABLE 2.6 Profiles of 150-nm thick CoNiP films A, B and C

		film A	film B	film C
Composition	[at%]	$Co_{31}Ni_{62}P_7$	$Co_{29}Ni_{65}P_6$	$Co_{39}Ni_{55}P_6$
M_s	[emu cc^{-1}]	550	550	600
$H_{c(\perp)}$	[kOe]	0.5	1.0	1.5
$H_{c(//)}$	[kOe]	0.23	0.45	0.70
Ku	[×10^6 erg cc^{-1}]	−1.1	−0.74	−0.48
$K_\perp$[†]	[×10^6 erg cc^{-1}]	0.48	0.83	1.8

† $K_\perp = Ku + 2\pi M_s^2$

ratio of the hcp region in the films makes the $H_{c(\perp)}$ value higher; film A with lower H_c, 500 Oe, consists of randomly oriented fcc structures and film C with higher H_c, 1500 Oe, mainly consists of c-axis perpendicularly oriented hcp crystallites. The pattern of film B with medium H_c, 1000 Oe, represents a mixture of these two kinds of crystallites. Moreover, as shown in Table 2.6, the intrinsic magnetic anisotropy constant, $K_\perp$, of the films increases with an increase in their H_c value. Hence, the perpendicular anisotropy of the films may be produced mainly from the shape anisotropy for film A and the magnetocrystalline anisotropy due to hcp structure may increase the perpendicular anisotropy of the films with an increase in $H_{c(\perp)}$ value, and finally both shape and magnetocrystalline anisotropies effectively work for film C.

It was also clarified that, at the initial deposition stage up of to about 30 nm, all the films show lower H_c; a typical example is shown in Fig. 2.20. It was interesting from the viewpoint of enhancement of output voltage in read/write properties that these films have an initial region with low coercivity similar to the case of CoNiReP/NiMoP DL medium described above.

The RHEED analysis of the films of various thickness clarified that such an initial region consists of randomly oriented fcc crystallites of low crystallinity, and that the upper region consists of perpendicularly oriented c-axis of hcp crystallites of high crystallinity.

Figure 2.21 shows representative cross-sectional TEM bright and dark field images of the 150-nm thick films. No ovbious grain structure is observed at the initial stage of all films, and the films develop different features in the upper region, due to a variation in H_c values. In the upper region, a columnar structure of about 30 nm diameter is clearly formed in the case of film C with higher H_c. On the other hand, such a columnar structure

Film A   Film C

Film B

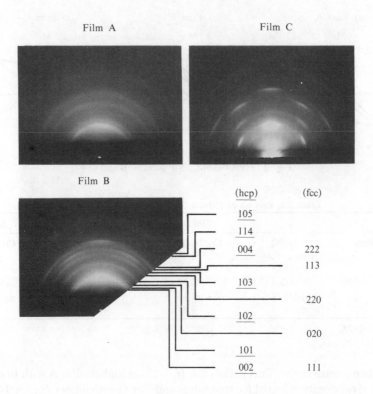

(hcp)	(fcc)
105	
114	
004	222
	113
103	
	220
102	
	020
101	
002	111

Fig. 2.19 Representative RHEED patterns of 150 nm-thick CoNiP films A, B, and C.

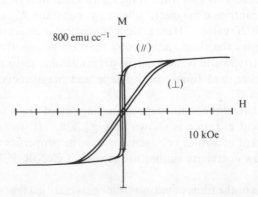

Fig. 2.20 Representative MH loops of 25-nm thick CoNiP film.

is not clearly observed in film A or B with lower $H_{c(\perp)}$ values.

The compositional analysis of ultra-small regions of film C confirmed that the initial region was in Ni-rich condition.   Similar to the case of the CoNiReP/NiMoP DL medium described above, such a preferential deposition of Ni forms randomly oriented fcc crys-

medium A   medium B   medium C

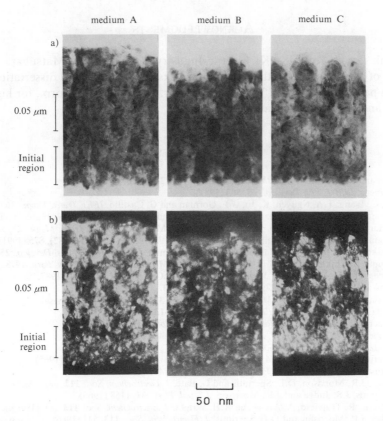

a)

0.05 μm

Initial
region

b)

0.05 μm

Initial
region

50 nm

Fig. 2.21 TEM cross-sectional images of CoNiP films A, B, and C; (a) bright field images and (b) dark field
images.

tallites with low M_s and low H_c, while the Co content increases with film growth, forming
a columnar structure consisting of c-axis perpendicularly oriented hcp crystallites.   Thus,
the CoNiP films show suitable magnetic properties for perpendicular magnetic recording
media.

2.7   Conclusion

We described high density magnetic recording media produced by electroless-plating, in
particular for perpendicular magnetic recording system, on the basis of our research
works.   If we understand the features of the electroless-plating method, e.g., mass-
productivity, uniformity of deposits on large and/or nonflat substrate, and also the barrier
of spiritual hesitation for open and complicated system as compared with dry processes, we
can effectively use this wet process, *i.e.*, electroless-plating method, in magnetic recording
media as demonstrated in the text.

ACKNOWLEDGMENTS

We thank Drs. I. Koiwa, OKI Electric Industry Corp., and H. Matsubara, Nagaoka University of Technology, for their research works on their doctoral dissertations, which comprise a part of this work. We also thank Mr. F. Goto, NEC Corp., for his valuable discussion and help in our research.

REFERENCES

1. T. Noyes and W.E. Dickinson, *IBM J. Res. Develop.*, **1**, 72 (1957).
2. L.D. Stevens, *IBM J. Res. Develop.*, **25**, 663 (1981).
3. T. Yogi, C. Tsang, T.A. Nguyen, K. Ju, G.L. Gorman and G. Castillo, *IEEE Trans. Magn.*, **26**, 2271 (1990).
4. M. Futamoto, F. Kugiya, M. Suzuki, H. Takano, H. Fukuoka, Y. Matsuda, N. Inaba, T. Takagaki, Y. Miyaumura, K. Akagi, T. Nakao, H. Sawaguchi and T. Munemoto, *IEEE Trans. Magn.*, **27**, 5280 (1991).
5. H. Wakamatsu, K. Kiuchi, M. Shinohara and Y. Miura, *J. Magn. Soc. Jpn.*, **15(S2)**, 875 (1991).
6. J.M. Harker, D.W. Brede, R.E. Pattison, G.R. Santana and L.G. Taft, *IBM J. Res. Develop.*, **25**, 677 (1981).
7. for example, S. Chikazumi and S.H. Charap, *Physics of Magnetism,* Krieger, New York, 1978.
8. C.D. Mee and E.D. Daniel, eds., *Magnetic Recording,* McGraw-Hill, New York, 1987.
9. R. Angus, *Audio,* Aug. 1984, p. 27; *ibid,* Sept. 1984, p. 33.
10. Y. Nakamura and S. Iwasaki, *J. Met. Finishing Soc. Jpn.*, **35**, 482 (1984) (in Japanese).
11. S. Iwasaki and Y. Nakamura, *IEEE Trans. Magn.*, **MAG-13**, 1272 (1977).
12. A. Brenner and G.E. Riddell, *J. Research Nat'l Bur. Standards,* **37**, 1 (1946).
13. R.D. Fisher and W.H. Chilton, *J. Electrochem. Soc.*, **109**, 485 (1962).
14. Y. Moradzadeh, *J. Electrochem. Soc.*, **112**, 891 (1965).
15. D.E. Speriotis, J.R. Morrison and J.S. Judge, *IEEE Trans. Magn.*, **MAG-1**, 348 (1965).
16. L.D. Ransom and V. Zentner, *J. Electrochem. Soc.*, **111**, 1423 (1964).
17. J.S. Judge, J.R. Morrison, D.E. Speriotis and G. Bate, *J. Electrochem. Soc.*, **112**, 681 (1965).
18. D.E. Speliotis, J.S. Judge and J.R. Morrison, *J. Appl. Phys.*, **37**, 1158 (1966).
19. M.G. Miksic, R. Traivieso, A. Arcus and R.H. Wright, *J. Electrochem. Soc.*, **113**, 360 (1966).
20. J.S. Judge, J.R. Morrison and D.E. Speriotis, *J. Electrochem. Soc.*, **113**, 547 (1966).
21. J.R. DePew, *J. Electrochem. Soc.*, **120**, 1187 (1973).
22. R.D. Fisher and D.E. Koopman, *J. Electrochem. Soc.*, **111**, 263 (1964).
23. A.S. Frieze, R. Sard and R. Weil, *J. Electrochem. Soc.*, **115**, 586 (1968).
24. V. Morton and R.D. Fisher, *J. Electrochem. Soc.*, **116**, 188 (1969).
25. S.L. Chow, N.E. Hedgecock and M. Schlesinger, *J. Electrochem. Soc.*, **119**, 1614 (1972).
26. F. Pearlstein and R.F. Weightman, *Plating,* 714 (1967).
27. F. Pearlstein and R.F. Weightman, *J. Electrochem. Soc.*, **121**, 1023 (1974).
28. I. Tsu, *Plating,* **48**, 379 (1961); *ibid,* **48**, 1207 (1961).
29. J.S. Sallo and J.M. Carr, *J. Electrochem. Soc.*, **109**, 1040 (1962).
30. G.V. Elmore and P. Bakos, *J. Electrochem. Soc.*, **111**, 1244 (1964).
31. G. Bate and D.E. Speliotis, *J. Appl. Phys.*, **34**, 1073, (1964).
32. S. Iwasaki, K. Yasuda and A. Senda, *IECEJ Tech. Rep.*, **MR65-17** (1965) (in Japanese).
33. R. Sard, C.D. Schwartz and R. Weil, *J. Electrochem. Soc.*, **113**, 424 (1966).
34. S. Iwasaki, K. Ouchi and K. Yasuda, *IECEJ Tech. Rep.*, **MR66-18** (1966) (in Japanese).
35. J.H. Kefalas, *J. Appl. Phys.*, **37**, 1160 (1966).
36. S. Hattori, A. Tago, Y. Ishii, A. Terada, O. Ishii and S. Ohta, *Elec. Comm. Lab. Tech. J.*, **31**, 277 (1982) (in Japanese).
37. Y. Sato, A. Terada, S. Ohta and T. Miyamoto, *NTT Elec. Comm. Lab. Tech. J.*, **36**, 485 (1987) (in Japanese).
38. F. Goto, Y. Suganuma and T. Osaka, *J. Met. Finishing Soc. Jpn.*, **33**, 414 (1982) (in Japanese).
39. Y. Hirayama, *J. Met. Finishing Soc. Jpn.*, **38**, 378 (1987) (in Japanese).
40. M. Yanagisawa, *Tribology and Mechanics of Magnetic Storage Systems,* 2, ASLE Special Publication SP-19, 16 (1985).
41. M. Yanagisawa, *Tribology and Mechanics of Magnetic Storage Systems,* 2, ASLE Special Publication SP-19, 21 (1985).
42. T. Osaka, *Denki Kagaku,* **52**, 438 (1984) (in Japanese).
43. F. Goto and T. Osaka, *J. Chem. Soc. Jpn.* (Chemistry and Chemical Industry), **42**, 417 (1989) (in Japanese).

44. M. Nagao, Y. Suganuma, H. Tanaka, M. Yanagisawa and F. Goto, *IEEE Trans. Magn.*, **MAG-15**, 1543 (1979).
45. Y. Suganuma, H. Tanaka, M. Yanagisawa, F. Goto and S. Hatano, *IEEE Trans. Magn.*, **MAG-18**, 1215 (1982).
46. H. Tanaka, F. Goto, N. Shiota and M. Yanagisawa, *J. Appl. Phys.*, **53**, 2576 (1982).
47. J.S. Sallo, *Plating*, **54**, 257 (1967).
48. G. Bate, *J. Appl. Phys.*, **37**, 1164 (1966).
49. G. Bate and J.K. Alstad, *IEEE Trans. Magn.*, **MAG-5**, 821 (1969).
50. J.E. Williams, Jr. and C. Davison, *J. Electrochem. Soc.*, **137**, 3260 (1990).
51. M. Nagao, *J. Surf. Finishing Soc. Jpn.*, **42**, 273 (1991) (in Japanese).
52. J. Hokkyo, *IECEJ Tech. Rep.*, **MR65-22** (1965) (in Japanese).
53. D.E. Speriotis and J.R. Morrison, *IBM J. Res. Develop.*, **9**, 233 (1966).
54. H. Tanaka, N. Shiota, F. Goto, M. Yanagisawa and Y. Suganuma, *Trans. IECEJ*, **J67-C**, 82 (1984) (in Japanese).
55. D.D. Dressler and J.H. Judy, *IEEE Trans. Magn.*, **MAG-10**, 674 (1974).
56. N.R. Belk, P.K. George and G.S. Mowry, *IEEE Trans. Magn.*, **MAG-21**, 1350 (1985).
57. R.D. Fisher, *IEEE Trans. Magn.*, **MAG-2**, 681 (1966).
58. H. Matsuda and O. Takano, *J. Jpn. Inst. Met.*, **52**, 414 (1988) (in Japanese).
59. F. Goto, M. Kimura, N. Shiota, T. Yamamoto and M. Yanagisawa, 1989 Autumn Natl. Conv. Rec., IEICEJ, 5-164 (1989) (in Japanese).
60. H. Nagasaka, T. Michimori and H. Takano, *J. Surf. Fin. Soc. Jpn.*, **42**, 58 (1991) (in Japanese).
61. T. Osaka and H. Nagasaka, *J. Electrochem. Soc.*, **128**, 1686 (1981).
62. M. Mirzamaani, L.T. Romankiw, C. McGrath, J. Mahlke and N.C. Anderson, *J. Electrochem. Soc.*, **135**, 2813 (1988).
63. D. DiMilia, J. Horkans, C. McGrath, M. Mirzamaani and G. Scilla, *J. Electrochem. Soc.*, **135**, 2817 (1988).
64. H. Matsubara, M. Toda, T. Sakuma, T. Homma, T. Osaka, Y. Yamazaki and T. Namikawa, *J. Electrochem. Soc.*, **136**, 753 (1989).
65. E.M. Rossi, G. McDonough, A. Tietze, T. Arnoldussen, A. Brunsch, S. Doss, M. Henneberg, F. Lin, R. Lyn, A. Ting and G. Trippel, *J. Appl. Phys.*, **55**, 2254 (1984).
66. E. Teng and N. Ballard, *IEEE Trans. Magn.*, **MAG-22**, 579 (1986).
67. E.M. Shimpson, P.B. Narayan, G.T.K. Swami and J.L. Chao, *IEEE Trans. Magn.*, **MAG-23**, 3405 (1987).
68. T. Osaka, T. Homma, K. Inoue, H. Asai, H. Iidsuka, H. Yoshino and F. Goto, *J. Surface Finishing Soc. Jpn.*, **42**, 334 (1991) (in Japanese).
69. T. Matsunaga, M. Kaneko, Y. Miyamoto, M. Tagami and T. Tomita, *J. Surface Finishing Soc. Jpn.*, **42**, 339 (1991) (in Japanese).
70. J.S. Judge and D.E. Speliotis, *IEEE Trans. Magn.*, **MAG-23**, 3402 (1987).
71. A.S. Hoagland, *IBM J. Res. Develop.*, **2**, 91 (1958).
72. S. Iwasaki and K. Takemura, *IEEE Trans. Magn.*, **MAG-11**, 1173 (1975).
73. S. Iwasaki, *IEEE Trans. Magn.*, **MAG-16**, 71 (1980).
74. S. Iwasaki, *IEEE Trans. Magn.*, **MAG-20**, 657 (1984).
75. J. Hokkyo and F. Kugiya, *J. Magn. Soc. Jpn.*, **13(S1)**, 1 (1989).
76. Y. Nakamura and S. Iwasaki, *IEEE Trans. Magn.*, **MAG-20**, 105 (1984).
77. S. Yamamoto, Y. Nakamura and S. Iwasaki, *IEEE Trans. Magn.*, **MAG-23**, 2070 (1987).
78. H. Tamai and K. Tagami, *IEEE Trans. Magn.*, **MAG-21**, 1480 (1985).
79. H. Tamai and K. Tagami, *IEEE Trans. Magn.*, **MAG-23**, 2737 (1987).
80. N. Akutsu, M. Akimitsu and T. Mizoguchi, *IEEE Trans. Magn.*, **MAG-22**, 1170 (1986).
81. K. Ouchi, *J. Magn. Soc. Jpn.*, **13(S1)**, 611 (1989).
82. S. Iwasaki and K. Ouchi, *IEEE Trans. Magn.*, **MAG-14**, 849 (1978).
83. S. Iwasaki and K. Ouchi, *Trans. IECEJ*, **J63-C**, 238 (1980) (in Japanese).
84. Y. Maeda, S. Hirono and M. Asahi, *Jpn. J. Appl. Phys.*, **24**, L951-L953 (1985).
85. Y. Maeda and M. Asahi, *J. Appl. Phys.*, **61**, 1972 (1987).
86. Y. Maeda and M. Asahi, *IEEE Trans. Magn.*, **MAG-23**, 2061 (1987).
87. Y. Maeda and M. Takahashi, *IEEE Trans. Magn.*, **24**, 3012 (1988).
88. Y. Maeda and M. Takahashi, *J. Magn. Soc. Jpn.*, **13(S1)**, 673 (1989).
89. M. Sato and Y. Hoshino, *Denki Kagaku*, **35**, 111 (1967) (in Japanese).
90. S. Kawai and R. Ueda, *J. Electrochem. Soc.*, **122**, 32 (1975).
91. S. Kawai, *J. Electrochem. Soc.*, **122**, 1026 (1975).
92. S. Kawai and I. Ishiguro, *J. Electrochem. Soc.*, **123**, 1047 (1975).
93. T. Chen and P. Cavallotti, *Appl. Phys. Lett.*, **41**, 209 (1982).
94. T. Chen and P. Cavallotti, *IEEE Trans. Magn.*, **MAG-18**, 1125 (1982).
95. J. Horkans, D.J. Seagle and I-Chia Hsu Chang, *J. Electrochem. Soc.*, **137**, 2056 (1990).

96. T. Osaka, F. Goto, N. Kasai and Y. Suganuma, *Denki Kagaku,* **49**, 792 (1981) (in Japanese).
97. T. Osaka and N. Kasai, *J. Met. Finishing Soc. Jpn.,* **32**, 309 (1981) (in Japanese).
98. O. Takano, H. Matsuda, H. Izumitani and K. Ito, *J. Metal Finishing Soc. Jpn.,* **35**, 440 (1984) (in Japanese).
99. H. Matsuda and O. Takano, *J. Metal Finishing Soc. Jpn.,* **37**, 753 (1986) (in Japanese).
100. T. Osaka and I. Koiwa, *J. Met. Finishing Soc. Jpn.,* **38**, 362 (1987) (in Japanese).
101. T. Osaka, *Rep. Asahi Glass Found. Ind. Technol.,* **52**, 53 (1988) (in Japanese).
102. T. Osaka, H. Matsubara and N. Masubuchi, *J. Chem. Soc. Jpn., Chem. and Ind. Chem.,* **10**, 1659 (1989) (in Japanese).
103. T. Osaka and H. Matsubara, *Iron and Steel,* **75**, 1112 (1989) (in Japanese).
104. T. Homma and T. Osaka, *J. Kinki Institute of Aluminum Surface Finishing,* **146**, 1 (1990) (in Japanese).
105. T. Osaka and T. Homma, *J. Surface Finishing Soc., Jpn.,* **42**, 238 (1991).
106. T. Osaka, in: *Perpendicular Magnetic Recording,* (S. Iwasaki and J. Hokkyo, eds.) p. 189, Ohmusha, Tokyo (1991).
107. T. Osaka, I. Koiwa, and F. Goto, in: *New Materials & New Processes,* vol. 3, JEC Press Inc., (Nov. 1985), p. 108.
108. T. Osaka and I. Koiwa, in: *Storage Devices for Personal, Computer,* Triceps Ltd., (Nov. 1985), p. 222 (in Japanese).
109. F. Goto, T. Osaka, N. Kasai, I. Koiwa, H. Tanaka, M. Aoyama and Y. Suganuma, *Proc. of Symp. on Inst. Elec. Comn.,* Tohoku Univ., 197 (1982) (in Japanese).
110. T. Osaka, F. Goto, N. Kasai, I. Koiwa and Y. Suganuma, *J. Electrochem. Soc.,* **130**, 568 (1983).
111. T. Osaka, N. Kasai, I. Koiwa and F. Goto, *J. Electrochem. Soc.,* **130**, 790 (1983).
112. T. Osaka, I. Koiwa, Y. Okabe, H. Matsubara, A. Wada and F. Goto, *Denki Kagaku,* **52**, 197 (1984) (in Japanese).
113. T. Osaka, I. Koiwa, Y. Okabe, H. Matsubara, A. Wada, F. Goto, N. Shiota and J. Nakashima, *IECEJ Tech. Rep.,* **MR84-15** (1984) (in Japanese).
114. F. Goto, T. Osaka, I. Koiwa, Y. Okabe, H. Matsubara, A. Wada and N. Shiota, *IEEE Trans. Magn.,* **MAG-20**, 803 (1984).
115. T. Osaka, I. Koiwa, Y. Okabe, H. Matsubara, A. Wada, F. Goto and N. Shiota, *Bull. Chem. Soc. Jpn.,* **58**, 414 (1985).
116. I. Koiwa, Y. Oakabe, H. Matsubara and T. Osaka, *J. Met. Finishing Soc. Jpn.,* **36**, 204 (1985) (in Japanese).
117. T. Osaka, I. Koiwa, Y. Okabe and K. Yamanishi, *Jpn. J. Appl. Phys.,* **26**, 1674 (1987).
118. T. Osaka and I. Koiwa, *J. Met. Finishing Soc. Jpn.,* **36**, 365 (1985) (in Japanese).
119. I. Koiwa, Y. Okabe, H. Matsubara, T. Osaka and F. Goto, *J. Magn. Soc. Jpn.,* **9**, 83 (1985); translated in *IEEE Translation J. Magn. Jpn,* **TJMJ-1**, 443 (1985).
120. I. Koiwa, M. Toda and T. Osaka, *J. Electrochem. Soc.,* **133**, 597 (1986).
121. I. Koiwa, H. Matsubara, T. Osaka, Y. Yamazaki and T. Namikawa, *J. Electrochem. Soc.,* **133**, 685 (1986).
122. T. Osaka, I. Koiwa, M. Toda, T. Sakuma, Y. Yamazaki and T. Namikawa, *J. Magn. Soc. Jpn.,* **10**, 5 (1986); translated in *IEEE Translation J. Magn. Jpn,* **TJMJ-2**, 208 (1987).
123. T. Osaka, I. Koiwa, M. Toda, T. Sakuma, Y. Yamazaki, T. Namikawa and F. Goto, *IEEE Trans. Magn.,* **MAG-22**, 1149 (1986).
124. I. Koiwa, T. Osaka, Y. Yamazaki and T. Namikawa, *IEEE Trans. Magn.,* **MAG-23**, 2800 (1987).
125. T. Osaka, H. Matsubara, T. Sakuma, T. Homma, S. Yokoyama, Y. Yamazaki and T. Namikawa, *J. Magn. Soc. Jpn.,* **12**, 77 (1988); translated in *IEEE Translation J. Magn. Jpn,* **TJMJ-4**, 39 (1989).
126. I. Koiwa, H. Matsubara, K. Yamanishi, H. Mizutani and F. Goto, *IEEE Trans. Magn.,* **MAG-23**, 2356 (1987).
127. H. Matsubara, S. Mitamura, K. Noda, T. Osaka and F. Goto, *J. Magn. Soc. Jpn.,* **13**, 153 (1989); translated in *IEEE Translation J. Magn. Jpn,* **TJMJ-5**, 276 (1990).
128. H. Matsubara, K. Yamanishi, H. Mizutani and T. Osaka, *J. Met. Finishing Soc. Jpn.,* **37**, 708 (1986) (in Japanese).
129. T. Homma, K. Saito and T. Osaka, *J. Surface Finishing Soc. Jpn.,* **40**, 140 (1989) (in Japanese).
130. T. Homma, K. Saito and T. Osaka, *Jpn. J. Appl. Phys.,* **29**, 1701 (1990).
131. T. Osaka, T. Homma, K. Saito, K. Noda, F. Goto, N. Shiota and T. Yamamoto, *IEICEJ Tech. Rep.,* **MR90-10** (1990) (in Japanese).
132. T. Osaka, T. Homma, K. Inoue and K. Saga, *Denki Kagaku,* **58**, 661 (1990) (in Japanese).
133. T. Osaka, H. Sawai, F. Otoi and K. Nihei, *J. Metal Finishing Soc. Jpn.,* **31**, 661 (1980) (in Japanese).
134. S. Iwasaki and K. Ouchi, *IEEE Trans. Magn.,* **MAG-26**, 97 (1990).
135. S. Nasu, K. Matsumoto, M. Isurugi and K. Saiki, *Digests of Ann. Conf. of Magn. Soc. Jpn.,* p. 293, 1988 (in Japanese).
136. T. Homma, K. Noda, T. Watanabe and T. Osaka, *Jpn. J. Appl. Phys.,* **30**, 1971 (1991).
137. T. Osaka, T. Homma, K. Noda, T. Watanabe and F. Goto, *IEEE Trans. Magn.,* **27**, 4963 (1991).
138. T. Homma, T. Watanabe, T. Osaka and F. Goto, *J. Magn. Soc. Jpn.,* **15(S2)**, 305 (1991).
139. T. Osaka, T. Homma, K. Inoue, Y. Yamazaki and T. Namikawa, *J. Magn. Soc. Jpn.,* **13**, 85 (1989); translated

in *IEEE Translation J. Magn. Jpn,* **TJMJ-5**, 155 (1990).

140. M. Hansen and K. Anderko, in: *Constitution of Binary Alloys,* p. 486, McGraw-Hill, New York, 1958.
141. T. Osaka, T. Homma, K. Inoue, Y. Yamazaki and T. Namikawa, *J. Magn. Soc., Jpn.,* **13(S1)**, 779 (1989).
142. T. Osaka, T. Homma and K. Inoue, *J. Electrochem. Soc.,* **138**, 538 (1991).
143. I. Koiwa, K. Yamada, M. Usuda and T. Osaka, *Denki Kagaku,* **54**, 514 (1986) (in Japanese).
144. T. Osaka and I. Koiwa, *J. Metal Finishing Soc. Jpn.,* **34**, 330 (1983) (in Japanese).
145. I. Koiwa, M. Usuda, K. Yamada and T. Osaka, *J. Electrochem. Soc.,* **135**, 718 (1988).
146. H. Matsubara, H. Mizutani, S. Mitamura and T. Osaka, *Jpn. J. Appl. Phys.,* **27**, 1895 (1988).
147. H. Matsubara, H. Mizutani, S. Mitamura, T. Osaka and F. Goto, *IEEE Trans. Magn.,* **24**, 3018 (1988).
148. H. Matsubara, S. Mitamura, K. Noda and T. Osaka, *J. Magn. Soc. Jpn.,* **13(S1)**, 679 (1989).
149. T. Osaka, H. Matsubara, T. Homma, S. Mitamura and K. Noda, *Jpn. J. Appl. Phys.,* **29**, 1939 (1990).
150. T. Homma, K. Inoue, H. Asai, K. Ohrui, T. Osaka, Y. Yamazaki and T. Namikawa, *J. Magn. Soc. Jpn.,* **15(2)**, 113 (1991) (in Japanese).
151. T. Homma, K. Inoue, H. Asai, K. Ohrui and T. Osaka, *IEEE Trans. Magn.,* **27**, 4909 (1991).

3

Metallurgical Analysis of Mechanical Properties of Electroless Copper Deposits

S. NAKAHARA and Y. OKINAKA*

AT&T Bell Laboratiories, Murray Hill, New Jersey 07974, U.S.A.

3.1   Introduction

In printed circuit boards (PCBs), one of the most important structural elements is the through-hole, an electrical conduction path connecting one side of the board to the other.   As the through-holes are made smaller and the boards get thicker, the demand for uniform plating of copper inside the high aspect-ratio ($= L/D$, $L =$ board thickness and $D =$ hole diameter) through-holes in multi-layer PCBs has become more stringent in recent years.   The electronics industry now requires PCBs with plated through-holes (PTHs) having an aspect-ratio close to 10 : 1; this will increase to 20 : 1 in the near future.[1]   The full-additive technology that uses only an electroless copper process is ideally suited for this application.   The advantage of the full-additive process lies in its ability to economically plate small diameter and high aspect-ratio holes with high throwing power.[2]   Electroless copper deposits for this application, however, must possess mechanical properties, which are required to resist against cracking, because during soldering operation and/or field usage, it is exposed to severe thermal shock or thermal cycling stresses due to a difference in thermal expansion coefficient between the copper and the substrate.   Typically, the laminate materials used as the substrate expand more than copper during heating.   If the mechanical property of the copper is poor, the differential thermal expansion in the direction of board thickness causes a tensile cracking in the copper of the PTH, thus losing a part of the electrical conduction path.

Electroless copper grown on the wall of the PTH is a critical element that determines the reliability of the PCBs.   Corner (or knee) and barrel cracks are commonly observed failures in copper plated inside the through-holes (see Fig. 3.1).   The solder float (288°C for 10 sec.) and the thermal cycling (−55 to 125°C , 100 cycles) tests, which simulate the soldering operation and the field usage, respectively, are performed for determining mechanical reliability of the electroless copper.[3]   It has been claimed[4] that elongation (ductility) of at least 6% is required to pass the solder float test, and tensile strength of −50 kpsi (−345 MPa) is needed to endure fatigue cracking during the thermal cycling. Therefore, two mechanical properties, ductility and tensile strength, have been used extensively as a measure for qualifying electroless copper deposits for the PCB application.

In this review, we will describe several key factors that affect the mechanical properties (ductility

---

* Retired.

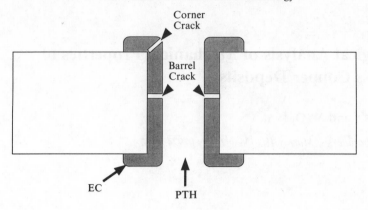

EC = Electroless Copper
PTH = Plated Through-Holes

Fig. 3.1 A schematic illustration showing the cross-section of the plated through-hole used in
         the printed circuit board.   Two types of cracks (corner and barrel cracks) are shown
         to form in electroless copper grown on the through-hole

and tensile/yield strength*) of electroless copper.   Emphasis will be placed on the effect of
incorporated molecular hydrogen and associated void volume on the ductility.

3.2   Electroless Copper for PCB Applications

For evaluating electroless copper for PCB applications, it is important to measure the
mechanical properties of electroless copper deposited on the cylindrical wall of the through-
holes.   However, the deposit grown on the PTHs cannot be easily subjected to conventional
mechanical tests like a tensile or a bulge test.   Consequently, no direct measurements of the
mechanical properties of the PTH copper have been done in the past.   Instead, a more
primitive but tedious way of detecting cracks in the PTHs after the thermal shock and/or
thermal cycling tests has been performed using metallographic cross-sectioning or electrical
continuity tests.   In addition, a chemical etching method was recently developed[5] to reveal
defective regions in the cross section of the PTHs.

For the practical evaluation of mechanical properties, electroless copper films deposited
on large flat plastic or metallic (copper or stainless steel) substrates are customarily used,
because flat substrates are much more convenient for making test specimens.   However,
thermal stresses received by copper in the PTH area are very complex due to its geometrical
irregularities and are not the same as external stresses applied to conventional flat
specimens.   In addition, the nucleation and growth pattern of electroless copper on the
small cylindrical walls of the high aspect-ratio PTHs may be different from that on the flat
surface.   Nevertheless, it is important to keep in mind that electroless copper deposits

---

* When the material reaches a stress level at which defromation is no longer elastic but plastic, the stress is said to
  have reached the yield stress.   At the yield stress level, the slope of the stress-strain curve starts deviating from
  the elastic modulus.   With further deformation, the material undergoes work-hardening and the stress reaches
  a maximum at the ultimate tensile strength, followed by the development of necking.   The ultimate tensile
  strength is generally taken to be the tensile strength of the material.   Ductility is the strain that a material can
  withstand before fracture.

grown on flat substrates provide only general information on the mechanical properties. For more specific information, one should directly measure the properties of electroless copper deposited inside the through-holes.

As an alternative to performing direct measurement, several attempts[6-8] were made to evaluate thermal stress fields generated around the PTH area using a computer simulation, which predicts the location of possible cracks formed during thermal cycling.   Iannuzzelli[7] applied the finite element method of structural analysis to the low-cycle fatigue case of copper in the PTH.   The model showed that for thin (<6 μm) deposits, failure is likely to occur near the center of the PTH and in the barrel (barrel crack), whereas for very thick (>50 μm) deposits, the failure always occurs in the knee (corner crack) (see Fig. 3.1). Vecchio and Hertzberg[6] found in their calculation that the incorporation of an internal copper land in multilayer boards significantly increases the PTH barrel stress.   These theoretical predictions provide useful guides for designing reliable PCBs.

3.3   Microstructure of As-Plated Electroless Copper

Based on our previous studies,[9-11] it is possible to illustrate several important micro-structural characteristics of as-deposited electroless copper (see Fig. 3.2).   Crystalline defects like dislocations, twins, and grain boundaries, which are also commonly observed in other thin metallic films prepared by vapor deposition and sputtering, are present abundantly in electroless copper deposits.[9-10]   For example, the density of the dislocations is on the order of $\sim 10^{12}/cm^3$.   Atomic or molecular forms of impurities are incorporated from the electrolyte, including constituents of basic electroless copper bath chemistries and additives.   These impurity inclusions were directly observed[12] by transmission electron microscopy (TEM), but their chemical composition analysis was generally done only by other analytical techniques, such as fusion gas analysis.[13]

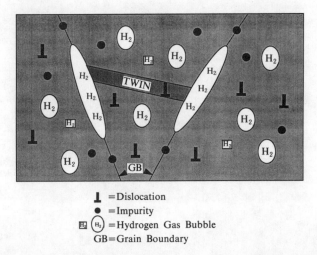

$\perp$ =Dislocation
● =Impurity
🄷₂ (H_2) =Hydrogen Gas Bubble
GB=Grain Boundary

Fig. 3.2 Microstructure of electroless copper deposits showing various internal defects, such as dislocations, grain boundaries, twins, impurity inclusions, and hydrogen gas bubbles. Three kinds of hydrogen gas bubbles are present: small spherical and cuboidal ones inside the grain, and large elongated ones at the grain boundaries.

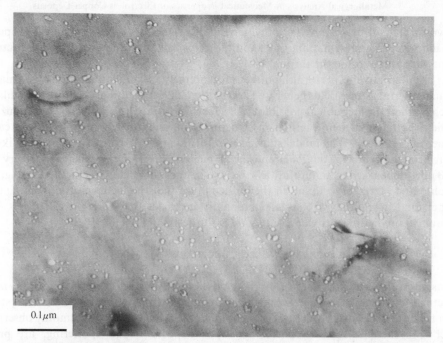

0.1μm

Fig. 3.3 TEM micrograph showing a high density of spherical voids inside an electroless copper grain.

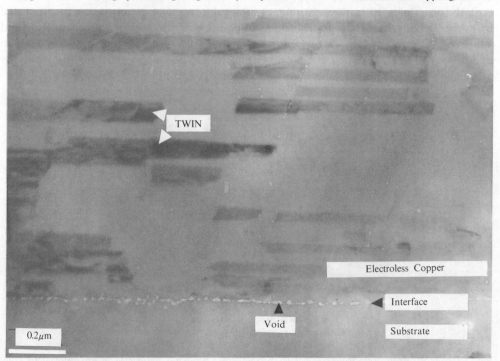

TWIN

Electroless Copper

Interface

Void

Substrate

0.2μm

Fig. 3.4 Cross-section TEM micrograph showing twins and voids in an electroless copper deposit grown epitaxially on a large-grained copper substrate. Note the line of voids along the electroless copper/ copper substrate interface.

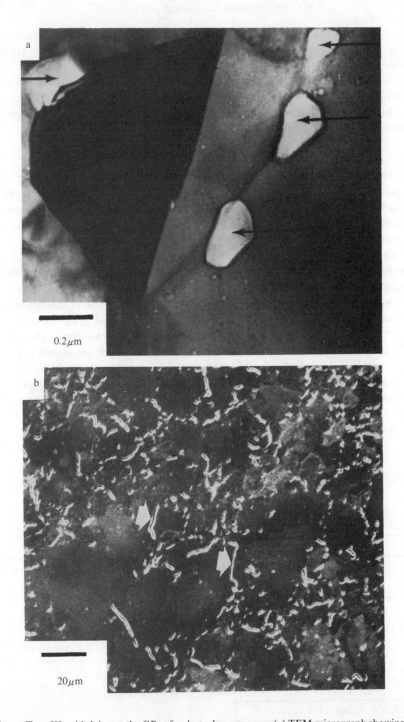

Fig. 3.5 Large Type III voids lying at the GBs of a electroless copper. (a) TEM micrograph showing elongated GB voids as marked with four black arrows and (b) SEM micrograph showing GB voids (indicated by two white arrows) on the electropolished surface of an electroless copper.

Voids or gas bubbles are characteristic defects in electroless copper deposits. In the electroless copper deposition process, copper is deposited through the autocatalytic-reduction of an alkaline solution of a copper complex by formaldehyde. The deposition of copper accompanies simultaneous evolution of hydrogen gas as a result of splitting of the C–H bond in the formaldehyde molecule and the subsequent recombination of hydrogen atoms at the copper surface. The overall reaction of the electroless copper deposition can ben expressed[14] as

$$Cu(II) + 2HCHO + 4OH^- \longrightarrow Cu + 2HCOO^- + H_2 + 2H_2O$$

Since this reaction involves the production of hydrogen as well as copper, it is possible that a small portion of the hydrogen is incorporated in the copper deposit in the atomic (interstitial) and/or molecular (gas bubbles) form(s). The presence of gas bubbles or voids is, therefore, an integral part of unique microstructures that develop in electroless copper deposits (see Figs.3.3 and 3.4).

Three kinds of gas bubbles are found[11] in electroless copper deposits. Their overall density is generally high (10^{14}–10^{15}/cm³). The incorporation of gas bubbles formed on the growing surface of electroless copper results in two kinds of internal gas bubbles, depending on their absorbed sites; small (20–300 Å) spherical bubbles (Type I) inside the granis and large (–2000 Å) elongated lenticular bubbles (Type III) at the grain boundaries (GBs). Because of the surface anisotropy, bubbles inside the grains are spherically shaped and those at the GBs are lenticular (see Fig. 3.2). Large Type III GB voids are shown in Fig. 3.5. In addition, a low (–10^{10}/cm³) density of small (–50 Å) faceted cuboidal bubbles (Type II) is formed by internal nucleations, resulting from the supersaturation and agglomeration of incorporated intersitial hydrogen atoms. It will be shown that small Type I and II bubbles contribute to an increase in the tensile/yield strength of copper, whereas large Type III GB bubbles cause a decrease in the ductility.

ELECTROLESS COPPER

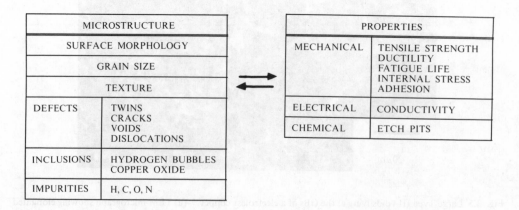

MICROSTRUCTURE				PROPERTIES	
SURFACE MORPHOLOGY				MECHANICAL	TENSILE STRENGTH DUCTILITY FATIGUE LIFE INTERNAL STRESS ADHESION
GRAIN SIZE					
TEXTURE					
DEFECTS	TWINS CRACKS VOIDS DISLOCATIONS			ELECTRICAL	CONDUCTIVITY
				CHEMICAL	ETCH PITS
INCLUSIONS	HYDROGEN BUBBLES COPPER OXIDE				
IMPURITIES	H, C, O, N				

Fig. 3.6 Microstructure-property relationship in electroless copper.

3.4 Factors Affecting Mechanical Properties of Electroless Copper

Measurements of the mechanical properties were first performed by Grunwald *et al.*,[15,16] who studied the effect of high-temperature (100–1000°C) annealing on ductility and tensile strength. Since this work, a number of key factors that influence the mechanical properties of electroless copper have been identified. Fig. 3.6 summarizes how the microstructure of electroless copper deposits affects their properties, including the mechanical, electrical, and chemical properties. In this review, discussion will be limited to the mechanical properties, in particular, ductility and tensile/yield strength. As seen in Fig. 3.6, there are many important factors that affect the mechanical properties of electroless copper. In addition to these microstructure-related parameters, post-annealing treatments also change the property significantly.

3.4.1 Impurities

Various impurity elements,[*1] such as carbon, oxygen, and hydrogen, in electroless copper deposits are quantitatively analyzed by many investigators. Among all the impurity elements, hydrogen represents probably the most important element that affects the mechanical properties of electroless copper. The effect of hydrogen on the ductility has been studied most systematically and is now well understood. A series of papers[9–13,17,18] demonstrates how hydrogen affects the properties of electroless copper.

A. Hydrogen

Hydrogen can exist in several forms in electroless copper films: interstitial and molecular hydrogen, copper hydride, and organic/inorganic molecules containing hydrogen as one of the atomic elements. We will discuss the role of these hydrogens in the order of importance.

Okinaka and Straschil[13] have shown that the ductility improves with annealing (150°C) time and reaches a constant level after about 24 hours. Concurrently, the hydrogen content[*2] decreases with time, then becomes constant after 24 hours (see Fig. 3.7). The two curves clearly demonstrate the existence of a close correlation between the ductility and the hydrogen content. From the trend of the hydrogen curve, they discovered the presence of two kinds of hydrogen in the deposit: "diffusible hydrogen" that diffuses out upon the 150°C annealing and "residual hydrogen" that cannot be removed by the annealing. The diffusible hydrogen diffuses out completely after the 150°C, 24-hour annealing.

Subsequently, Graebner and Okinaka[19] confirmed using a calorimetric method that the diffusible hydrogen is molecular hydrogen trapped entirely inside voids and diffuses out upon annealing. In addition, based on void volume data obtained by density measurements, they estimated that the internal pressure of hydrogen-containing voids prior to the annealing is ∼700 atm, which is roughly the same as the yield stress (∼680 atm[20]) of polycrystalline bulk copper. In other words, the hydrogen gas pressure is in mechanical equilibrium with the copper lattice. It should be emphasized that this pressure (∼700 atm)

[*1] In this paper, impurities are referred to as those incorporated in the deposits and should be distinguished from those used as organic/inorganic additives, which are deliberately added to the plating bath to improve the properties of electrodeposits. Subjects dealing with the effect of additives on the properties are beyond the scope of this paper and will not be discussed here.

[*2] For expressing the amount of hydrogen, both atomic and weight ppm are used; 1 wt. ppm H=0.5 wt. ppm H_2=63.54 at. ppm H=31.77 at. ppm H_2.

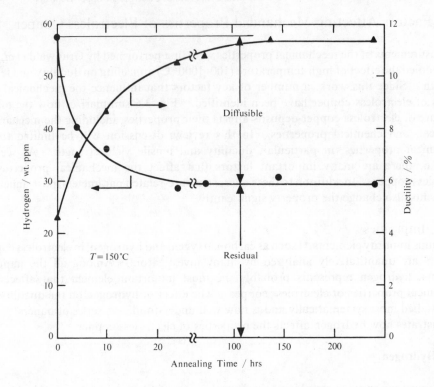

Fig. 3.7 A change in the hydrogen content and ductility of electroless copper deposits during annealing at 150°C.

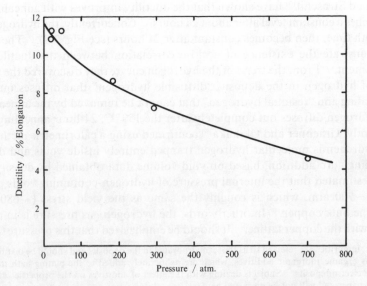

Fig. 3.8 Ductility change plotted as a function of hydrogen gas pressure.   Data for this plot was taken from Fig. 3.4.

is the upper limit; if the pressure exceeds 700 atm, the copper around the voids is most likely to be deformed plastically by punching out dislocations. This process, accompanied by the enlargement of voids, will continue until the pressure decreases to the yield stress. Such a dislocation punch-out process, which was indeed observed by TEM,[11] will maintain the pressure elastically at the level of the yield stress. Since the hydrogen diffusivity in copper is low ($\sim 10^{-14}$ cm^2/s) at room temperature, the outdiffusion of hydrogen is slow and thus as-deposited electroless copper is expected to hold this pressure (~ 700 atm) for a long period of time (up to a few months). The gas pressure can, of course, be lower than the yield stress, depending on how much hydrogen gas is left in voids after outdiffusion during room-temperature storage or post-annealing.

The close correlation between the diffusible hydrogen content and the ductility indicates that the slow release of high-pressure molecular hydrogen out of voids[*1] leads to the gradual ductility recovery. Since no other related microstructural changes were observed by the 150°C annealing, Okinaka and Straschil[13] concluded that electroless copper was embrittled by the classical pressure effect,[21] supporting an earlier speculation given by Okinaka and Nakahara.[9]

From the above discussion, it is reasonable to assume that the equilibrium pressure of hydrogen gas bubbles included in the as-deposited film is on the order of ~ 700 atm. We assume that the hydrogen content of as-deposited films in Fig. 3.7, i.e. 57 wt. ppm taken at zero annealing time, is kept in voids at a pressure of 700 atm. It is then possible to convert the remaining values of the hydrogen content into the hydrogen gas pressure. Based on this assumption, the ductility in Fig. 3.7 is re-plotted as a function of hydrogen gas pressure in Fig. 3.8.

The ductility is seen to decrease with the pressure, demonstrating the pressure effect on the ductility; a 50% reduction in ductility is achieved at a pressure of 700 atm.

The proposal that the upper limit of 700 atm is the equilibrium gas pressure can be further tested using a cathodic charging of hydrogen in combination with the 150°C annealing treatment. We found that after all the diffusible hydrogen is removed by the annealing, nearly the same amount of hydrogen can be charged back by the 15-hour[*2] cathodic charging into the voids. At the same time, the ductility is brought down to the same level as before. Further annealing removed the diffusible hydrogen completely and brought back the ductility (see Table 3.1). This result suggests that both the hydrogen content and the ductility can be reversibly changed by alternating charging/annealing treatments. The charging/annealing sequence is illustrated in Fig. 3.9. It can be envisioned from this experiment that (1) there is an upper limit to the amount of hydrogen that can be charged in, and the maximum equilibrium pressure is most likely to be in the neighborhood of 700 atm, and (2) the ductility change is caused only by the pressure change.

The effect of interstitial hydrogen on the ductility of electroless copper cannot be studied directly using electroless copper films, because the amount of interstitial hydrogen cannot easily be determined. Furthermore, the equilibrium solubility of hydrogen in copper at ambient temperatures is negligibly small (3.7×10^{-5} at.ppm). It is therefore doubtful that the copper contains sufficient interstitial hydrogen to affect the ductility. In addition,

---

[*1] The voids in as-deposited electroless copper are gas bubbles, as they contain high-pressure hydrogen gas. After the 24-hour annealing at 150°C, however, the gas bubbles become genuine voids, as all molecular hydrogen diffuses out. Because of this dual nature, both terminologies will hereafter be used interchangeably.

[*2] The period of 15 hours is ssconsidered to be sufficient to saturate the voids with hydrogen.

TABLE 3.1 Effect of cathodic charging of hydrogen and annealing on ductility of
electroless copper deposits
Charging conditions: 0.05M H_2SO_4, 0.001M As_2O_3, 10 mA/cm², 15 hrs.

Thermal History	Ductility (%)	Diffusible Hydrogen Content	
		at.ppm	wt.ppm
As-deposited	2.1	2775	44
After Anneal[†]	6.5	0	0
After Charging	3.8	2356	37
After Re-anneal[†]	6.4	0	0

†, 150°C, 24 hrs.

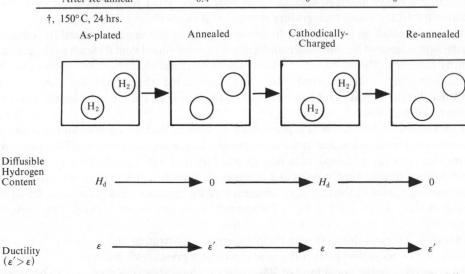

Fig. 3.9 A schematic diagram showing the sequence of charging/annealing that reversibly changes the diffusible
hydrogen content and the ductility of electroless copper deposits.

because of the presence of a high density of voids in electroless copper, it is difficult to
separate the effect of interstitial hydrogen from that of molecular hydrogen.   Therefore, we
studied the effect of interstitial hydrogen on the ductility of copper *in-situ* using a void-free
copper foil by charging hydrogen cathodically.   In this way, we insured that the copper was
supersaturated continuously with interstitial hydrogen, while a bulge test was being
conducted.   We found[11] no effect of interstitial hydrogen on ductility.

It is known that copper hydride can be produced by a chemical reduction method using
hypophosphite.[22]   Therefore, it was suspected that copper hydride might form during
electroless copper plating.   From the covalently bonded wurtzite structure of copper
hydride (CuH),[23] the ductility of this compound is believed to be much lower than that of
copper.   The presence of copper hydride should reduce the ductility and increase the tensile
strength by dispersion hardening.   However, an electron diffraction analysis[24] failed to
detect its presence.   The hydrogen concentration of as high as 200 wt. ppm corresponds to
only $CuH_{0.013}$, whose stoichiometric ratio is too small to be detectable as CuH.   If CuH
should exist in electroless copper deposits, the low-temperature annealing[13] could have
decomposed the hydride phase and driven out hydrogen as diffusible hydrogen.   The total
amount of diffusible hydrogen, however, accounts only for the total amount of molecular
hydrogen stored in voids.   Thus, the possibility of the presence of a CuH phase has been

ruled out.

In summarizing the effect of hydrogen, it is clear that reducing the hydrogen incorporation is a key to ductility improvement. Fo example, the addition of a non-ionic surfactant to the electroless copper bath redeuced the entrapment of hydrogen bubbles, resulting in ductility improvement.[25]   As will be discussed, the presence of hydrogen gas bubbles reduces the ductility not only by the pressure effect, but also by the void effect by creating many structurally weak sites in the copper lattice.

B. Copper Oxide (Cu_2O)

Dissolved oxygen plays an important role in stabilizing full-build electroless copper baths against spontaneous decomposition.[26,27]   Bubbling the bath with air increases dissolved oxygen in the bath.   If the dissolved oxygen level becomes too high, it creates two deleterious effects[28]: (1) a decrease in the ductility of electroless copper deposits and (2) "skip-plating" due to surface passivation.   In both cases, the bath starts depositing non-catalytic copper oxide together with copper.   The addition of a cyanide compound to an electroless copper bath suppresses the formation of Cu_2O by promoting the generation of cuprous ions on the copper surface.[29]   Hirohata et al.[30] thought that the formation and incorporation of Cu_2O is a cause of the low film ductility, and complexing agents other than cyanide ions should be able to suppress the Cu_2O production, thus controlling the ductility.   Based on this idea, they investigated various complexing agents that form soluble cuprous species and found that complexing agents having $-N=C-C=N-$ radicals improve the ductility.   However, no direct observations of the oxide inclusions have been reported to substantiate the effect of Cu_2O inclusions on the ductility.

C. Other Impurities

Various impurities are codeposited in electroless copper deposits.   Compounds and ions present in the plating solution are possible sources of impurities, which include H_2O, HCHO, EDTA, $H_2C(OH)O^-$, $HCOO^-$, OH^-, and CO_3^{2-}.[13]   Non-volatile residual hydrogen, determined by low-temperature (100–150°C) annealing,[13] belongs to this class of impurities and probably originates from impurities containing hydrogen.   Based on an impurity analysis that yielded an atomic ratio of $H:O:C:N=2:1:1:0.2$, Murakami et al.[31] thought that in addition to the diffusible hydrogen, EDTA used as the complexing agent for copper ions is incorporated into the deposits as one of the impurities.

Direct TEM observations[12] have indeed revealed the presence of small (~ 20 Å) impurity molecules in electroless copper.   In addition, in-situ heating experiments[32] inside a TEM have also shown the presence of small liquid inclusions, which were observed to boil when heated above 180°C.   This observation demonstrates the possibility of trapping of the plating solution in the deposit.   There is one other piece of evidence that supports the possible entrapment of plating solution.   During the course of ductility measurements, Straschil[33] discovered that the clamped circular edge of electroless copper specimens used for the mechanical bulge tester[34,35] is often stained green in spots after the test.   This stain is thought to originate from entrapped electroless copper solution, which was squeezed out to the surface from the internal region of the clamped area of the test specimen.   Large GB voids are most likely to be the sites for trapping the solution.   These results raise a serious question whether or not the atomic ratio of various elements determined by chemical analysis can accurately predict the type of impurities incorporated, because the occluded electroless copper solution is expected to contain all possible impurities mentioned above.   In other words, elemental analysis alone may not clearly provide the chemical structure of impurity inclusions.

It is clear from the above discussion that it is difficult to determine the exact chemical structure of incorporated impurity molecules from elemental analyses.   However, we recently found[12] that the carbon content can provide some measure of impurity level in the deposits.   Impurities represented by carbon analysis reduce the degree of ductility recovery during low-temperature annealing by slowing down the recrystallization and grain growth processes.   This subject will be discussed further in the section on annealing effect.

3.4.2 Void Effect

Ductile metals like copper do not rupture uniformly throughout the volume, but the fracture is initiated from a number of microscopically small regions where voids are nucleated.   Tensile fracture eventually proceeds by the growth and coalescence of these voids.   Inclusions or intermetallic particles are known to provide the nucleation sites of these voids.[36]   In the case of electroless copper deposits, voids, particularly large GB voids, are already present prior to a plastic deformation; therefore fracture can occur prematurely without void nucleation.   In other words, pre-existing voids serve as mechanically weak sites in copper and accelerate ductile fracture during tensile deformation, thus reducing the ductility.

The effect of voids on the ductility can be demonstrated by low-temperature (100–200°C) annealing experiments.   The ductility, expressed in terms of % elongation before and after the 150°C annealing, is plotted against diffusible hydrogen content in Fig. 3.10.   The ductility at the zero diffusible hydrogen was taken from that of an 11 µm-thick well-annealed bulk copper foil.   The ductility (solid circles) of the as-plated films is seen to decrease with increasing hydrogen content (the upper horizontal axis), which varies from 0 to ~2300 at.ppm.   It was shown in Fig. 3.7 that the 150°C, 24-hour annealing treatment removes all the diffusible hydrogen from gas bubbles, leaving voids behind.   Consequently, the upper horizontal axis can be converted into the void volume fraction in the lower horizontal axis.   The curve (open circles) for the annealed films shows that the ductility decreases with increasing void volume fraction.   The ductility difference between the as-plated and the annealed films is considered to reflect the pressure effect of hydrogen, whereas the ductility decrease of the annealed films from the ductility at the zero void volume fraction represents the void effect on ductility.   For a given void volume fraction, therefore, we can determine the relative contribution of the pressure effect and the void effect to the ductility, provided the annealing causes only the outdiffusion of hydrogen from voids.

Diffusible hydrogen content provides a measure of void volume fraction, because it is entirely contained in voids.   Furthermore, if we assume that the average void diameter is 1000 Å[10] and the gas pressure is 700 atm, we can estimate the number density of voids from the diffusible hydrogen content.   This result is shown in Table 3.2.   It is interesting to note that even for the 1 wt.ppm hydrogen, the void density is very high and amounts to as high as $2.7 \times 10^{11}/cm^3$, which is slightly less than the density of dislocations ($\sim 10^{12}/cm^3$).[10]   Therefore, it is not surprising to observe a high density of voids in electroless copper

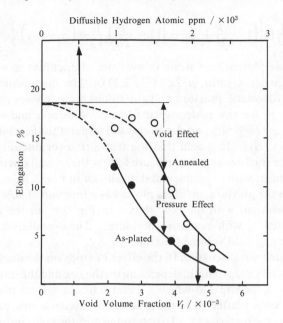

Fig. 3.10 Ductility (% elongation) of various as-deposited (solid circles) and annealed (open circles) electroless copper deposits plotted against diffusible hydrogen content.   The annealing treatment was performed at 150°C for 24 hours.   As this annealing drives out all the diffusible hydrogen, the horizontal axis (upper scale) can be expressed only in terms of void volume fraction for the annealed deposits.

deposits containing even very little diffusible hydrogen.   In electroless copper films deposited at room temperature, Kalikhman et al.[37] indeed mentioned that the voids are so numerous that it was impossible to produce specimens suitable for TEM.

A theoretical model describing ductile fracture by the coalescence of voids was found to explain qualitatively an experimental trend for the ductility change with void volume fraction.   According to Thomason's theory[38] of ductile fracture, the material is assumed to deform homogeneously until localized deformation along a fracture path of voids becomes energetically more favorable.   After the onset of nonhomogeneous deformation, the material between the voids is assumed to neck down at such a small increase of the overall strain that the fracture strain equals the strain at the beginning of localized deformation. Based on Thomason's original formulations, Melander[39] derived the following upper-bound solution for the fracture strain, ε_f, as a function of void volume fraction, V_f, internal pressure (tensile hydrostatic pressure), p, and the yield shear stress, k:

TABLE 3.2 Calculated values of void fraction and void density at various H_2 content
(Void diameter = 1000Å; Pressure of H_2 = 700 atm)

H₂ Content		Void Volume Fraction	Void Density (#/cm³)
wt.ppm	at.ppm		
1	64	0.00014	2.7×10¹¹
5	320	0.00071	1.4×10¹²
50	3200	0.0071	1.4×10¹³
125	8000	0.018	3.4×10¹³

$$\varepsilon_f = \frac{1}{2} \ln\left[\left(1 - \frac{p}{2k}\right)\frac{1}{\sqrt{V_f}} - \left\{\left(1 - \frac{p}{2k}\right)\frac{1}{V_f} - \left(\frac{1}{\sqrt{V_f}} - 1\right)^2\right\}^{1/2}\right] \qquad (3.1)$$

Using this equation, we plotted true strain (a measure of ductility) as a function of void volume fraction, V_f, and the ratio, $p/2k$ (Fig. 3.11). The dimensionless term, $-p/2k$, represents a tensile hydrostatic pressure and the minus sign denotes tensile. Since the internal gas pressure, p, for the as-deposited films is ~ 700 atm and $k = 680$ atm[20] for copper, the two cases, $p/2k = -0.5$ and 0, roughly correspond to the as-deposited and the annealed films, respectively. It is seen that the true strain (or ductility) decreases with increasing void volume fraction and the pressure lowers the overall ductility. This result is in qualitative agreement with experimental data shown in Fig. 3.10.

The true strain, ε, vs the pressure, $-p/2k$, is plotted as a function of void volume fraction, V_f, in Fig. 3.12. Consistent with the plot shown in Fig. 3.8, all the curves indicate a decreasing trend of ductility with increasing pressure. The overall ductility curve moves downward with increasing void volume fraction.

So far, we have limited our discussion to the effect of voids on the ductility. The voids can also affect the tensile/yield strength, depending on the size and the internal gas pressure of voids. Yield stress is the stress at which a metal starts to deform plastically, and it is structure-sensitive; its value is affected by the presence of foreign atoms, precipitates, voids, and grain boundaries in the material.[40] To determine how the voids influence the ductility or the tensile/yield strength, it is necessary to know the equilibrium strain around pressurized voids. The equilibrium strain around pressurized spherical voids in copper is expressed[41] as

$$\varepsilon = \frac{4\gamma - Pd}{4\mu d} \qquad (3.2)$$

where ε is the strain around the void, d the void diameter, P the internal pressure, γ the surface energy of copper and μ the shear modulus.

Based on Eq. (3.2), we plotted strain ε vs. void size d for the internal pressures of 0,700, 1000, and 2000 atm in Fig. 6.13. It is seen that both Type I (20–300 Å) and II (–50 Å) voids are under high compression, regardless of the size and the magnitude of the internal pressure (0–700 atm). Large compressive stresses associated with these small voids act as obstacles to the motion of dislocations during tensile deformation, contributing to the hardening of electroless copper. Small voids (Type I and II voids) under compression, therefore, increase the tensile/yield strength. Unfortunately, there are no systematic studies that report the effect of small voids on the tensile/yield strength of electroless copper deposits. For other fcc metals like aluminum, Manusmare and Leighly[42] reported that the yield strength of bulk aluminum with a high density of voids, which were produced by quenching and aging treatment, was increased by the presence of voids. It was shown that the void density of more than $10^{12}/cm^3$ was needed to obtain a measurable increase in the yield strength. Electroless copper deposits contain voids on the order of 10^{14}–$10^{15}/cm^3$,[11] which should be sufficient to cause a significant increase in the yield strength. Equation (3.2) also predicts that large (>900 Å) voids (Type III) are weakly strained or slightly under tension if they contain hydrogen gas at a high pressure. Large voids, therefore, do not contribute to the hardening, but serve instead as preferential sites for stress concentration and reduce the ductility by promoting ductile fracture, as discussed above.

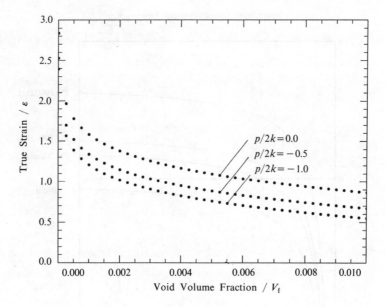

Fig. 3.11 Theoretical curves showing the relationship between true strain, ε, and void volume fraction, V_f, where p = hydrostatic pressure and k = shear yield stress.

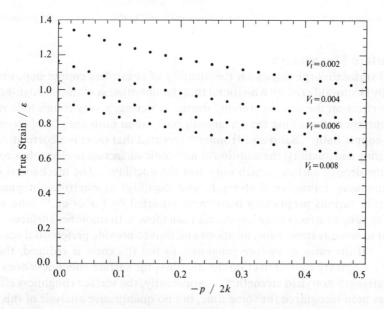

Fig. 3.12 Theoretical plots of true strain, ε, vs. $-p/2k$ as a function of void volume fraction, V_f, where p = hydrostatic pressure and k = void volume fraction.

Strain from Gas Bubbles or Voids

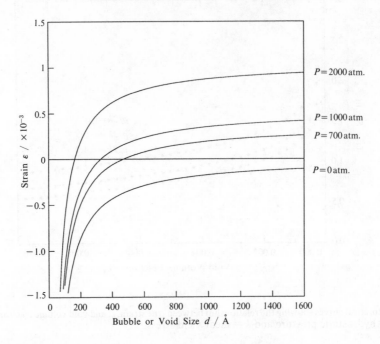

Fig. 3.13 Calculated strain from gas bubbles or voids as a function of bubble or void size and internal gas pressure, p.

3.4.3   Surface Morphology

Effect of surface morphologies on the ductility of electroless copper deposits was first suggested by Grunwald et al.,[43] who found that the smoothness of the through-hole surface has a large effect on the deposit stability during soldering; a very rough hole results in a greater occurrence of cracking than a smooth hole, when both are plated from the same electroless copper bath.   Saito and Honma[44] reported that there is a correlation between surface leveling and ductility; the addition of non-ionic surfactant to electroless copper bath smoothes the deposit surface, which improves the ductility.   The mechanical properties (Young's modulus, tensile/yield strength, and ductility) of electroless copper deposits obtained from various proprietary baths were reported by Lin et al.,[45] who found that deposits with rough surfaces were less ductile than those with smoother surfaces.   Crevices are thought to serve as stress concentrations and thus to provide preferential sites for crack nucleation.   If the ratio of surface roughness to foil thickness is reduced, the ductility increases.[6]   Contrary to the effect on the ductility, the surface roughness does not affect the tensile strength nor yield strength.[45]   Apparently, the surface roughness effect on the ductility has been recognized for some time, but no quantitative analysis of this effect has been done in the past to substantiate its significance.

A theoretical analysis[46] for a metal sheet with a groove subjected to biaxial tension can be used for understanding the effect of surface roughness on ductility.   The analysis shows that the depth of the groove, which represents the surface crevice, strongly affects the

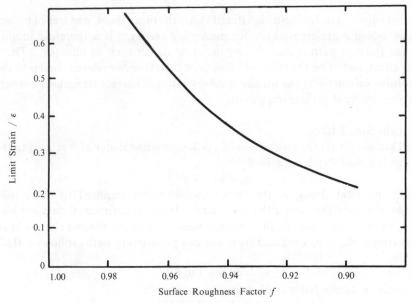

Fig. 3.14 Theoretical plot showing the limit strain ε, vs. surface roughness factor, f (see text).

ductility.   The result is shown in Fig. 3.14 as a function of surface roughness factor f (= t_g/t, where t_g is the thickness at the groove and t the thickness outside the groove).   The ductility decreases with increasing surface roughness; even a 7% thickness change from f=0.97 to 0.90 appears to produce a significant reduction (by~61%) in ductility.   The result clearly indicates the importance of surface roughness.   More experimental data are needed to confirm the surface roughness effect.

A hillock or a nodule is one type of surface defect commonly observed on the surface of electroless copper deposits.   The hillock is roughly mushroom-shaped and is surrounded by void or low-density regions (see Fig. 3.15).   Because of the void region, the presence of a hillock creates a locally thin area, which provides a preferential site for crack nucleation.   Most recently, we found[47] that electroless copper foils grown on activated plastic substrates exhibit a large scatter in ductility.   A careful metallographic analysis of the fracture edge has revealed that the foil with low ductility always contained a hillock along

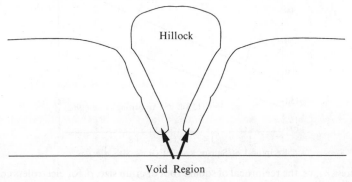

Fig. 3.15 A schematic showing the cross-sectional view of a hillock, which is surrounded by a void region.

the fractured edge.   The foil with high ductility, on the other hand, was free of hillocks.   A hillock was indeed a preferential site for nucleating cracks.   It is therefore important to examine the fracture path if there is any localized defect such as hillocks.   The surface roughness effect, including the effect of hillocks, is therefore considered similar to the effect of void volume on ductility; the former involves external surface irregularity, whereas the latter involves internal surface irregularity.

3.4.4   Grain Size Effect

It is well known[48] that the yield stress of a polycrystalline material is related to the grain size through the Hall-Petch equation[49,50];

$$\sigma_y = \sigma_0 + kd^{-1/2} \qquad (3.3)$$

where σ_y is the yield stress, σ_0 the lattice friction stress required to move individual dislocations, k a constant, and d the grain size.   When experimental data are plotted in terms of σ_y vs. $d^{-1/2}$, they usually fit a straight line.   Lin et al.[45] found that yield stress of electroless copper deposits obtained from various proprietary baths follows a Hall-Petch relationship;

$$\sigma_y = 40.6 + 140.6d^{-1/2} \qquad (3.4)$$

This result can be compared with that for bulk copper[51];

$$\sigma_y = 26 + 113.8d^{-1/2} \qquad (3.5)$$

Equations (3.4) and (3.5) are plotted in Fig. 3.16 for comparison.   It is seen that their slopes are similar but the line of electroless copper lies slightly above that of bulk copper.   In other words, for a given grain size, the yield stress of electroless copper is about 30% larger than that of bulk copper.   In a previous section we suggested that the yield stress of electroless copper can be higher because of the presence of Type I and II voids.   One possible explanation for the difference in the yield stress is that in addition to the grain size effect, a high density of voids contribute to the strengthening of electroless copper and thus increases

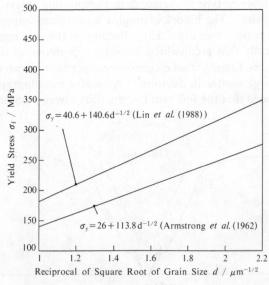

Fig. 3.16 Yield stress, σ_y, vs. the reciprocal of square root of grain size, d, for electroless copper deposits and bulk copper.

Large-Grained (10–40μm) Electroless Copper

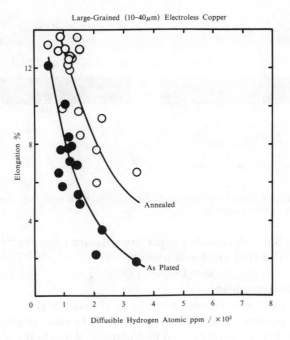

Fig. 3.17 Ductility of large-grained (10–40 μm) electroless copper deposits plotted against diffusible hydrogen content.

Fine-Grained (0.2–2μm) Electroless Copper

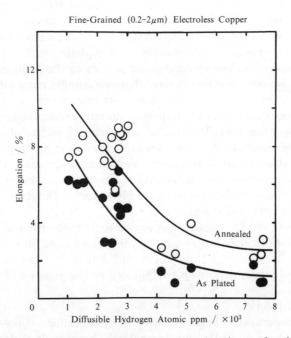

Fig. 3.18 Ductility of fine-grained (0.2–2 μm) electroless copper deposits as a function of diffusible hydrogen content.

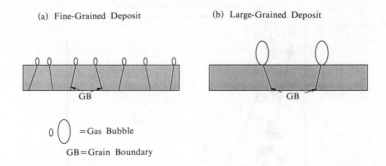

Fig. 3.19 A schematic illustration showing the distribution of GB voids in (a) fine-grained and
          (b) large-grained deposits.

the yield strength.   Since electroless copper deposits are generally brittle, their tensile
strength also follows[45] a Hall-Petch relationship;

$$\sigma_t = 133.8 + 153.7d^{-1/2} \qquad (3.6)$$

where σ_t is the tensile strength and d the grain size.

Contrary to the Hall-Petch relationship for the yield strength/grain size, there is no well-
defined relationship between grain size and ductility.   The effect of grain size on ductility
in electroless copper deposits is found[17] to be complicated due to the presence of voids at
the GBs.   To determine the grain size dependence of film ductility for electroless copper,
two types of copper substrates were prepared.   The substrate used to obtain large-grained
epitaxial deposits was a section of 11 µm-thick annealed OFHC copper foil consisting of
grains measuring 10–40 µm.   Fine-grained deposits were grown on the same copper foil
coated with a thin (~0.4 µm) layer of fine-grained (<1000 Å) gold electrodeposit.   The two
types of substrates were plated simultaneously in each plating bath.   Electroless copper
deposits grew epitaxially on these substrates and replicated the grain sizes.   Comparing
Figs. 3.17 with 3.18, we note that fine-grained deposits contain more diffusible hydrogen
and more void volume than large-grained deposits.   In other words, under identical plating
conditions, fine-grained deposits tend to trap more gas bubbles than large-grained ones.   It
was shown[17] previously that the GBs emerging at the growing surface of electroless copper,
which are seen as line segments, are grooved and therefore can provide stronger retaining
force to gas bubbles than the non-GB region.   Fine-grained deposits, which have greater
line segments per unit growth surface area than large-grained ones, are expected to trap gas
bubbles, which are smaller in size and more closely spaced.   In fact, we did observe this
difference.   This concept is illustrated in Fig. 3.19.

Combining Figs. 3.17 and 18 yields a graph similar to that shown in Fig. 3.10.   Although
the data were taken for two grain size ranges, they indicate a trend for the void effect rather
than the grain size effect.   It can thus be concluded that the grain size dependence of
ductility in electroless copper deposits is complicated by the presence of GB voids.

3.4.5   Annealing Effect

The mechanical properties can be greatly affected by annealing.   Low-temperature (20–
250 °C) annealing has been studied[9-13] most extensively, because electroless copper deposits
are exposed to heating/cooling environments in this temperature range during the PCB

fabrication and/or its field usage.   During low-temperature annealing, electroless copper deposits undergo primarily two processes[12] that contribute to the ductility improvement: (1) the outdiffusion of molecular hydrogen trapped in voids and   (2) recrystallization and grain growth via a GB diffusion mechanism.   The low-temperature ductility recovery, therefore, comes from both the pressure release and the recrystallization and grain growth.   The outdiffusion of hydrogen trapped in voids occurs first by dissociation of molecular hydrogen into hydrogen atom, *i.e.* $H_2 \rightarrow 2H$, followed by interstitial diffusion in copper lattice.   The recrystallization stage involves the migration of incoherent large-angle GBs which sweep through the whole crystal structure and replace it by less distorted material.

These two processes are schematically illustrated in Fig. 3.20.   In an earlier study,[13] it was reported that the first process was predominant and the second process was not present.   The absence of the second process can be attributed to the use of large (10–40 μm)-grained copper, in which the enlargement of the grain size was not obvious.   For fine-grained ($\sim$0.1 μm) deposits, we did observe[12] recrystallization and grain growth, accompanied by ductility increase.   The annealing effect is small for large-grained deposits, but large for fine-grained deposits.   The driving force for the recrystallization and grain growth processes comes primarily from the GB energy.   In this temperature range (20–250°C), only the GB diffusion process is active and assists the GB migration.   Impurities or voids lying at the GBs or inside the grains can exert a pinning force, making the motion of GBs difficult.   Even the GBs initially free of impurities will eventually meet impurities included within the grains during their migration, causing pinning.   Therefore, recrystallization and grain growth occur to a lesser extent in electroless copper containing more impurities and more voids.

The effect of impurities and voids on the recrystallization behavior of electroless copper was recently studied by Nakahara *et al.*[12]   The amount of ductility increase after 150°C annealing plotted as a function of both void volume fraction and carbon content can provide some insight into how voids and impurities affect the annealing behavior.   We assume that the carbon content gives a measure of impurity content in the deposits.   The ductiliy increase, $\Delta\varepsilon$, generally decreases with increasing void volume fraction.   In addition, if each set of data is grouped together according to the amount of impurity content, we obtained several families of descending curves, as shown schematically in Fig. 3.21.   The slope of the curves becomes smaller with increasing impurity content.   Based on microstructural analysis together with the results in Fig. 3.10, we classified fine-grained electroless copper deposits into four types.   Type I deposits are free of both impurities and voids.   The GBs of this type of deposit are clean so can migrate eailsy without being pinned.   Therefore, the deposits can readily recrystallize *via* a GB diffusion mechanism during the annealing, improving the ductility.   Type II deposits lying on the same curve as Type I are free of impurities but contain a high density of voids, which serve as pinning sites for the GB motion during the annealing.   Therefore, this type of deposit does not recrystallize easily, resulting in only a small amount of ductility recovery by the outdiffusion of hydrogen in voids (a relief of pressure effect).   Type III deposits are void-free but contain a large amount of impurities.   The ductility of Type III deposits does not recover easily by recrystallization because impurities pin the motion of the GBs.   Type IV deposits, which lie on the same curve as Type III deposits, contain a high density of both impurities and voids.   Because of numerous voids, the initial ductility is already low, thus

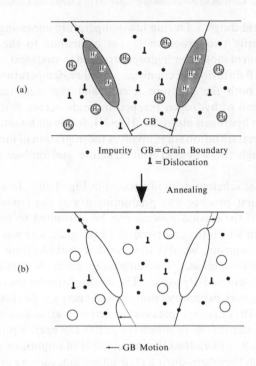

(a)

Impurity   GB = Grain Boundary
⊥ = Dislocation

Annealing

(b)

← GB Motion

Fig. 3.20 A schematic view illustrating how the microstructure of as-deposited electroless copper changes upon 150°C annealing.   The GB migration occurs via a GB diffusion mechanism.   The migration, however, can be impeded by incorporated voids (or hydrogen gas bubbles) and impurities lying on the boundaries.

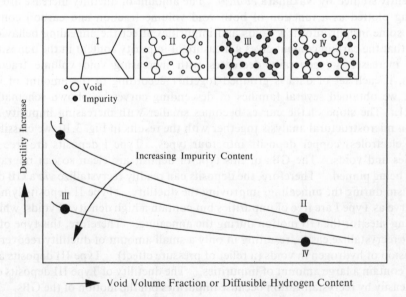

Fig. 3.21 A diagram illustrating how a ductility increase brought about by annealing can be affected by diffusible hydrogen, voids, and impurities.   Four typical microstructures, I, II, III, and IV, are illustrated.

the recoverable amount of the ductility is also low.   Consequently, the ductility improvement resulting from removal of the pressure effect will also be small.   This schematic illustration clearly demonstrates that both impurities and voids affect the extent of the ductility recovery through their effects on the extent of recrystallization.

3.5   Classification of Electroless Copper

Several attempts have been made to classify the type of electroless copper deposits based on their mechanical properties.   Paunovic and Zeblisky[52] first classified crack-free electroless copper after a solder shock test (288°C, 10 sec.) into two types: Class 1 with high tensile strength (~579 MPa) and Class 2 with high elongation (~7.1%). Characteristics of these deposits are listed in Table 3.3.   Both types of deposits, having markedly different properties, apparently pass the thermal shock test.   The second classification is found in the Japanese Industrial Standard[53] (see Table 3.4).   This classification is based on the type of applications: Class 1 is for general use and Class 2 for high-reliability applications.   It should be noted that this classification is different from that of Paunovic and Zeblisky.[52]

A third classification is based on the ductility recovery behavior observed upon annealing.   Four types[12] have been described in a previous section.   In addition, Godbole and Pedraza[54,55] and Minten and Toth[56] made detailed studies on two kinds of electroless copper deposits, classified as high-elongation (HE) and high-strength (HS) types.   They found that the recrystallization temperature of the HS type was 100K higher than that of HE type.   They claimed that the HS copper is less pure than HE copper.   Dinella and Mak[57] studied two types of fine-grained electroless copper deposits.   They found that one type of deposit exhibited a large change in both ductility and strength upon thermal cycling but the

TABLE 3.3 Two Types of Electroless Copper Deposits (after Paunovic and Zeblisky[52])

Type of Deposit	Class 1	Class 2
Elongation (%)	4.3	7.1
Tensile Strength (MPa)	579	213
Grain Size (μm)		
Size Parallel to the Substrate	0.3	0.7
Size Perpendicular to the Substrate	7	6

TABLE 3.4 Two types of electroless copper classified by Japanese Industrial Standard[53]

Type of Deposit	Class 1	Class 2
Minimum Elongation (%)	3	7
Minimum Tensile Strength (MPa)	195	295

other type did not show a significant change.   These classifications are primarily based on mechanical properties, which are considered to play an important role in determining the reliability of the PCBs.

3.6   Concluding Remarks

We have reviewed various important factors that affect the mechanical properties (ductility and tensile/yield strength) of electroless copper deposits.   It has been shown that hydrogen inclusions, particularly molecular hydrogen, reduce the ductility both by the pressure effect and by the void effect.   Surface morphology was also shown to affect the ductility significantly, although its effect has not been investigated sufficiently.   Low-temperature (20–250°C) annealing generally increases the ductility by removing the pressure effect and/or by inducing recrystallization and grain growth.   The extent of the ductility recovery by the recrystallization process is limited by the impurity and void content of the deposits.   The tensile strength of electroless copper deposits can be related to the grain size through the Hall-Petch equation, and it is higher for a given grain size than that of bulk copper.   The increased yield strength can be attributed to the void-strengthening effect due to the presence of numerous voids in the deposits.

One of the most important factors not discussed in this review is the additive effect.   Additives are known to play an important role in modifying the properties of electroless copper deposits.   We found a number of references dealing with the subject of additive effect.   However, understanding of the mechanistic aspect of the additive effect is still far from complete and is not yet well established.   We hope that this subject will be dealt with elsewhere in the near future.

REFERENCES

1. M. Goodenough and K. J. Whitlaw, *Trans. Inst. Metal Finish.*, **67**, 57 (1989).
2. J. J. D'Ambrisi, D. Ferrier, P. E. Kukanskis and R. A. Letiza, *P. C. Fab.*, **12**, 30 (1989).
3. Military Standard Specification, MIL-8TD-202DM107C;MIL-P-55110C.
4. E. K. Yung, L. T. Romankiw and R. C. Alkire, *J. Electrochem. Soc.*, **136**, 206 (1989).
5. H. Akahoshi and K. Murakami, Extended Abstract, 88-2, ECS Mtg., Chicago, Oct. 9–14 (1988).
6. K. S. Vecchio and R. W. Hertzberg, *Microelectron. Reliab.*, **26**, 715 (1986).
7. R. J. Iannuzzelli, *Electronic Manufacturing,* **35**, 18 (1989).
8. Y. Kitamura and T. Takahama, *Proc. 5th Ann. Tech. Mtg. Printed Circuit Soc. Japan,* p. 133, Nov. 1990.
9. Y. Okinaka and S. Nakahara, *J. Electrochem. Soc.,* **123**, 475 (1976).
10. S. Nakahara and Y. Okinaka, *Acta Met.,* **31**, 713 (1983).
11. S. Nakahara, *Acta Met.,* **36**, 1669 (1988).
12. S. Nakahara, C. Y. Mak and Y. Okinaka, *J. Electrochem. Soc.,* **138**, 1421 (1991).
13. Y. Okinaka and H. K. Straschil, *J. Electrochem. Soc.,* **133**, 2608 (1986).
14. R. M. Lukes, *Plating,* **51**, 1066 (1964).
15. J. J. Grunwald, H. Rhodenizer and L. Siominski, *Plating,* **58**, 1004 (1971).
16. J. J. Grunwald, L. Slominski, and A. Landau, *Plating,* **60**, 1022 (1973).
17. S. Nakahara, Y. Okinaka and H. K. Straschil, *J. Electrochem. Soc.,* **136**, 1120 (1989).
18. S. Nakahara and Y. Okinaka, *Mater. Sci. & Eng.,* **A101**, 227 (1988).
19. J. E. Graebner and Y. Okinaka, *J. Appl. Phys.,* **60**, 36 (1986).
20. T. Gela, in:*Mechanical Design and Systems Handbook* (ed. H. A. Rothbart), pp. 17–19, McGraw-Hill, New York (1964).
21. A. R. Troiano, in:*Hydrogen in Metals* (eds. I. M. Bernstein and A. W. Thompson), American Society for Metals, Metals Park, OH (1974).
22. J. C. Warf, *J. Inorg. Nucl. Chem.,* **19**, 304 (1961).

23. J. C. Warf, *J. Inorg. Nucl. Chem.,* **28**, 1031 (1966).
24. S. Nakahara and Y. Okinaka, *Script. Met.,* **19**, 517 (1985).
25. H. Honma and S. Mizushima, *J. Metal Finish. Soc. Japan.,* **34**, 290 (1983).
26. M. C. Agens, U. S. Patent 2,938,805 (1960).
27. M. Matsuoka and T. Hayashi, *Jitsumu Hyōmen Gijutsu,* **31**, 362 (1984) (in Japanese).
28. T. F. Schaaf, K. L. Morton and B. S. Madsen, *Proc. 1st AES Electroless Plating Symp.,* St. Louis, MO., March 23–24 (1982).
29. H. Hirohara, M. Oita and K. Honjo, *J. Met. Finish. Soc. Japan,* **21**, 485 (1970).
30. H. Hirohata, M. Oita and K. Honjo, *J. Met. Finish. Soc. Japan,* **21**, 550 (1970).
31. K. Murakami, H. Akahoshi and M. Wajima, *Proc. 70th Ann. Tech. Mtg. Metal Finish. Soc. Japan,* 17B-2 (1984).
32. S. Nakahara, Unpublished Results (1988).
33. H. K. Straschil, Private Communication (1986).
34. S. Nakahara, Y. Okinaka and D. R. Turner, *J. Testing & Evaluation* **5**, 178 (1977).
35. S. Nakahara, Y. Okinaka and H. K. Straschil, in:*Testing of Metallic and Inorganic Coatings,* ASTM STP 947 (eds., W. B. Harding and G. A. Di Bari), ASTM, Philadelphia, 1987, pp. 32–51.
36. D. Broek, *International Metallurgical Reviews,* **19**, 135 (1974).
37. V. L. Kalikhman, Ya. S. Umanskii, I.A. Tribunskaya, S.V. Bunsheva and V.A. Osadchenko, *Protection of Metals,* **20**, 611 (1984).
38. P. F. Thomason, *J. Inst. Metals,* **96**, 360 (1968).
39. A. Melander, *Mater. Sci. & Eng.,* **39**, 57 (1979).
40. A. H. Cottrell, in:*Theoretical Structural Metallurgy,* Edward Arnold Publishers Ltd., London (1965), p.241.
41. L. M. Brown and D. J. Mazey, *Phil. Mag.,* **10**, 1081 (1964).
42. P. G. Manusmare and H. P. Leighly, Jr., *Acta Met.,* **24**, 1047 (1976).
43. J. J. Grunwald, L. Slominski, and A. Landau, *Proc. 4th AES Plating in the Electronics Industry Symp.,* Indianapolis, Ind., Jan. 31 & Feb. 1 (1973).
44. M. Saito and H. Honma, *J. Metal Finish. Soc. Japan,* **29**, 190 (1978).
45. K. Lin, I. Kim, and R. Weil, *Plat. & Surf. Finish.,* **75**, 52 (July 1988).
46. Z. Marciniak and K. Kuczynski, *Int. J. Mech. Sci.,* **9**, 609 (1967).
47. S. Nakahara, C. Y. Mak and Y. Okinaka, to be published (1991).
48. R. B. Nicholson, in:*Strengthening Methods in Crystals,* (eds. A. Kelly and R. B. Nicholson), John Wiley & Sons, Inc., New York, 1971.
49. E. O. Hall, *Proc. Phys. Soc. (London),* **64B**, 747 (1951).
50. N. J. Petch, *J. Iron Steel Inst.,* **174**, 25 (1953).
51. R. Armstrong, I. Codd, R. M. Douthwaite and N. J. Petch, *Phil. Mag.,* **7**, 45 (1962).
52. M. Paunovic and R. Zeblisky, *Plat. & Surf. Finish.,* **72**, 52 (1985).
53. Japanese Industrial Standard (JIS), Electroless Copper Platings, JIS H 8646 (1991).
54. A. J. Pedraza and M. J. Godbole, *Script. Met.,* **24**, 1185 (1990).
55. M. J. Godbole and A. J. Pedraza, *Script. Met.,* **24**, 1191 (1990).
56. K. Minten and J. Toth, *Trans. Inst. Metal Finish.,* **69**, 20 (1991).
57. D. Dinella and C. Y. Mak, *Proc. Printed Circuit World Convention V,* Tech. Paper B 5/1, Glasgow, Scotland, June, 1990.

4

Synthesis of Advanced Materials by Electrochemical Processing in Nonaqueous Media

Donald R. SADOWAY

Department of Materials Science and Engineering, Massachusetts Institute of Technology, Cambridge, Massachusetts 02139-4307, U.S.A.

4.1 Introduction

Advanced materials are characterized not only by their specialized chemistries, *i.e.*, purity, doping level, etc., but also by their tailored microstructures. Through processing one attains compositional and microstructural goals and produces materials to specification. This chapter discusses electrolysis from the perspective of materials processing, in particular, the potential of electrochemical processing to generate advanced materials. These include thin films, epitaxial layers, powders, and various nonequilibrium structures such as metastable phases, compositionally graded microstructures, and compositionally modulated microstructures.

Electrolysis is based upon electron-transfer with ionic species. Why, then, electrolysis in nonaqueous media? Unfortunately, aqueous solutions are unsuitable as media for processing reactive elements. At decomposition potentials negative enough to deposit these elements hydrogen evolution occurs. Furthermore, in certain cases the elements so deposited immediately react with water in a metallothermic reduction. To a first approximation aqueous electrochemistry is restricted to the energy window bounded by the hydrogen and oxygen evolution reactions. Kinetic factors extend these limitations somewhat, but not far enough to allow electrolysis of highly reactive metals and their compounds. Hence, there is a need to exploit nonaqueous electrolytes, of which there are three categories, characterized primarily by their temperature regimes of stability: at ambient temperature, organic electrolytes; at elevated temperatures, molten salts; at subambient and cryogenic temperatures, liquefied gases. This article is confined to a discussion of the latter two. In metallurgical applications organic electrolytes play a very small role. This is in part due to their poor ionicity, which results in low electrical conductivity and inability to dissolve reactants. As well, organic electrolytes can have some or all of the following characteristics: low flash point, carcinogenic, react violently with water.

To repeat, then, electrodeposition in nonaqueous media may be the only way to deposit certain elements. However, for other elements that can be deposited from aqueous solutions, electrolysis in nonaqueous media may offer advantages in terms of the specific resulting composition and microstructure of the deposit. For example, chromium deposits produced by fused salt electrolysis in halide melts are very low in hydrogen, a condition difficult to achieve in deposits generated in aqueous media. Furthermore, fused salt electrolysis offers opportunities to make coatings on easily oxidizable metals which are difficult to plate in aqueaous media. For example, niobium and tantalum can be electroplated with platinum group metals only by fused salt electrolysis despite the fact that the latter are easily electrodeposited from aqueous media.

By way of introduction to the field of molten salts the reader is directed to the collections by Blander,[1] Sundheim,[2] Mamantov,[3] and Mamantov and Marassi,[4] as well as the monographs by Lumsden[5] and Bloom[6]. A brief overview can be found in the two-volume set by Richardson[7]. Electrochemistry of molten salts is treated in the monograph by Delimarskii and Markov.[8] Basic property data have been compiled by Janz in a handbook[9] with supplements published in the *Journal of Physical and Chemical Reference Data* (Refs. 10 and 11, for example). The properties of the most common solvent systems have been collected by Plambeck[12]. The industrial applications of molten salts are treated in books edited by Lovering[13] and Kuhn.[14] Current research and reviews are reported in several series: *Advances in Molten Salt Chemistry,*[15] *Molten Salt Techniques,*[16] as well as in proceedings volumes from international symposia held under the umbrella of the Electrochemical Society.[17] As for archival publications, the journals where molten salt research is apt to be reported include the *Journal of the Electrochemical Society, Electrochimica Acta* and the *Journal of Applied Electrochemistry.* There is a substantial amount of activity in the former Soviet Union, especially in Russia and Ukraine, with the result that much of the molten salt literature is not published in English, e.g., *Rasplavy*, or Melts, published in Sverdlovsk, and *Ukrainskii Khimicheskii Zhurnal*, or the Ukrainian Journal of Chemistry, published in Kiev.

4.2   Characteristics of Electrochemical Processing

Electrolysis is an electrochemical process, *i.e.*, a process in which chemical reaction is accompanied by electron transfer. Electrolysis is performed in a reactor called an electrochemical cell, which is a device that enables electrical energy to do chemical work, which in the context of this article is the generation of an element or a compound. This, in turn, must first be dissolved in an ionic solution from which elements are deposited by the passage of electrical current with its attendant electron-transfer reactions at each electrode. Fig. 4.1 shows a prototypical electrolysis cell in which the electrolyte is a molten salt. Its principal components are the electrolyte, the electrodes, and the container (sidewalls and floor). The electrolytes are multicomponent melts of either chlorides or fluorides.

Chlorides offer the advantages of a lower operating temperature and of a greater choice of electrode and container materials. As for disadvantages, chlorides react with moisture: some are hydroscopic, even deliquescent, while others decompose by hydrolysis. Hydrolysis prevents dehydration, *i.e.*, simple heating will not result in the removal of the water of hydration from niobium pentachloride:

$$NbCl_5 \cdot H_2O = NbCl_5 + H_2O . \tag{4.1}$$

Instead, hydrolysis occurs to convert the pentachloride to oxychloride with attendant emission of hydrogen chloride gas:

$$NbCl_5 \cdot H_2O = NbOCl_3 + 2 \, HCl . \tag{4.2}$$

Niobium oxychloride, $NbOCl_3$, is much stabler than $NbCl_5$ and thus much more difficult to

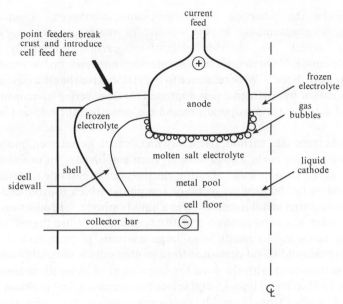

Fig. 4.1 Prototypical Electrolysis Cell.

electrolyze.   Furthermore, the oxychloride contains oxygen which at the carbon anode reacts in preference to chlorine and forms carbon monoxide and carbon dioxide; the result is an increase in anode consumption rate.   To assure metal purity it is imperative that the electrolyte be free of the impurities formed by reaction with moisture.   This adds to the number of unit operations in cell feed preparation from source materials and furthermore puts strict requirements on the operating conditions of the electrolysis cell.

Fluorides, on the other hand, have the advantage of being less reactive with moisture.   Additionally, fluorides can dissolve oxides directly.   This avoids fluorination which requires reaction with ammonium bifluoride, for example.   The use of an oxide-based cell feed in principle simplifies the process flowsheet and reduces capital and operating costs.   Unfortunately, the higher melting points and greater corrosivity of the fluorides severely limit the choice of materials of construction in the physical plant.   In the case of materials processing, this means greater risk of inflicting thermal damage on the substrate.   Another disadvantage is the relatively low solubility of refractory-metal oxides in molten fluorides.   Since the limiting current density scales directly with concentration the low solubility of oxide feed in fluoride melts limits cell productivity by setting a rather low ceiling on the maximum practical operating current density.

During electrolysis electric current is passed from the anode through the electrolyte to the cathode.   The electrolyte must be strictly an ionic conductor, while the electrodes must be electronic conductors.   The anode can be either consumable or nonconsumable.   Consumable anodes are found in various electrolytic processes.   In electrorefining, the anode consists of an impure form of the metal to be purified.   In electroplating, the consumable anode may act as the feedstock for the deposited metal.   In electrowinning, the consumable anode consists of a material that reacts with the products of the anodic reaction, e.g., a carbon anode in the presence of evolving anodic oxygen. Used primarily in electrowinning, nonconsumable anodes consist of materials inert to chemical and electrochemical attack. In chloride electrolytes carbon commonly serves as a nonconsumable anode. There is no fully satisfactory nonconsumable anode for use with fluoride-based electrolytes. With reference to the Hall cell for the electrolytic extraction of aluminum this author has defined a new approach for discovering nonconsumable anodes for use in fused salt electrolysis operations and has described the relevant set of selection criteria.[18]

As for cathode materials, carbon, refractory metals such as tungsten, molybdenum, and tantalum, as well as low carbon steel have all been employed. In practice, the cathode functions only as the current lead. During electrolysis the cathode material is separated from the electrolyte by the product metal or compound which is produced in solid form unless a host low melting metal is employed as a liquid cathode. Production of solid metal and liquid alloy each has its advantages and disadvantages. When the cell product is solid metal it is not necessary to purify it of large amounts of host cathode metal. The disadvantage is that solid metal deposited from molten salts is invariably dendritic. This results in salt entrainment with the need for some form of subsequent treatment for salt removal. The production of liquid metal solves the morphological problem and facilitates easy removal of product from the cell by siphoning; however, this approach has its faults, the principal one being the need to refine the refractory metal out of the product cathode metal alloy.

The electrolyte is contained in a steel shell lined with carbon block. With chlorides a lining of ceramic or low carbon steel is acceptable. It is also possible to operate with a sidewall of frozen electrolyte. Current densities are in the neighborhood of 1 A cm^{-2} for electrowinning molten metal; for reasons related to assuring morphological stability current densities in electoplating cells are about an order of magnitude lower and range from 10 to 100 mA cm^{-2}. Cell operating temperatures span 400° to 1000°. Cell voltages depend upon the particular melt chemistry and cell design which determines the contribution of the ohmic resistance of the bath. During electrolysis the voltage required to drive the process is substantially higher than the reversible potential as calculated by the Nernst equation, which for metal halide, MX_n, in a multicomponent molten salt solution and in equilibrium with pure metal, M, and pure gas X_2 at atmospheric pressure, can be expressed as

$$\mathscr{E}_{MX_n} = -\Delta_f G°_{MX_n}/(n\mathscr{F}) - (RT/n\mathscr{F})\ln a_{MX_n}, \qquad (4.3)$$

Where $\Delta_f G°_{MX_n}$ is the standard Gibbs free energy of formation of MX_n, $\mathscr{F}$ is the Faraday constant, 96487 C mol^{-1}, R is the gas constant, 8.314 J mol^{-1} K^{-1}, T is the temperature in Kelvins, and a_{MX_n} is the activity of MX_n in the electrolyte solution. $\mathscr{E}_{MX_n}$ is a function of electrolyte composition and temperature. The difference between the equilibrium potential and the applied voltage is due to kinetic factors which increase the energy consumption of the cell. The cell voltage for the electrolytic decomposition of MX_n is given by[19]

$$V_{cell} = \mathscr{E}_{MX_n} + (\eta_a + \eta_c)_{cathode} + (\eta_a + \eta_c)_{anode}$$
$$+ \eta_{electrodes} + \eta_{ohmic}, \qquad (4.4)$$

where $\mathscr{E}_{MX_n}$ is the reversible potential or equilibrium decomposition potential given by the Nernst equation; η_a is the activation overpotential at the electrode and is a function of electrolyte composition, current density and temperature; η_c is the concentration overpotential at the electrode and is a function of electrolyte composition, current density and temperature; $\eta_{electrodes}$ includes the voltage drops associated with the electrodes themselves, with the bus bars, and with the electrical contacts between them; and η_{ohmic}, the ohmic overpotential or IR drop, is due to the electrical resistance of the electrolyte itself and is proportional to current density and interelectrode distance and inversely proportional to the electrical conductivity of the electrolyte and to the electrode area.   Existing industrial molten salt electrolysis cells operate at voltages three to five times the value of the Nernst potential.

Cell productivity is expressed in terms of several figures of merit.   Current efficiency can be loosely defined as the ratio of the number of equivalents of metal product to the number of moles of electrical charge delivered to the cell by the power supply.   As such, current efficiency is effectively a measure of compliance with Faraday's laws of electrolysis.   In electrowinning cells cathodic current efficiencies of 60 to 80 per cent are not uncommon.   These figures are well below those reported for the electrolytic production of aluminum which typically attains current efficiencies exceeding 90 per cent.   Voltage efficiency is the ratio of the equilibrium decomposition potential to the applied cell voltage.   Quite simply, voltage efficiency expresses the deviation from the Nernst equation and is a measure of inefficiency due to kinetic factors cited above.   In the electrolysis of fluorides voltage efficiencies are typically below 50 per cent, while in the electrolysis of chlorides values below 25 per cent have been reported.

4.3   Electroplating

Fused salt electrolysis can also generate coatings.   Representative of the types of coatings so formed are those comprising the refractory metals.   By way of illustration the following treatment draws upon results for refractory metals.   The range of compositions includes elements, alloys, and compounds.   Indeed, electroplating of refractory metals has received somewhat more attention than electrolytic extraction of these metals.   At least on the basis of reports in the open literature, the most thoroughly studied metals from the perspective of electroplating are molybdenum[20-23] and titanium.[24,25]   Other metals, however, continue to receive attention: niobium,[26,27] tantalum,[26,28,29] chromium,[30-33] and tungsten.[34]   Electrodeposited coatings can be pure metal, metal alloy, or compounds.   Reports of research on the electrodeposition of alloys include Mo–Nb,[35] Ni–Ta,[36] and Ni–Nb.[36]

As for electrodeposition of compounds containing refractory metals, the earliest work was concentrated on the production of carbides, largely for the purposes of generating abrasion-resistant coatings.[34,37]   Coatings of titanium diboride have been deposited both to impart corrosion resistance against attack by liquid metal[38,39] and to offer abrasion resistance.[40-42]   More recently, investigators have begun studying the associated electrode processes.[43]   Generation of tungsten carbide coatings has been driven by the desire to form material for use in abrasion-resistant coatings.[34,44,45]   Studies of electrochemical fundamentals have begun.[46-50]   Other refractory metal compounds whose electrosynthesis has been reported include zirconium diboride,[48,50] chromium boride,[51] molybdenum disilicide,[52] tantalum carbide[53] and molybdenum carbide.[54]   More recently, attention has turned to a broader array of materials syntheses, including metal matrix composites[55] and refractory-metal oxides containing controlled subvalent forms of the refractory-metal ion.[56]   In the case of the latter, electrosynthesis from fused salts has facilitated the generation of compounds otherwise produced thermochemically at high temperatures and high pressures.

An alternative to electrosynthesis of refractory-metal oxide compounds is anodization.   The distinction between the two processes is that anodization is a process for the faradaic oxidation of elemental metal present as the anode substrate.   In contrast, electrosynthesis is a process for the faradaic discharge of both metal and oxygen (both present in the electrolyte) to form a compound on an electrode substrate.   While refractory metals can be anodized in aqueous media, fused salt anodization offers certain advantages in product quality, both in terms of chemical composition and microstructure.[57]

4.4   Cryogenic Electrolytes

Cryogenic electrolytes do not appear in contemporary metallurgical technology.   Electroplating of elemental refractory metal from subambient and cryogenic liquids has been reported, but not at the commercial scale.[58]   At the time of this writing the viability of electrosynthesis of compounds in cryogenic media is under investigation in the author's laboratory at the Massachusetts Institute of Technology.[59]   Reference is made below to future prospects for electrochemical processing in these media.

4.5   Future Directions

When viewed in the context of materials processing, fused salt electrolysis has many fine attributes.   However, unresolved technical issues continue to impede its further commercialization.   These include low cathode current efficiency, anode effect (restricted to fluoride-based electrolytes processing oxide feed), purity of metal product, corrosion of cell components, and heat balance of the cell.   Losses of power efficiency can be traced to the fact that the refractory metals exhibit multiple valency in these melts.   This can lead to redox looping or parasitic reaction of subvalent ions with metal product.   Furthermore, as mentioned above, most cells produce solid metal.   Solid electrodeposits obtained in molten salts are typically dendritic or powdery, but rarely smooth, especially when the metal is of high purity.   To deal with multiple valency one can optimize bath chemistry,[60,61] use a diaphragm to separate specified ions from one another while allowing selected mass transfer between regions of the cell, an approach very popular with designers of titanium electrowinning cells,[62-64] or invent divided cells featuring staged reactions.[65]   The morphological problem has been attacked in some cases by employing molten metal cathodes (Refs. 66 and 67, for example).   The use of leveling agents, while potentially beneficial, has been examined for electroplating,[20] but evidently not for electrowinning where the goal is to produce metal of the highest purity.

Besides the strictly technical issues there are other concerns.   For example, in designing new electrolytic processes one must look carefully at capital costs as well as operating costs.   If fused salt electrolysis is to compete effectively with nonelectrochemical materials processing, steps must be taken to design flowsheets with a minimum number of unit operations.   More attention must be paid to environmental, health and safety issues.   Clearly, the ecological soundness of new processes must be considered from the time of their invention. It is the opinion of this author that electrolysis is uniquely positioned to tackle these problems which, if left unsolved, threaten to cripple the metals industry.

From the perspective of a technology capable of generating advanced materials, fused salt electrolysis looks attractive.[68] Advanced materials are characterized not only by their specialized chemistries, *i.e.*, purity, doping level, etc., but also by their tailored microstructures, which fused salt electrolysis has the potential to generate. These include thin films, epitaxial layers, powders, and various nonequilibrium structures. Powders of a number of refractory metals and their compounds have been produced by fused salt electrolysis: titanium,[69-71] niobium,[72] tantalum,[72] chromium,[70] tungsten,[70,73] tungsten carbide[45] and in general.[74] As for nonequilibrium structures, fused salt electrolysis has the capacity to produce metastable phases, compositionally graded microstructures, and compositionally modulated microstructures. To date there has been very little use of fused salt electrolysis to generate nonequilibrium structures of refractory metals. There are isolated reports in the literature of metastable phase formation[75] and deposition of single crystals with preferred orientation.[76] These results were restricted to refractory *metals* and not their *compounds*. Among the layered structures reported in the literature is molybdenum carbide on diamond.[77] Overall, this field is severely underexploited.

Earlier in this article liquefied gases were named as a class of inorganic electrolytes. What is their potential role in the electrosynthesis of advanced materials? What is to be gained by processing in such media? First of all, these electrolytes are anhydrous and chemically stable. Thus, in principle, one should be able to electrodeposit elements that cannot be plated from aqueous solutions. Secondly, the processing temperatures are very low with the result that thermal damage to the substrate is minimized. Thirdly, at these low processing temperatures the kinetics of deposition are expected to be controlled by charge transfer rather than by mass transfer. This tends to favor surface smoothing and the production of coatings of uniform thickness; alternatively, the process can be said to have good throwing power. There are other microstructural consequences. Low temperature processing enhances nucleation and restrains growth. Deposits are expected to be microcrystalline, or perhaps even amorphous. If sharp interfaces are sought, electrodeposition at cryogenic temperatures is unique in that it is a process operative at low temperatures and driven by low energy. Diffusion distances are extremely short; diffusion times are extremely long. These are precisely the process characteristics necessary for materials processing at nanoscalar dimensions. Fourthly, the preparation of the electrolyte involves the condensation of a gas with the result that the solutions have the potential to be uncommonly free of contaminants. This puts cryogenic electrolytes at an advantage over high temperature electrolytes which tend to dissolve, albeit sparingly, even the most refractory crucibles. When high purity is a concern, cryogenic electrolytes are excellent processing media.

As a consequence of the fact that the data base for these media is almost nonexistent cryoelectrodeposition has been conducted to date on an empirical basis to a large extent. Vital information such as compound solubilities and decomposition potentials, which are essential in describing the chemistry and electrochemistry of the process, is unreported. Even the state of the metallic ion in solution is unknown. There is much to be done in researching the physical chemistry of these liquids before commercial viability can be properly assessed.

4.6   Conclusion

While molten salt electrolysis has proven its viability in metallurgical processing , in the opinion of this author the technological applications of electrochemical processing in nonaqueous media have not been exhausted.   As an example, the electrosynthesis of refractory metal compounds in cryogenic electrolytes represents enormous commercial potential.   Finally, as environmental quality standards rise beyond the capabilities of classical metals processing technologies to comply, electrolysis may prove to be the only acceptable route from ore to metal.

REFERENCES

1. M.Blander, ed., *Molten Salt Chemistry*, Interscience, New York, 1964.
2. B.R. Sundheim, ed., *Fused Salts*, McGraw-Hill, New York, 1964.
3. G. Mamantov, ed., *Molten Salts*, Marcel Dekker, New York, 1969.
4. G. Mamantov and R. Marassi, ed., *Molten Salt Chemistry*, D. Reidel Pub., Dordrecht, Holland, 1987.
5. J. Lumsden, *Thermodynamics of Molten Salt Mixtures*, Academic Press, New York, 1966.
6. H. Bloom, *The Chemistry of Molten Salts* , Benjamin, New York, 1967.
7. F.D. Richardson, *Physical Chemistry of Melts in Metallurgy*, Vols. 1 & 2, Academic Press, London, 1974.
8. Iu.K. Delimarskii and B. F. Markov, *Electrochemistry of Fused Salts* (ed. Adam Peiperl), The Sigma Press, Washington, DC, 1961.
9. G.J. Janz, *Molten Salts Handbook*, Academic Press, New York, 1967.
10. G.J. Janz et al., *Journal of Physical and Chemical Reference Data*, **3(1)**, 117–140 (1974).
11. G.J. Janz, *Journal of Physical and Chemical Reference Data*, **9(4)**, 791–829 (1980).
12. J.A. Plambeck, *Encyclopedia of Electrochemistry of the Elements*, vol. 10 (ed. A. J. Bard), Marcel Dekker, New York, 1976.
13. D.G. Lovering, ed., *Molten Salt Technology,* Plenum Press, New York, 1982.
14. A. Kuhn, ed., *Industrial Electrochemical Processes*, American Elsevier Pub., New York, 1971.
15. G. Mamantov, C.B. Mamantov and J. Braunstein, eds., *Advances in Molten Salt Chemistry*, vol. 6, Elsevier Science Pub., Amsterdam, 1987.
16. D.G. Lovering and R. J. Gale, eds., *Molten Salt Techniques,* vol. 3, Plenum Press, New York, 1987.
17. C.L. Hussey et al., eds., Proceedings of the Seventh International Symposium on Molten Salts, The Electrochemical Society, Pennington, N. J., 1990, 892 pp.
18. D. R. Sadoway, *Light Metals 1990*, (ed. C. A. Bickert), TMS, Warrendale, PA, 1990, 403–407.
19. V.V. Stender, P.B. Zivotinsky and M.M. Stroganoff, *Trans. Electrochem. Soc.*, **65**, 189–213 (1934).
20. G.J. Kipouros and D.R. Sadoway, *J. Appl. Electrochem.*, **18(6)**, 823–830 (1988).
21. V.I. Shapoval, A.N. Baraboshkin, Kh.B. Kushkhov and V.V. Malyshev, *Elektrokhimiya*, **23(7)**, 942–946 (1987).
22. K. Koyama, Y. Hashimoto and K. Terawaki, *J. Less-Common Met.*, **134(1)**, 141–151 (1987).
23. T. Hatusika, M. Miyake and T. Suzuki, *Kenkyu Hokoku - Asahi Garasu Kogyo Gijutsu Shoreikai*, **49**, 289–293 (1986).
24. X. Gu, S. Duan and D. Inman, *Xiyou Jinshu*, **7(3)**, 182–186 (1988).
25. A. Robin, J. De Lepinay and M.J. Barbier, *J. Electroanal. Chem. Interfacial Electrochem.*, **230(1-2)**, 125–141 (1987).
26. P. Taxil and J. Mahenc, *J. Appl. Electrochem.*, **17(2)**, 261–269 (1987).
27. G.P. Capsimalis, E.S. Chen, R.E. Peterson and I. Ahmad, *J. Appl. Electrochem.*, **17(2)**, 253–260 (1987).
28. A.W. Berger, *Chem.-Anlagen Verfahren*, no. 3, 82–84 (1980).
29. P. Los, J. Josiak, A. Bogacz and W. Szklarski, *Arch. Hutn.*, **29(4)**, 515–527 (1984).
30. T. Vargas, R. Varma and A. Brown, in: *Molten Salts*, ECS Symposium Vol. 87-7 (ed. G. Mamantov, M. Blander, C. Hussey, C. Mamantov, M.-L. Saboungi, and J. Wilkes), The Electrochemical Society, Pennington, NJ, 1987, 1018–1027.
31. A.M. Emsley and M.P. Hill, *J. Appl. Electrochem.*, **17(2)**, 283-293 (1987).
32. T. Vargas and D. Inman, *J. Appl. Electrochem.*, **17(2)**, 270–282 (1987).
33. R.A. Bailey and T. Yoko, *J. Appl. Electrochem.*, **16(5)**, 737–744 (1986).

34. H. Yabe, Y. Ito, K. Ema and J. Oishi, in: *Molten Salts*, ECS Syposium Vol. 87-7 (ed. G. Mamantov, M. Blander, C. Hussey, C. Mamantov, M.L. Saboungi and J. Wilkes), The Electrochemical Society, Pennington, NJ, 1987, 804–813.
35. Z.I. Valeev, A.N. Baraboshkin, Z.S. Martem'yanova and N.O. Esina, *Elektrokhimiya*, **24(1)**, 59-63 (1988).
36. Z. Qiao and P. Taxil, *Jinshu Xuebao*, **23(2)**, B76–B83 (1987).
37. K.H. Stern and S.T. Gadomski, *J. Electrochem. Soc.*, **130(2)**, 300–305 (1983).
38. K. Matiasovsky, K. Grjotheim and M. Makyta, *Metall* (Berlin), **42(12)**, 1196, 1198–1200 (1988).
39. D.W. Townsend and L.G. Boxall, in: *Light Metals 1984*, TMS, Warrendale, PA, 1984, 555–571.
40. W.S. Ricci, J.L. Wong, M. Levy and K.J. Bhansali, "Fused salt electrodeposited titanium boride coatings on high speed steel twist drills," Report MLT-TR-87-48, 1987, 25 pp., Chem. Abs. 109 (20): 174183w.
41. S. Nishikida and F. Matsuno, inventors, Sumitomo Metal Industries, Ltd., assignee, "Ceramic coatings on steels," Japanese patent, no. 62, 112, 782 A2, May 23, 1987.
42. A. Bogacz, P. Los, W. Szklarski and J. Josiak, *Rudy Met. Niezelaz.*, **28(4)**, 134–139 (1982).
43. M. Makyta, K. Matiasovsky and V.I. Taranenko, *Electrochim. Acta*, **34(6)**, 861–866 (1989).
44. K.H. Stern and M.L. Deanhardt, *J. Electrochem. Soc.*, **132(8)**, 1891–1895 (1985).
45. V.I. Shapoval, Kh.B. Kushkhov and I.A. Novoselova, *Zh. Prikl. Khim.* (Leningrad), **58(5)**, 1027-1030 (1985).
46. H. Yabe, K. Ema and Y. Ito, *Elektrochim. Acta*, **35(1)**, 187–189 (1990).
47. B. Hofman and H. Scholl, *Elektrokhimiya*, **24(9)**, 1264–1267 (1988).
48. J.M. Gomes and K. Uchida, "Electrolytic preparation of Titanium and zirconium diborides using a molten sodium salt electrolyte," U.S. patent no. 3, 775, 271 (November 27, 1973).
49. H. Wendt, K. Reuhl, and V. Schwarz, *Electrochim. Acta*, **37**, 237–244 (1992).
50. V.I. Taranenko *et al.*, *Electrochim. Acta*, **37**, 263–268 (1992).
51. T. Arai and Y. Sugimoto, inventors, Toyota Central Research and Development Laboratories, Inc., assignee, "Formation of carbide or boride coatings of Group VB metals or chromium on carbon product surface," Japanese patent, no. 52, 029, 500, March 5, 1977.
52. N. Petrescu, M. Petrescu, M. Britchi and L. Pavel, *Rev. Roum. Chim.*, **18(11)**, 1853–1858 (1973).
53. K.H. Stern and S.T. Gadomski, *Rev. Int. Hautes Temp. Refract.*, **24(2)**, 71–83 (1987).
54. V.I. Shapoval, Kh.B. Kushkhov, V.V. Malyshev, P.V. Nazarenko and N.P. Baydan, *Zashch. Met.*, **4**, 564–566 (1986).
55. G.A. Hope and R. Varma, *Aust. J. Chem.*, **41(8)**, 1257–1259 (1988).
56. M.E. De Roy and J.P. Besse, *Rev. Int. Hautes Temp. Refract.*, **24(2)**, 71–83 (1987).
57. V.P. Yurkinskii, E.G. Firsova, A.G. Morachevskii and A.A. Maiorov, *Zh. Prikl. Khim.* (Leningrad), **57(3)**, 695–698 (1984).
58. R.M. Rose and D.R. Sadoway, inventors, "Cryoelectrodeposition," U.S. patent, no. 4, 517, 253, May 14, 1985.
59. D.R. Sadoway and R.M. Rose, inventors, Massachusetts Institute of Technology, assignee, "Cryoelectrosynthesis," U.S. patent, no. 4, 971, 663, November 20, 1990.
60. A.L. Glagolevskaya, S.A. Kuznetsov, E.G. Polyakov and P.T.Stangrit, *Rasplavy*, **1(6)**, 81–85 (1987).
61. A.V. Kovalenskii, A.E. Mordovin, I.F. Nichkov, V.I. Shishalov and A.V. Kovalevskii, *Izv. Vyssh. Uchebn. Zaved., Tsvetn. Metall.*, no. 5 (1987), 115–116.
62. Sony Corp., assignee, "Diaphragm for fused salt electrolysis," Japanese patent, no. 56/5832 [81/5832], Feb. 6, 1981.
63. E. Chassaing, F. Basile and G. Lorthioir, in: *Titanium '80 Science and Technology* (ed. H. Kimura and O. Izumi), TMS-AIME, Warrendale, PA., 1980, 1963–1967.
64. G.Cobel, J. Fisher and L.E. Snyder, in: *Titanium '80 Science and Technology*, (ed. H. Kimura and O. Izumi), TMS-AIME, Warrendale, PA., 1980, 1969–1976.
65. M.V. Ginatta, private communication, "Industrial plant for the production of electrolytic titanium, Ginatta technology," report RT 88-03-077, Ginatta S.A., Torino, Italy, March 1988.
66. G.F. Warren, A. Horstik, A. Corbetta, R.E. Malpas, A. Honders, and G.J. Van Eijden, inventors, Shell Internationale Research Maatschappij B.V., assignee, "Process for the electrolytic production of metals," European patent appl., no. 219, 157 A1, Apr. 22, 1987.
67. M. Onozawa, inventor, Nippon Steel Corp., assignee, "Preparation of titanium or its alloy by fused salt electrolysis," Japanese patent, no. 63/118089 A2 [88/118089], May 23, 1988.
68. D.R. Sadoway, in: *Proceedings of the Elliott Symposium on Chemical Process Metallurgy*, (ed. L. Kuhn *et al.*), Iron & Steel Society, Warrendale, PA., 1991, 189–196.
69. G.P. Dovgaya, V.V. Nerubashchenko, S.P. Chernysheva and L.K. Mineeva, *Poroshk. Metall.* (Kiev), no. 10 (1987), 6–10.
70. A.B. Suchkov, A.S. Vorob'eva, V.N. Kryzhova, L.V. Ryumina, A.G. Kaganov, I.V. Chikunova and B.F. Kovalev, *Poroshk. Metall.* (Kiev), no. 6 (1987), 1–4.
71. S.L. Gol'dshtein, S.V. Gudkov, S.P. Raspopin, and G.B. Smirnov, *Izv. Vyssh. Uchebn. Zaved., Tsvetn. Metall.*, no. 2 (1986), 58–61.
72. C.F. Rerat, inventor, Fansteel, Inc., assignee, "Tantalum and niobium powder," U.S. patent, no. 4, 149, 876,

Apr. 17, 1979.

73. V.A. Pavlovskii and V.A. Reznichenko, *Poroshk. Metall.* (Kiev), no. 11 (1986), 1–3.

74. M. Armand, "Process for elaboration of transition metal powders in molten salt baths," French patent, no. 2, 592, 664 Al, July 10, 1987.

75. K.A. Kaliev, A.N. Baraboshkin and S.M. Zakhar'yash, *Elektrokhimiya*, **20(3)**, 328–331 (1984).

76. A.N. Baraboshkin, Z.S. Martem'yanova, S.V. Plaksin and N.O. Esina, *Elektrokhimiya*, **14(1)**, 9–15 (1978).

77. V.I. Shapoval, Kh.B. Kushkhov, V.V. Malyshev, V.T. Vesna and V.P. Maslov, *Poroshk. Metall.*, 7, 43–45 (1986).

II

New Methods of
Electrochemical Approaches

5

The Electrochemical
QCM (Quartz Crystal Microbalance) Method

William H. Smyrl and Mary Lien

Corrosion Research Center, Department of Chemical Engineering and Materials Science, University of Minnesota, Minneapolis, MN 55455, U. S. A.

5.1 Introduction

As a mass sensor, piezoelectric quartz found early applications as a monitor in thin film formation by physical vapor deposition processes. The use of the quartz crystal as a microbalance can be traced to the work of Lord Raleigh,[1] Onoe,[2] and Sauerbrey.[3] Lord Raleigh demonstrated that the frequency of vibration of a quartz crystal can be perturbed by a small change of inertia. Onoe considered the problem of the vibration of a quartz plate loaded by a surface film. Sauerbrey suggested using the quartz crystal as a sensing device for measuring the thickness of thin films. The extraordinary sensitivity was exploited by the development of the quartz crystal microbalance (QCM) to monitor the thickness of micron and submicron thick films, and in this application the QCM has become standard equipment in thin film laboratories. This was soon followed by other applications whereby a deposited film responded to chemical or physical interactions to give mass responses. Thus, humidity sensors and other chemical sensors were developed in an explosive growth that still continues. The major advantage of the quartz crystal microbalance is that it is very sensitive, it is simple to construct and operate, and it can be deployed in a wide variety of circumstances. In addition, it is readily available and inexpensive. The sensitivity, on the other hand, also makes it susceptible to interferences because it is not specific. This has led to the development of complementary techniques which can be used in concurrent measurements to connect the mass change to a specific reaction or process. As we shall see below, the lack of specificity and the use of concurrent measurements is also encountered in applications in liquid systems.

The second major wave of development of the QCM began in the early 1980s when it was found that the technique could also be used in the liquid phase. Nomura et al.[4-6] carried out electrodeposition and microweighing experiments which demonstrated that the QCM could be used for liquid phase studies. The major impetus came, however, when Kanazawa and Gordon[7,8] were able to show that when used in the liquid phase, the QCM would have the same sensitivity as in the gas phase. The work of these investigators and their colleagues at IBM, along with studies in the laboratory of Bruckenstein have led to the demonstration that the QCM can be used for a wide range of investigations regarding film formation and film reactions. In addition, the remarkable sensitivity of the device has made it a valuable adjunct to surface studies at the solid-liquid interface. Melroy and colleagues[9-11] have used the QCM to study underpotential deposition of metals, surface reconstruction of metal surfaces, and surface adsorption in electrochemical systems, for example. These and other studies have stimulated many other groups to use electrochemical techniques in conjunction with the QCM, and the number of such studies continues to increase.

A third stage of development is taking place as liquid phase measurements continue to expand. Namely, QCM measurements along with electrochemical measurements of charge for example are not sufficient to completely eliminate interferences, and other complementary techniques are used in conjunction to clarify the chemical interactions and physical processes that occur in individual systems. Thus, optical, spectroscopic and electrical impedance measurements have been shown to add sufficient information to characterize surface roughness or viscoelastic behavior of films, and this permits more complete treatment of surface events. This third wave will bring the field to maturity, so that the QCM will become a standard device in most electrochemical laboratories.

In the present paper, the principles of the QCM and other piezoacoustic sensors will be reviewed with particular emphasis on applications in electrochemical systems. Combined measurements of mass and charge will be illustrated for three kinds of systems. In the first, simple deposition and dissolution of metal films will be discussed because of their similarity to physical vapor deposition processes. The extension of the studies to corrosion applications will then be discussed. The second general study to be illustrated here is that in which chemical or electrochemical interactions with a metal film lead to the deposition of a product layer. Also, insertion of ions into electroactive solid oxide or polymeric films increase the mass on the QCM, and the stoichiometry of the reaction can be clarified by concurrent charge measurements. The review of these investigations will be both illustrate the power of the QCM to facilitate the characterization of electrochemical reactions in terms of stoichiometry and dynamics, as well as to indicate how future studies might be designed to overcome the limitations. Other recent reviews on the subject have been written by Ward and Buttry,[12] by Buttry,[13] by Deakin and Buttry,[14] and by Smyrl and Naoi.[15]

It should be noted that other piezoelectric quartz monitors such as the surface acoustic wave (SAW) and surface harmonic acoustic wave monitor (SHAWM) have also been introduced for gas and liquid phase studies. Some mention of these devices will be made here for completeness, but more detail may be obtained from a companion paper in this volume.

5.2 Fundamental Principles of Bulk and Surface Acoustic Resonators

When a pressure is applied to a piezoelectric material, an electrical field is developed and the magnitude of the field is proportional to the mechanical stress. The converse is also true, *i.e.* when a voltage is applied across a piezoelectric material, a mechanical deformation is observed. If the sign of the voltage is reversed, the deformation is reversed as well. A crystal is compressed when an electric field of one sign is applied, and when the field is reversed, the crystal will be expanded (tension).

Of the thirty-two crystal classes, twenty satisfy the conditions for piezoelectricity. In order for an ionic crystal to be piezoelectric, the structure must lack a center of inversion so that a mechanical distortion can separate the centers of concentration of the positive and negative charges. If electrodes are placed on either side of a thin sheet of material, charge buildup can be monitored by current flow from one electrode to the other. A peak in current appears when the crystal is stressed, and an opposite peak is detected when the pressure is released.   If a sinusoidal stress is applied, an alternating current will flow.   On the other hand, an alternating stress is produced when an alternating voltage is applied to the electrodes.   The latter is the more normal mode for operation of piezoelectric resonators.[16]

Crystalline, α-quartz is the most widely used piezoelectric material because it is readily available, stable, and inexpensive.   It has one axis of three-fold symmetry and three axes of two-fold symmetry, and does not possess a center of inversion.   Electrodes placed on either side of a quartz crystal plate and subjected to an alternating voltage will cause the crystal to vibrate at the frequency of the applied voltage.   Except for a few frequencies, these vibrations are forced, and as a consequence, are of small amplitude.   As the frequency approaches one of the natural (mechanical) frequencies of the plate, resonance occurs and the deformation amplitude is maximized.   Different vibration modes and their overtones (harmonics) will lead to different maxima of strain amplitude.   The resonant frequency is virtually independent of the electric circuit, especially if the crystal is operated in air or vacuum, but depends on the dimensions of the plate and on the elastic properties of quartz.   The resonant frequencies are also influenced by the "cut" or orientation of the quartz crystal plate with respect to the crystallographic axes.   For example, for a given orientation a crystal only vibrates in a specific mode, and the others are prevented by the cut.[17]   Also, the effect of temperature on the frequency can be reduced by using the crystal cuts which minimize the temperature effect.   Specifically, both the AT and BT orientations have small temperature coefficients near ambient conditions.   The former has the lowest temperature effect between 0–70°C.   Both orientations exhibit shear waves in the thickness direction, and are used in the frequency range of 1 to 10 MHz.   The former property is very important for liquid phase applications as we shall see below.   Other factors which influence the mode of vibration are the orientation of the exciting electrodes and the method by which the crystals are clamped into the supporting structure.   The characteristics of the AT, BT, and ST cuts are discussed in detail elsewhere.[18,19]   We conclude this part of the discussion by noting that the AT orientation is by far the most commonly used for electrochemical investigations.   The BT cut is used for certain investigations of stress effects in deposited films, and the ST cut is used for the surface harmonic device discussed below.

When close to a resonant frequency, the shear mode mechanical vibrations of AT quartz are a function of the vibrating mass, and of the mechanical elasticity and damping losses of the vibrating crystal.   Placed in an electrical circuit, the electrical response of the crystal can be represented by an equivalent circuit which includes an inductance, a capacitance, and

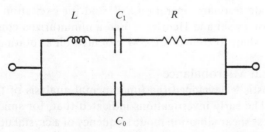

Fig. 5.1 Equivalent circuit of a quartz crystal near resonance in a gas.

a resistance.   The inductance reflects the mechanical inertia (including the mass loading), the capacitance the mechanical elasticity, and the resistance the frictional resistance and energy losses in the crystal structure.   In Fig. 5.1 is shown the equivalent circuit of a quartz crystal near resonance, where the mass, the mechanical elasticity, and the mechanical damping are represented by L, C_1, and R respectively.[19,20] C_0 represents the capacitance between the electrodes when the crystal is perturbed at a frequency far from resonance where it acts as a passive dielectric.   Also shown in the figure are representative values for an AT-cut quartz crystal.   Resonance occurs when the circuit is resistive at a given frequency.[19,20]   Series resonance occurs when the impedance is minimized,

$$\omega_s = 1/\sqrt{(LC_1)} \tag{5.1}$$

and parallel resonance when the impedance is maximized,

$$\omega_p = \omega_s(1 + C_1/2C_0) \tag{5.2}$$

where

$$1/LC_0 \gg (R/L)^2 \text{ and } C_1/C_0 \ll 1$$

The frequency of zero phase shift, ω_o, is related to the series resonant frequency by

$$\omega_o = \omega_s[1 + (C_1/C_0)/Q^2]$$

where Q is the quality factor given by Ref.20

$$Q = \omega_s L/R$$

For large values of Q, the series resonant frequency coincides with the frequency of minimum impedance, ω_m, since

$$\omega_m = \omega_s[1 - (C_1/C_2)/Q^2].$$

Most quartz crystal bulk resonators used for quartz crystal microbalances operate in the series resonance mode, both to avoid dependence of the resonant frequency on C_0, and because the electrical resonator circuits are low impedance output devices.[21]   In most cases, the difference in resonant frequency is only of the order of 0.3%.[21]   The quality factor, Q, for a quartz crystal oscillator is usually about 10^6 (unloaded) and 10^4 (loaded). Q represents the ratio of the (time averaged) energy stored in the crystal compared to the energy dissipated per cycle.   The equivalent circuit representation is valuable for analyzing the impedance behavior of a crystal under nonideal conditions.   For example, when a deposited film is not rigid, but is viscoelastic, it is marginally useful to determine the resonant frequency alone.   Additional information may be obtained by measurements on the loaded crystal with an impedance analyzer or vector voltmeter that can be used for a more comprehensive description of the surface behavior.

The equivalent circuit description facilitates the design of the electronic oscillator circuit which is used to drive the crystal.   Several circuits have been published in the literature for both fundamental mode resonant operation,[22-26] and for excitation of higher harmonic frequencies.[9]   Grzegorzewski and Heusler[27] used a miniaturized control circuit that was housed in the rotating shaft to control a QCM mounted on a rotating disk.

5.2.1   Quartz Crystal Microbalance

Sauerbrey[3] and Lostis[28] developed the fundamental analysis of the QCM for gas or vacuum operation.   The early investigations indicated that, for small mass changes, the decrease in the thickness shear vibration mode frequency of a crystal upon which a thin film is deposited is linearly proportional to the deposited mass.   Sauerbrey argued that the elastic properties of the deposited film cannot contribute to the resonance frequency since the film is thin and located entirely within the antinodal region of the resonator where no shear deformation occurs, either in the film or in the quartz crystal near the surface.   The unloaded resonant frequency f_Q is found[29] from the condition that the bulk material thickness d is an integral multiple n of half-wavelength λ_Q, i.e., $d = n\lambda_Q/2 = nV_Q/2f_Q$, where V_Q is the shear wave velocity in quartz.   Therefore,

$$f_Q = nV_Q/2d \tag{5.3}$$

and if one assumes that at the fundamental frequency ($n=1$), $N_{AT} = df_Q$ is the frequency constant of the commonly used AT-cut crystal and is 0.1666 MHz·cm.[19]   A change of thickness of the quartz plate will cause a change of frequency as given by

$$\Delta f/f_Q = \Delta d/d \tag{5.4}$$

The density, mass, and thickness of the quartz are related by $d = M_Q/A\rho$ where A is the surface area, and this yields

$$\Delta f/f_Q = -\Delta M_Q/dA\rho \tag{5.5}$$

The change in frequency resulting from the deposition of a thin, uniform film of any foreign substance would be equal to that resulting from a layer of quartz of the same mass.[3,29]   Using the relationship between the thickness and N_{AT}, one obtains

$$\Delta f = -\Delta Mf_Q^2/A\rho n_{AT} \tag{5.6}$$

where ΔM is the mass of film of any substance added to the quartz plate.   Using values of the constants quoted,

$$\Delta f = -2.275 \times 10^6 f_Q^2(\Delta M/A) \tag{5.7}$$

where Δf is the change in frequency due to the added film (Hz), f_Q is the resonant frequency of the quartz plate without the deposited film (MHz), ΔM is the mass of deposited film (g), and A is the area (cm^2).   For a 6 MHz crystal, one finds

$$\Delta M = -1.221 \times 10^{-8} A\Delta f \tag{5.8}$$

so that the mass sensitivity is 1.221×10^{-8} g/cm^{2}Hz.   Equation (5.8) is the fundamental relationship which relates the frequency decrease to the increase of mass loading on the quartz crystal, and it reveals that the mass sensitivity can be calculated from first principles.

Equations (5.7) and (5.8) predict that the QCM is sensitive to submonolayer amounts of material deposited on the quartz plate, and that the sensitivity increases as the square of the frequency of the plate, f_Q.   Since f_Q is inversely proportional to the thickness of the plate, the mass sensitivity may be increased by reducing the thickness of the plate, but the fragility of the quartz probably limits the frequency to about 20 MHz.   This exceptional sensitivity is the basis for the considerable interest in the QCM for both gas and liquid phase applications.   A second way to increase the sensitivity is to excite the frequency of one of the higher (odd) harmonics.   The third and fifth overtones have been used, with appropriate electronic control circuits, to study the behavior of underpotential deposits of metal monolayers.[22,30]   When a higher harmonic n is used, the mass-frequency relationship analogous to Eq. (5.7) is

$$\Delta f = -2.275 \times 10^6 f_Q^2(\Delta M/nA) \tag{5.7b}$$

The mass sensitivity is thereby increased to 3.66×10^{-8} g/cm^{2}Hz and 6.11×10^{-8} g/cm^{2}Hz for the third and fifth harmonics, respectively.

A second measure of the QCM to be compared with other gravimetric sensors is the sensitivity function quantity Sm where[29]

$$S_m = \lim(A\Delta f/f_Q \Delta M) \text{ as } \Delta M \to 0 \tag{5.9}$$

S_m is also given by the relationship (e.g. AT-cut quartz)

$$S_m = -2/\rho\lambda_Q = -13.659 \text{cm}^2/\text{g}] \tag{5.10}$$

Equation (5.9) is analogous to (5.8), so that

$$\Delta M = A\Delta f/f_Q S_m. \tag{5.11}$$

and Eq.(5.11) is identical to (5.8). The extension for operation at higher harmonics is straightforward.

The analysis for operation of the QCM in a liquid is somewhat more complex because of the viscous coupling. That is, the shear mode vibration of an AT crystal is parallel to the surface and induces the adjacent liquid to move because of the no-slip boundary condition expected at the interface. The general treatment of the fluid motion induced by an oscillating solid boundary was first given by Stokes.[31] In an alternate treatment specifically for the QCM, Kanazawa and Gordon[7,8] showed that the change in resonant frequency was a function of the density and viscosity of the liquid and of the frequency as

$$\Delta f_{vis} = -(f_Q^2/N_{AT}\rho A)(\rho_L\eta_L/\pi f_Q)^{1/2} \tag{5.12}$$

It has been found that Δf_{vis} caused by immersion in water is 800 Hz for a 5 MHz crystal[13] as compared to 700 Hz calculated from Eq. (5.12). The importance of the result is that the change of mass sensitivity is not significant, and one may expect to have the same sensitivity in low viscosity liquids (e.g., water) as in the gas phase.[32-34] Therefore, to measure relative changes in the liquid phase one may use either Eq. (5.8) or (5.11) with the sensitivity calculated from first principles.

The change in resonant frequency is seen from Eq. (5.12) to depend linearly on $(\rho_L\eta_L)^{1/2}$. Muramatsu et al.[35] extended the analysis to show that the viscous coupling influences R in the equivalent circuit description of the QCM (Fig. 5.1), and that R is proportional to $(\rho_L\eta_L)^{1/2}$. Therefore, it is seen that the energy dissipated by the crystal increases as the liquid viscosity increases, and this reduces the quality factor, Q, for the resonator. The result is to decrease the sharpness of the resonant frequency, and the effect increases with the viscosity.[13]

The sinusoidal velocity wave is damped exponentially with distance from the surface as (Kanazawa and Gordon,[7,8] see also Ref. 31),

$$v(z,t) = v_o\exp(-z/\delta) \cos(k_1 z - 2\pi f_Q t) \tag{5.13}$$

where $v(z,t)$ is the fluid velocity as a function of distance from the surface, z, and time, t. The boundary layer (penetration depth) of the shear wave, δ, is given by

$$\delta = \left(\frac{v_L}{\pi f_Q}\right)^{1/2} \tag{5.14}$$

where v_L, the kinematic viscosity, is the ratio η_L/ρ_L. For a 6 MHz crystal immersed in water at 20°C, the decay length is 230 nm. Liquid outside this region is unperturbed by the oscillating crystal surface.

Hager[36] discussed the velocity distribution in the liquid near the oscillating surface, and considered the effect of the gaussian distribution of velocity *amplitude* of the quartz surface. That is, the maximum amplitude of vibration and the maximum velocity of the crystal surface is considered to be at the center of the vibrating surface, with smaller amplitude near the edge of the metal electrode (Ref. 37 and references therein). Pulker et al.[38] also called attention to the local sensitivity distribution which varies with position on the vibrating surface.   The integrated mass sensitivity (*cf.* Buttry[13]), however, remains valid and equal to the value given in Eq. (5.8), especially for the relatively thick films considered here (we take the substrate electrode as well as the electrochemically deposited film, and any entrained liquid, to give the total film that loads the crystal).   Returning to the question of the velocity at the surface, Hager[36] found that the local velocity could be replaced by the average velocity, and the hydrodynamic motion of the liquid was similar to that given by Stokes,[31] except for a geometrical constant for the crystal.   He was then able to show experimentally that the hydrodynamic coupling can be used to evaluate the product $(\mu\rho)^{1/2}$ on a single QCM crystal.   Separation of the product could be done by measurements on several crystals together.

The QCM has been used to measure the viscosity of liquids.[39,40]   Because the viscosity sensor operates at high frequency (MHz), it is necessary to account for relaxation effects in the liquid.[16]   The shear behavior is that of a Newtonian viscoelastic fluid when $\omega\tau \ll 1$.   It behaves more as an amorphous solid (with a shear modulus μ) when $\omega\tau \gg 1$.   Here, τ is the liquid relaxation time.   Liquid relaxation times can be related to viscosity through the high-frequency rigidity modulus μ by[41]

$$\tau = \eta/\mu$$

where η is the viscosity of the fluid.   Since τ is proportional to η, relaxation effects become important as the liquid viscosity increases, resulting in power loss saturation of the oscillation system.   A critical viscosity, $\eta_c = \mu/\omega$, which can be defined at which $\omega\tau = 1$, delineates two distinct regions of behavior.   In the first region, when $\eta \ll \eta_c$, the liquid behaves as a Newtonian liquid and follows the behavior shown by Kanazawa and Gordon[7,8] for the QCM, and by Ricco and Martin[42] for the plate mode device (see below).   In most liquids, the variation of viscosity with temperature is larger than the variation of the density, and may lead to a significant temperature effect in operation of the QCM for example.   When $\eta \ll \eta_c$, no significant molecular diffusion occurs during one wave period and the fluid behaves as a solid, and this sets the upper limit on the range of viscosity which can be measured by this technique.   Ricco and Martin found[42] that a single rigidity modulus could be used to relate τ to η for a variety of pure liquids and mixtures.   For polar liquids, the lowest frequency relaxation process is associated with molecular rotation, and shear relaxation times calculated from μ agreed well with dielectric relaxation times.[42]   This suggests that the chemical nature of the liquid is not as important for the viscous coupling as is the nature of the physical interface.   In particular, it is necessary that the liquid wet the solid uniformly for the coupling to be efficient.   The detection of gas bubbles at an electrode surface has been proposed for QCM studies,[42] but bubble evolution does not always lead to a frequency shift.[44]   It is concluded that the viscosity of liquids and a number of near surface properties can be studied by either the QCM or the plate mode device.   It should be noted that rigid films will obey the Sauerbrey equation Eq. (5.8), but viscoelastic films will not.   As the frequency of the oscillator increases, δ decreases Eq. (5.14), and viscoelastic materials will approach rigid behavior.

Viscoelastic effects have been treated more exactly recently for the QCM by Reed *et al.*[45]   The treatment was suggested to be valid until the frequency decrease due to loading is approximately 2% of the unloaded frequency.   If one uses an impedance analyzer to measure the shape of the resonance plot versus frequency, the characteristics of the film can be measured more completely and additional information may be obtained.   Benes[21] earlier proposed an equivalent circuit analysis for fully elastic overlayers.   Lu and

Lewis[46] developed the "impedance match" technique, again for elastic overlayers, and this extends the loading limit for the QCM to frequency shifts that are nearly 40% of the unloaded frequency. Using an impedance analyzer with the QCM for example enables one to obtain values for the individual equivalent circuit elements. Physical properties are then calculated from, the electrical circuit parameters, as discussed by Buttry,[13] and Ward and Buttry.[12] For example, Buttry[13] has found that measurement of the quality factor, Q, of the crystal as one deposits a film is an unambiguous way to establish whether a film behaves in a rigid manner. In particular, Q decreases as the result of deposit viscosity for a viscoelastic film, and this provides a measure of the limits of film thickness for which there is a rigid response. It should be noted that a linear relationship between frequency and film thickness is sufficient to establish rigit layer behavior.

Thus we see that at one limit, a deposited film may be rigid and obey Eq. (5.8). In the other limit, when the "film" is thick and liquid, the viscosity of the liquid causes a frequency shift that is proportional to $(\rho_L \eta_L)^{1/2}$. Films which are thin and viscoelastic fall between the two limits. To be more specific, if a viscoelastic film has a thickness, λ, which is much smaller than δ, the viscous boundary layer thickness for the material, the film can be considered to be rigid. This behavior has been confirmed for a polymeric photoresist film.[47] More quantitative treatment for systems where δ is unknown can be provided by impedance measurement procedures. The latter approach is rapidly developing for polymer and organic films.

In addition to sensitivity to mass changes, the QCM has been found to be sensitive to lateral stress in thin films deposited on the surface by EerNisse.[48-50] Where both mass and stress effects are small, the two contributions are independent and can be superimposed. In many studies the mass change is much larger, so the measurement of stress will be uncertain. In order to definitively measure the stress, EerNisse recommended a double resonator technique.[48,49] The AT and BT cuts of quartz have stress coefficients of the opposite sign[50] as illustrated schematically in Fig. 5.2. Simultaneous measurements on both orientations will then yield the desired separation of frequency changes. For the simplest case, the stress is assumed to be uniformly distributed in the thin film, and ΔS is the change of the integral of stress through the film (dyne/cm). For an AT-cut crystal, one obtains[49]

$$\Delta f^{AT} = -\left(\frac{\Delta M^{AT}}{A}\right)\left(\frac{f_{QAT}^2}{\rho N_{AT}}\right) + K^{AT}\left(\frac{\Delta S^{AT}}{A}\right)\left(\frac{f_{QAT}^2}{N_{AT}}\right) \tag{5.15}$$

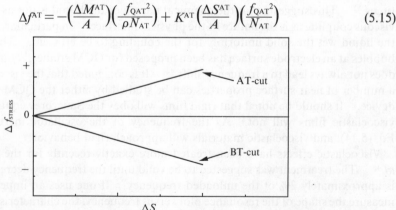

Fig. 5.2 Schematic of the frequency change due to lateral stress in a thin film on quartz crystal resonators in either the AT-cut (increase of resonant frequency) or BT-cut (decrease of resonant frequency) orientation.

written in analogy to Eq. (5.6).   Likewise, one writes for the BT-cut,

$$\Delta f^{\mathrm{BT}} = -\left(\frac{\Delta M^{\mathrm{BT}}}{A}\right)\left(\frac{f_{\mathrm{Q_{BT}}}^2}{\rho N_{\mathrm{BT}}}\right) + K^{\mathrm{BT}}\left(\frac{\Delta S^{\mathrm{BT}}}{A}\right)\left(\frac{f_{\mathrm{Q_{BT}}}^2}{N_{\mathrm{BT}}}\right) \tag{5.16}$$

Here, K^{AT} and K^{BT} are constants of proportionality which have been evaluated,[50]

$$K^{\mathrm{AT}} = 2.75 \times 10^{-12} \ \mathrm{cm^2/dyne}$$
$$K^{\mathrm{BT}} = -2.65 \times 10^{-12} \ \mathrm{cm^2/dyne}.$$

and which reflect the opposing effects of stress in the two orientations.   In the simplest case, one adds equal mass to the two resonators, and has equal stress in the two films, so that

$$\Delta M^{\mathrm{AT}} = \Delta M^{\mathrm{BT}} = \Delta M$$
$$\Delta S^{\mathrm{AT}} = \Delta S^{\mathrm{BT}} = \Delta S$$

Equations (5.15) and (5.16) then become two equations with two unknowns (ΔM and ΔS)

$$\Delta f^{\mathrm{AT}} = -(\Delta M/A)\left(\frac{f_{\mathrm{Q_{AT}}}^2}{\rho N_{\mathrm{AT}}}\right) + (\Delta S/A)K^{\mathrm{AT}}\left(\frac{f_{\mathrm{Q_{AT}}}^2}{N_{\mathrm{AT}}}\right) \tag{5.17}$$

$$\Delta f^{\mathrm{BT}} = -(\Delta M/A)\left(\frac{f_{\mathrm{Q_{BT}}}^2}{\rho N_{\mathrm{BT}}}\right) + (\Delta S/A)K^{\mathrm{BT}}\left(\frac{f_{\mathrm{Q_{BT}}}^2}{N_{\mathrm{BT}}}\right) \tag{5.18}$$

The constant N_{BT} is the product of the thickness of the BT crystal and the fundamental frequency, i.e., $d_{\mathrm{BT}}f_{\mathrm{QBT}}$.

EerNisse[49] notes that K^{AT} and K^{AT} are evaluated for quartz, but it is necessary to specify whether ΔS is given for the film or for the quartz. ΔS in the quartz is equal and opposite to that in the film.   The equations above were written for ΔS in the film.   That is, a positive sign for ΔM is an addition of mass to the film, and a positive value for ΔS is appropriate for tension in the film.

Several additional cases where the stress and mass effects can be resolved by the double resonator technique were also given by EerNisse.[49]   A recent example where the double resonator was used was reported by Cheek and O'Grady[51] for hydrogen and deuterium charging of Pd films.   It would appear that the technique can be used to advantage to study stress generation by thin anodic oxide film growth on metals.   There are no reports of such studies.   Studies of the effects of differential pressure across a quartz crystal were reported by Heusler et al.[52]   The deflection of the crystal was measured interferometrically, and related to the frequency change.

5.2.2   Surface Acoustic Wave (SAW) Resonators

Surface Acoustic Wave devices are transducers based on high frequency mechanical oscillators.[53]   The characteristic wave energy is constrained to the surface region of the substrate, a feature that also accounts for their versatility as chemical and physical sensors.   The surface waves are generated by interdigitated fingers deposited on the surface of the piezoelectric substrate.   One may excite a variety of elastic waves with the interdigitated array, including the Rayleigh surface waves on which the SAW devices are based.   A second set of fingers detect the surface waves traveling across the sample.   In a typical application, the velocity of the surface wave is monitored, and changes in velocity have been found to depend on the surface mass loading.   Wenzel and White[29] have discussed the fundamental operation of the SAW resonators where the sensitivity function

$$S_{\mathrm{m}} = \lim(\Delta V/V_{\mathrm{Q}}\Delta M) \text{ as } \Delta M \to 0 \tag{5.19}$$

and V_Q and V are the unloaded and loaded phase velocities on the SAW device and $\Delta V = V - V_Q$. We assume here that the piezoelectric is quartz, but other piezoelectric materials may be used in an analogous way.   In most cases the resonator is controlled in such a way that

$$\Delta f / f_Q \simeq \Delta V / V_Q$$

and therefore

$$\Delta M = A \Delta f / f_Q S_m \qquad (5.20)$$

S_m is -91 cm^2/g for ST-cut quartz, and with an operating frequency of 112 MHz,[29)] one obtains

$$\Delta M = -9.81 \times 10^{-11} \Delta f \qquad (5.21)$$

and the mass sensitivity is 9.81×10^{-11} g/cm^{2}Hz.   Much of the increased sensitivity is due to the higher operating frequency.

The SAW resonator is used for gas phase applications based on the sensitivity of the surface wave to changes occurring in a thin surface film.   One may characterize the chemical interactions of thin metal films with an adjacent aggressive environment.   The majority of the applications rely on the mass sensitivity of the sensor to determine such properties as adsorption/desorption isotherms[54)], pore size, surface area, vapor diffusivity,[55)] and corrosion of microelectronic and contact materials.[56)]

Both the amplitude and the velocity of the Rayleigh surface wave can be used to monitor changes in the surface medium, but velocity is used most often.[53)]   As is seen in equation[55)], changes in the velocity are manifested as changes in the frequency of oscillation, similar to the QCM.   Both resonators utilize a piezoelectric substrate, but unlike the QCM, which has electrodes on opposite sides of the crystal, SAW resonators have electrodes deposited on the same side of the crystal in the form of interdigitated finger arrays.   When the

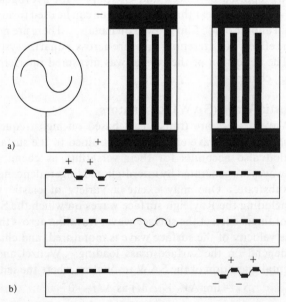

Fig. 5.3 Propagation of a surface wave in an SAW device between interdigitated arrays for launching and receiving the signal.   (Reproduced with permission from Ballantine and Wohltjen[53)])

potential is applied to the material, the crystal deforms in the region of the surface and propagates as an acoustic wave.   In Fig. 5.3, one set of fingers launches the surface wave, and the second set acts as a receiver.   As suggested above (Eq. (5.14)), the sensitivity of the device is superior to the QCM (at least in gas phase studies) because of the higher operating frequency.   In addition, the dimensions of SAWs decrease with frequency and smaller devices may be fabricated with lower absolute limits of detectability.   With the arrangement shown in Fig. 5.2, the SAW resonator has uniform sensitivity over the entire active surface.   The surface wave is also confined to the surface which has some advantage as compared to the QCM, but the Rayleigh wave has a component of the amplitude normal to the surface and thus is quite sensitive to damping in liquid environments.   That is, in addition to viscous damping in liquids of the component of the wave parallel to the surface (similar to QCM) with a small energy loss, there will be energy loss from the crystal because of damping of the compressional wave in the liquid from the component of the wave normal to the surface of the SAW.   The increased sensitivity that would be expected at high frequencies (e.g. 100 MHz) cannot be utilized in liquids[42] because of the attenuation of the Rayleigh wave.   SAW sensors have been used in liquids for example, but at lower frequency (10 MHz), by Bastiaans[57] for bioassay and biochemical sensing.

5.2.3   Plate Mode Piezoelectric Mechanical Oscillators

In addition to the bulk (QCM) and surface Rayleigh wave (SAW) resonators already discussed, several other elastic waves can be generated and have been adapted to gravimetric studies in liquids.   Ballantine and Wohltjen[53] have described several of the elastic waves as shown in Fig. 5.4.   For Lamb waves, the acoustic energy is present on both surfaces of the substrate and has both a longitudinal and vertical component, similar to Rayleigh waves.   The zero order mode amounts to a flexural motion of the substrate.   Devices of this type have been fabricated (ZnO on silicon nitride) and have been claimed to have a value of S_m of -1014 cm^2/g when operated at 2.6 MHz, *in liquid*, a considerable improvement in sensitivity at lower frequency over either QCM or SAW devices.[29,58]

Ricco and Martin [42,59–61] have described an acoustic plate mode device (SHAPM) that is structurally similar to the conventional SAW device but can operate efficiently in liquids.   The interdigital transducer is capable of exciting other waves, one of which is better suited for such applications.   Bulk waves can be generated and propagated parallel to the surface when excited at the frequency $f = V_Q/d$, where d is the transducer periodicity and V_Q is the velocity of the bulk wave propagating at zero angle to the surface.[62,63]   The waves propagate at 5060 m/s in ST-quartz, and are called horizontally polarized shear waves.   The essential feature that is improtant for liquid phase sensing is that it has only a single polarization direction, lying in the plane of the surface and normal to the propagation direction (Fig. 5.5).   The absence of a surface-normal component permits this wave to propagate efficiently at the solid/liquid interface, while surface mass loading perturbs the in-plane component.   A two-port design of interdigitated finger arrays for transmitter and receiver is used to excite the acoustic waves.   A variant on the design has aslo been used by this group[54] whereby the interdigitated arrays are arranged on one side of the quartz plate, but the sensor side exposed to the liquid environment is on the opposite side of the plate (Fig. 5.6).   An advantage to the latter arrangement is that the metalized finger array can be located outside any potential liquid exposure.   The shear horizontal plate mode devices have been used for liquid sensing of viscosity,[42,62] for mass sensing of silver

Horizontally polarized shear wave

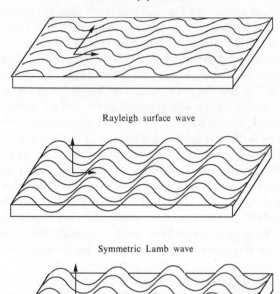

Rayleigh surface wave

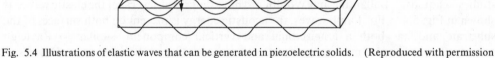

Symmetric Lamb wave

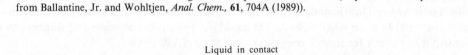

Fig. 5.4 Illustrations of elastic waves that can be generated in piezoelectric solids. (Reproduced with permission from Ballantine, Jr. and Wohltjen, *Anal. Chem.,* **61**, 704A (1989)).

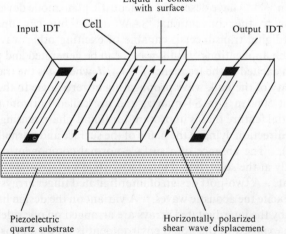

Fig. 5.5 Plate mode oscillator with interdigitated transmitter and receiver arrays for exciting the in-plane waves. Also shown is the arrangement for liquid phase sensing. (Reproduced with permission from Ricco and Martin, *Appl. Phys.,* **68**, 1993 (1990)).

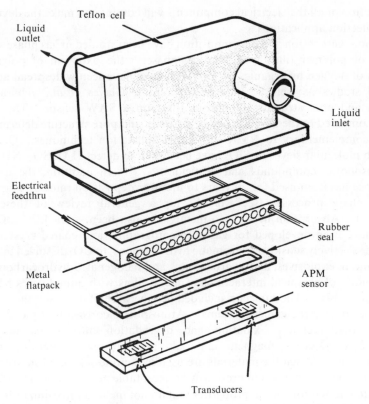

Fig. 5.6 Exploded view of an acoustic plate mode device with a flow-through cell to contain the liquid in contact with the side of the crystal opposite the transducers. (Reproduced with permission from Ricco *et al.*, *Chemical Sensors and Microinstrumentation,* Vol. 403, American Chemical Soc., Washington, 1989)

electrodeposition and for formation and removal of surface oxide on gold surfaces.[62]   For mass sensing, it was found that an equation analogous to the Sauerbrey equation was obeyed, that is

$$\Delta M = A\Delta f/f_Q S_m \qquad (5.22)$$

where S_m is -1998 cm^2/g at 159 MHz,[62] or a mass sensitivity of 3.15×10^{-12} g/cm^{2}Hz at 159 MHz.

5.3 General Applications of QCM and Other Gravimetric Mechanical Oscillators

Alder and McCallum,[64] and Hlavay and Guilbault[65] have reviewed the applications of the QCM to mass and chemical sensing.   Aerosols and suspended solids have been studied by deposition on a QCM on which an adhesive layer was attached.   Particles larger than about 0.1 μm were deposited and detected without difficulty, and low concentrations of aerosols were detected.[66-72]   The major attractions of aerosol measurement using quartz crystal microbalance techniques are high sensitivity, good agreement with theoretical response, and wide mass and frequency response range.   Electronic data processing and miniaturization of all the electrical components will continue to make the devices useful in particle collection applications.

Adsorption, desorption and decomposition have been studied in gas phase systems, e.g., formation of polymer films from the gas phase,[73] the oxdation of polymers,[74] and adsorption of oxygen by organics.[75] SAW devices have seen widespread application in adsorption studies as well.[53] In a recent report, Glaves et al.[76] characterized the adsorption and pore structure of porous films on a SAW sensor. The results were favorably compared to the BET method of pore size and pore structure determination, and also were complementary to NMR spin-lattice relaxation techniques. Quartz crystals coated with molecular sieves or SiO_2 have been used to detect H_2O, SO_2, NH_3, H_2S, HCl, organophosphorus compounds and pesticides.[65,77-79] In addition, the quartz crystal microbalance has been used for 20 years to monitor deposition rates by evaporation and other gas phase processes (see Ref. 17 for a general review of these and other applications). Absorption of H_2 into metals has also been studied.[17] QCM sorption detectors have been developed for gas chromatography, and coated crystals have been found to be selectively sensitive to aromatic hydrocarbons, to CO_2 dissolved in H_2O, to CO, CN^- in solution, explosives, and hydrocarbons and halogenated hydrocarbons.[64,65]

QCM studies of chemical interactions of metal films with humid gases have not been reviewed previously. The subject is included here because of its close connection to other QCM studies in electrochemical systems. Atmospheric corrosion of metals is a general description that includes oxidation and degradation and limits the lifetime of microelectronic materials, magnetic materials, magneto-optic materials, and electrical contact materials. When the materials are used in continuous, thin film form, corrosion and degradation rates that would ordinarily be acceptable now become catastrophic. The materials are selected for special properties that do not include corrosion resistance, and in microstructures and thin film forms the materials are vulnerable. That is, only a small amount of material can be corroded or removed before the special properties are lost. The sensitivity to corrosion increases as the structures decrease in critical dimensions. The investigation of chemical interactions in aggresive gaseous environments has been aided by the development of gravimetric techniques that can be used to study degradation in early stages and in a wide range of environments. The QCM was first proposed for corrosion studies in 1966 by Littler (U.S. Patent 3,253,219, May 29, 1966), but the application was not widely used until recently. Interaction of metal and corrosive gases leads to the deposition of a product film on the surface of the metal. QCM, SAW, and plate mode devices have all been used in these studies.

The QCM can be used with diverse materials and offers several advantages over interferometric or capacitive methods to monitor the reactions because the optical properties do not have to be known, for example. In addition, because it is an *in situ* technique, it complements the surface analytical methods that are *ex situ* by nature. In gas phase interaction studies with the QCM, comparison of experimental data and models is facilitated by reporting results in the form of a change of mass as a function of time. The early stages of oxide film growth on metals, for example, are expected to obey a parabolic rate law whereby ΔM should be proportional to $(t)^{1/2}$. Other useful data formats are ΔM vs t and ΔM vs $\ln(t)$.

Lee et al.[80] were among the first to use the QCM, in studies of permalloy oxidation. Permalloy is a magnetic material ($Ni_{0.8}Fe_{0.2}$) that is used in both thick film and microstructured from, and is subject to oxidation in humid air and other gaseous environments.   The QCM was used to study the oxidation of thin evaporated films in O_2 at 185°C.   It should be noted that the QCM may be used in principle up to the phase transition temperature for α-quartz (513°C).   In practice however, it has not been used with much success above 400°C.   At each temperature of use the mass sensitivity will be different, but always given by Eq. 5.6 and the properties at the temperature of interest.   The mass change is shown as a function of time in Fig. 5.7, and as a function of the square root of time in Fig. 5.8   The latter figure demonstrates that the oxidation is parabolic in the

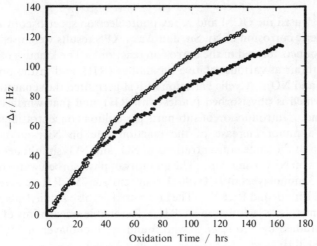

Fig. 5.7   QCM measurements of the mass increase caused by oxidation of permalloy films at 185°C, 1 atm O_2.   Films were deposited at 200° (O) and 350°C (●), respectively.   (Reproduced with permission from Lee et al., J. Electrochem. Soc., **124**, 1744 (1977)).

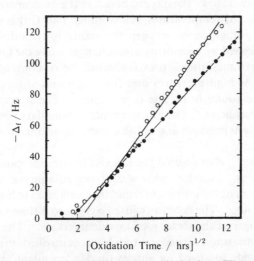

Fig. 5.8 Oxidation of permalloy films (Fig. 5.7) follows parabolic kinetics.   Films were deposited at 200° (O) and 350°C (●), respectively.   (Reproduced with permission from Lee et al., J. Electrochem. Soc., **124**, 1744 (1977)).

early stages.   The two curves in each figure were for films deposited at two different temperatures (*i.e.* 350°C and 200°C).   The sensitivity of the 5 MHz crystal is 17.7 ng/ Hz cm², enabling the detection of the first several atomic layers of oxide as it was formed.

Rice *et al.*[81] used a quartz crystal microbalance and other techniques to study the atmospheric corrosion of Co thin films.   The effect of humidity and other gases was investigated on films of 100 nm and 12 μm thickness.   Water absorbed from air caused the formation of complex oxyhydroxides.   The corrosion kinetics were linear with time and exponentially dependent on the relative humidity.   The partial pressure of SO_2, Cl_2, and NH_3 significantly influenced the corrosion rate, but little effect was noted for H_2S, NO_2, and O_3 gases.

Zakipour *et al.*[84] used the QCM and X-ray photoelectron spectroscopy (XPS) methods to study atmospheric corrosion of Ni, Sn, and Au.   XPS results were used to identify one or more of the products formed in the corrosion reaction.   The kinetics of the interaction was measured with air at various relative humidities (RH), and in the presence of small quantities of SO_2 and NO_2.   Cyclic variation of RH permitted the separation of adsorbed water into that which is physisorbed (varies with RH), and that which is chemically or permanently bound.   Introduction of sub-parts per million concentrations of SO_2 or NO_2 alone results in a minor increase of the reaction rate on Ni, and no increases on Sn.   Introduction of the same concentrations of SO_2 and NO_2 simultaneously resulted in an increase of mass on Ni, Sn and Au.   The quantity of physisorbed water on Ni amounted to approximately 3 monolayers of H_2O (90–100 ng/cm²) at 75% RH, in agreement with the previous results of Phipps and Rice.[85]   The latter workers also studied adsorption of water on several other metals as a function of RH.   Reversible adsorption of H_2O on oxide covered Cu was studied by Seo *et al.*[86] who found ~1 monolayer at 35% RH, and ~14 monolayers at 90% RH.

Anodic oxide films on Ta[82] and Ti[83] were subsequently treated in gaseous O_2 at elevated temperatures.   While heating amorphous anodic oxide films on Ta in vacuum at temperatures above about 150°C, the oxygen deficit in the oxide increases by dissolution of oxygen into the metal.   At temperatures below about 100°C this reaction stops almost completely, but after admission of oxygen the oxide is reoxidized.   The kinetics of reoxidation was investigated by measuring mass changes using the QCM.   At low oxygen pressures, and for short times after a pressure jump, the reaction at the phase boundary determines the rate.   At high pressures and for long times, diffusion of stoichiometric defects in the oxide was found to be rate determining.   The stoichiometric detects were assumed to be oxygen vacancies.   The rate of the phase boundary reaction was found to be proportional to the oxygen pressure and to the vacancy concentration.   The rate constant at 55°C was evaluated.

Gundlach and Heusler[83] also studied the kinetics of the incorporation of O_2 into non-stoichiometric TiO_2 films.   Anodic oxide was grown in aqueous solutions on Ti films evaporated on a quartz crystal microbalance, and then subjected to high vacuum conditions where Ti reacted with TiO_2.   The reaction caused oxygen to diffuse into the metal and thus created a diffuse boundary at the metal-metal oxide interface.   The QCM monitored the reoxidation of the films upon exposure to O_2 at controlled pressure.   The oxygen incorporation in the oxide followed an almost time-independent rate except for a short initial time.   The rate did not change with stoichiometry during the reaction.   The reaction order with respect to oxygen was 0.1.   With light of about 3 eV, oxygen was photodesorbed in high vacuum, but in the presence of oxygen the incorporation of oxygen was catalyzed. It was concluded from the experiments that neutral oxygen atoms were transferred from the surface to the bulk of the oxide. A mechanism of oxygen transfer was proposed by which the oxygen atoms were produced after a rate-determining reaction between two adsorbed oxygen radical ions, $O_{2,rad}$, in the dark. In the presence of light, a parallel rate-determining step becomes possible by transfer of a second electron to an adsorbed oxygen radical ion.

5.4　Electrochemical Studies with the QCM

Applications of the QCM to electrochemical systems have advanced rapidly from the first studies by Nomura et al.,[4-6] who used the technique to investigate the electrodeposition of Au, and of trace metals from solutions. Indeed, the sensitivity of the QCM for liquid investigations has been calibrated by electrochemical methods,[26,87-89] and found to be identical to that for gas phase studies. These calibration studies were carried out for deposition and dissolution of bulk metals (Ag, Au, Cu). Other investigations have exploited the high sensitivity of 5–20 MHz QCM resonators to determine the charge and mass involved in the deposition of metals in the underpotential deposition (UPD) region on Au. In this region, it has been demonstrated earlier that up to 1 monolayer of a metal may be deposited on a foreign metal. Many of the characteristics of the process have been extensively studied in ultra high vacuum. In UPD studies on the QCM, charge and mass may be measured simultaneously and in situ to determine the electrosorption valence, γ. For example, the value of γ was found to be identical to the valence of the metal ion for deposition of Pb (2.08),[9,10] Cd (2.0–1.6),[10] and Pd (1.8).[89] In addition, there is no alloy formation for the monolayer of either metal at short times. For other metals, UPD occurs with smaller values of γ, as shown in Table 5.1. Also included are the analogous values for monolayer deposition of anions on Au.

The QCM has been developed as an in situ monitor for electroplating to verify the current efficiency and incorporation of surface active agents in the deposit. Other processes such as simultaneous gas evolution, and the role of hydrides in the deposition and dissolution of Ni from a Watts bath have been reported.[92]

Electroless deposition of Cu from formaldehyde solutions has been studied with the QCM for kinetic analysis.[93] It was found that the balance of anodic and cathodic reactions in the process is strongly affected by chemical coupling as well. The electroless deposition of Ni has also been monitored by the QCM.[94]

These studies have confirmed that combining electrochemical measurements (of current

TABLE 5.1　Specific Charge Associated with Formation of Monolayers of the Ions on Au

Ion	UPD monolayer	Reference	Comments
Pb^{2+}	2.0	9,10	no alloy
Cd^{2+}	2.0 – 1.6	10	rapid alloy
Bi^{3+}	2.7	10	no alloy
Cu^{2+}	1.4	10	no alloy
Pd^{2+}	1.8	89, 90	slow alloy
I^-	1.0	11, 91	
Br^-	0.39	11	
Cl	0.06	91	
SO_4^{2-}	0.5	91	

and charge) with mass measurements on the QCM permits the *in situ* evaluation of the stoichiometry and other characteristics of simple surface processes.   These results serve as a basis on which other, more complex reactions may be probed.   Examples of the more complex studies are described below.

5.4.1   Electroformation of Films and Electrochemical Corrosion

Chemical interactions and liquid phase reactions with metals have been investigated to extend the QCM to complex systems.   The electrodissolution of metals provides a convenient baseline for the studies because in the first place it may be compared directly with theoretical predictions as discussed above.   In addition, chemical etching and corrosion reactions involve the coupling of the same (anodic or oxidation) reaction with the reduction of a second species such as oxygen.   The balance of these reactions locally on a homogeneous metal surface results in the uniform removal of the metal from the surface (*cf.* Smyrl[95]), if the reaction products are soluble.   For example, Hinsberg *et al.*[96] found that Cu films on QCM were etched uniformly by reaction with Ce $(NH_4)_2(NO_3)_6$ in H_2SO_4.   This maintains the surface roughness or morphology, and as we shall see below this is an extremely important characteristic.   In many systems, however, insoluble products are formed, or a mixture of both soluble and insoluble products are produced.   In the latter case, analysis of the QCM results becomes ambiguous and a more comprehensive study must be carried out to separate the contribution of the individual processes.   In the discussion below, we will review the application of the QCM to both film formation and dissolution processes.

Three different types of chemical interaction studies in the liquid phase have been carried out with the QCM.   These are: (1) anodic oxide formation on metals, (2) corrosion of metals with soluble products, and (3) surface reconstruction after oxide formation and subsequent reduction.   The mass change accompanying the corrosion reaction has been monitored in each case to establish the stoichiometry or yield of the process.   If the reaction is simple, simultaneous measurement of charge passed and mass change will provide confirmation of the mechanism, especially in studies of the first two types.   In reactions of type 3, the mass change alone is insufficient to establish the yield of the reaction, and other complementary measurements must be carried out.   Corrosion, which includes several processes such as oxide formation, surface roughening, and metal dissolution, may all affect the response of the QCM.   In this case, complete characterization of the processes requires the use of several complementary measurements along with the QCM.

Deakin and Melroy[23] recently monitored the growth of an anodic oxide film on aluminum with the QCM.   The oxidation of Al in a solution of ethylene glycol and ammonium pentaborate led to the formation of non-porous, barrier oxide films.   It had been established previously that the oxidation was 100% efficient, and in particular no dissolution of the film had been observed and no solvent was incorporated into the growing film.[96-98]   The mass-to-charge ratio was reported by Deakin and Melroy[23] to vary between 8.2 and 6.6 g/equivalent, as compared to the theoretical value of 8.0.   XPS and density measurements of the film confirmed the composition, which cannot be determined directly from the QCM alone.   The results demonstrated that the presence of large electric fields across the oxide films did not perturb the microbalance response.   As shown in Fig. 5.9, during the initial formation of the oxide film, the mass per equivalent of charge is greater than in the later stages of film formation.   It was concluded that the oxide film formed in

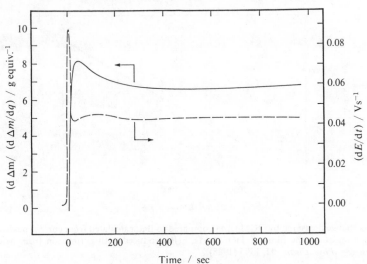

Fig. 5.9 QCM measurement of the kinetics of formation of thick anodic films on Al.   (Reproduced with permission from Deakin and Melory, *J. Electrochem. Soc.*, **136**, 349 (1989)).

the early stages differs slightly in composition from the oxide formed at longer times and higher voltages.   The effective mass increase of less than 8 g/equivalent at longer times suggests that some of the mass of the oxide film was lost through film dissolution.

Bruckenstein and Shay[33] observed the formation of a monolayer of electrosorbed oxygen at Au.   The simultaneous observations of mass change (QCM) and current-voltage curves led the authors to a mechanism of the monolayer formation.   A complete oxidation/ reduction cycle of the surface returned the QCM to the initial reading, which indicates that the surface roughness does not change.   After several cycles, the roughness apparently changes and this was interpreted as dissolution and redeposition of Au.   However, other authors found that the roughness was produced by reduction of oxide that was not of uniform thickness, *i.e.*, islands were formed.

The anodic oxide film formed on Ti film in H_2SO_4 was studied by Mueller *et al.*[44]   It was shown that only a fraction of the anodic charge passed through the cell leads to oxide formation.   In Fig. 5.10, the change of mass given by the QCM is plotted versus the change of mass calculated from the charge passed if it is assumed that only TiO_2 is formed.[44]   The slope of the line is constant and about 1/3.   It was concluded that the excess charge probably created oxygen that was released to the electrolyte, but no measurements were conducted to confirm the suggestions.   Other measurements were reported in which the oxide covered surface was cathodically charged with hydrogen in acidic and basic solutions, respectively.   In acid solutions, almost no change of resonant frequency of the QCM was observed, even though extensive hydrogen charging of the oxide occurred.   A large change of frequency was observed for hydrogen charging in alkaline solutions and this was interpreted as strong coupling of the surface with the electrolyte solution.   Hydrogen charging in either solution apparently caused only a small mass change, which was not detected.   The authors did not discuss the maximum hydrogen loading of the oxide (and metal) that would escape detection in their experiments.

Grzegorzewski and Heusler[27] studied the kinetics of deposition and dissolution of

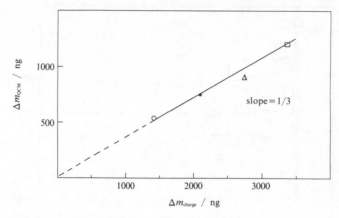

Fig. 5.10 Mass change measured by QCM (Δm_f compared to that calculated from current passed (Δm_q) during formation of anodic films of TiO_2 on Ti. (Reproduced with permission from Muller *et al., Ber. Bunsenges. Phys. Chem.*, **92**, 1395 (1988)).

manganese dioxide. The QCM was the central disk of a rotating ring-disk electrode. This unique application of the QCM enabled the detailed analysis of the oxidation and reduction of manganese dioxide electrodes in aqueous solution. In equilibrium, the water content of the oxide was found to be determined by the variable state of oxidation of the oxide. Proton transfer between the oxide and the electrolyte proceeded at a negligible rate. For an oxide like MnO_2, reduction and reoxidation amounted to changing the stoichiometry continuously so that metal cations and oxide anions crossed the interface in independent fluxes. The exchange current of manganese ions was much greater than the exchange current of oxygen ions. Manganese ions were transferred without water, but several water molecules were transferred with an oxygen ion. The same authors also investigated the influence of mass and stress on one side of a quartz crystal resonator.[52] Both investigations have helped to establish the QCM as a tool for studies in flowing liquid and gas streams.

   Grasjo *et al.*[97] found that oxide film formation and metal dissolution occurred simultaneously on Cu in borate solutions at pH 8.4. The mass change (QCM) during anodic oxidation corresponded to the sum of a mass loss due to metal dissoluion into solution and a mass gain due to oxide film formation. The amount of oxide formed was determined by subsequent cathodic reduction of the film, during which no copper is lost to solution. The mass due to metal dissolution in the initial oxidation was determined by difference. There was some scatter in the data which the authors noted might have been due to either stress in the film, or to morphology changes that were produced by oxide formation and subsequent reduction. Such morphology changes can be clarified by optical interferometric measurements.[148] It is known that changes of morphology cause frequency changes on the QCM by entrainment of liquid with the oscillating surface.

   Morphological changes of roughness with oxide formation was observed with Au,[24] and of Cu and Ag[25] in aqueous solution potential cycling. Upon oxidation of the respective metals, an oxide was formed on the surface and the resonant frequency of the QCM decreased as the mass increased. When the oxide was reduced completely, the frequency of the QCM increased to the original reading. It was found that about 20% of the observed mass change on Au was due to incorporation of oxygen into the metal surface (as the oxide) and the remainder arose from liquid confined in pockets of the roughened, oxidized surface.   Reduction of the oxide left a smooth surface after one oxidation/reduction cycle; this was confirmed by SEM micrographs.   Repeated cycling led to a final roughened surface.[24)   Subsequent measurements on Au revealed that pH had an effect on the interfacial oxide formation.[26)   Repeated cycling of the surface led to surface roughening and a frequency "gap" between the initial and final states of the surface.   Anodic and cathodic processes on platinum electrodes led to strong frequency changes, which are not related to mass changes in the usual way.[26)   It was proposed that chemisorbed hydrogen interacts with water and forms a kind of lattice that remains attached to the surface.   Presumably because the relaxation time for the lattice interaction is slow compared to the quartz resonant frequency, an apparent mass increase is seen.   This model was discussed in connection with IR spectroscopy measurements on the same surface in aqueous solution.   Upon cycling the electrode, there is a transition from the hydrophilic surface in the hydrogen region to a hydrophobic character in the double layer region on Pt.

Cu oxidation in aqueous solution led to an increased mass and a decrease of resonant frequency, similar to Au.   The current-voltage curve and the QCM frequency-time curve are seen in Fig. 5.11.   Upon reduction, a rough surface was produced after only one cycle, but the surface was observed to reconstruct and returned to the original smooth surface if the metal was held in the reduced condition for several minutes.   The QCM returned to the original reading as well.   Again, SEM micrographs confirmed the change of surface roughness in the reduced condition.[25)   The same authors also studied oxidation/reduction cycling of Ag.   A surface oxide was observed along with surface roughening as for the other metals, but the original smooth surface was not regenerated by reducing the oxide and

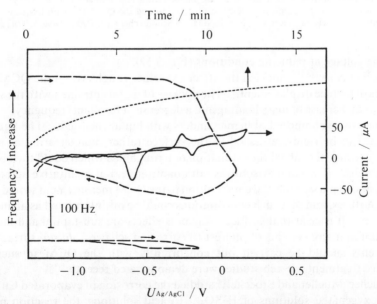

Fig. 5.11 Copper oxidation leads to an increased mass and a decrease of resonant frequency, which is reversed on reduction of the oxide.   Hysteresis is caused by a change of surface roughness.   (Reproduced with permission from Schumacher *et al., J. Electroanal. Chem.*, **216**, 127 (1987)).

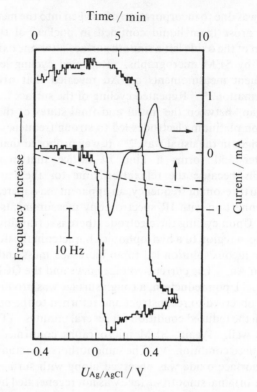

Fig. 5.12 The rough surface of Cu produced by an oxidation and reduction cycle returns to the original morphology as the result of surface reconstruction and the QCM resonant frequency returns to the initial value. (Reproduced with permission from Schumacher *et al., J. Electroanal. Chem.*, **216**, 127 (1987)).

holding the voltage at reducing conditions (Fig. 5.12).

Schumacher *et al.,*[24,25)] modeled the effect of surface roughness on the QCM for modest amplitudes of surface displacement. The pockets of liquid entrained with the surface leads to an apparent increase of mass loading and a decrease of resonant frequency. The surface was assumed to be composed of hemicylinders with liquid enclosed. The liquid enclosed was assumed to be rigidly attached to the surface rather than shearing as at a smooth surface. The model enabled the estimation of a roughness which could then be compared to micrographs. The comparison was not quantitative, but qualitative agreement led to the conclusion that a substanitial contribution to the QCM measurement would be expected for rough surfaces, and that such contributions could be misinterpreted as an increased rate of oxidation. It is clear that surface roughness effects are substantial and must be taken into account in many systems of interest to corrosion science. *In situ* surface roughness measurements should be carried out concurrently with the QCM in such cases for quantitative treatment. Such studies were demonstrated recently.[155)]

Schumacher, Mueller and Stoeckel[98)] studied the corrosion of evaporated Cu films on the QCM in oxygenated solutions of H$_2$SO$_4$. In acid solutions, the reaction products are soluble and no oxide film is formed. The dissolution rate was determined from the mass change on the QCM for dissolved oxygen concentrations of 1.6–9 μg/cm^2 and sulfuric acid concentrations of $1-60\ \mu g/cm^3$.   The rate was found to be linearly proportional to the dissolved O_2 concentration at all concentrations of acid, and was sufficiently slow so that the bulk solution concentration was not exhausted.   There was no dependence on the concentration of SO_4^{2-}.   The data were interpreted as a heterogeneous surface reaction for Cu dissolution.   The surface coverage of each of the electroactive species was assumed to be proportional to the bulk concentration of H^+ and O_2, *i.e.* a Langmuir behavior in the range considerably less than a monolayer coverage.   A nonagitated condition caused the rate to decrease, indicating some mass transport dependence.   The rate was extrapolated to a corrosion rate of zero at zero concentration of dissolved O_2, but there is measurable corrosion in deaerated alkaline solutions.   In the latter case, the mechanism is more complicated and the surface passivates.   The mechanism is expressed by the overall reaction

$$Cu + O_2 + 2H^+ = Cu^{2+} + H_2O_2$$

which would produce an equimolar buildup of Cu^{2+} and H_2O_2 in oxygenated H_2SO_4, which has been reported in the literature.   The dissolution rates were $1-10\times10^{-9}\ g/cm^2sec$ or corrosion currents in the $\mu A/cm^2$ range.

Hinsberg *et al.*[96] described uniform film etching studies on the QCM for Cu films and for photoresist polymer films.   Cu was etched in dilute H_2SO_4 containing ceric ammonium nitrate as the oxidant.   The products were soluble and the corrosion rate was relatively constant at about 20 Å/sec for the time required to completely remove a 4700-angstrom film.

Benje *et al.*[92] investigated the dissolution of Ni films that had been electrodeposited on Au.   The films appeared to be nickel hydride, NiH_x, where $0.6<x<1$.   The anodic oxidation produced nickel ions in solution and H_2 according to the reaction

$$NiH_x - > Ni^{2+} + 2e^- + x/2H_2$$

Good agreement was found between the QCM and the electrochemical measurements when this reaction was assumed.

Chandler[99] recently investigated the corrosion of both Cu and Co films in acidic solutions as a function of the concentration of dissolved O_2 (see also Ref. 100).   In both cases the metal films were evaporated onto the quartz crystal substrates.   The corrosion of Cu in halides occurs with the anodic reaction under mass transport control.[101-103]   The electrodissolution and corrosion in HCl have been studied previously in our laboratories with both steady state and impedance techniques.   At low oxidizer concentrations, it has been shown[103,104] that copper dissolves to a cuprous state stabilized by the formation of the dihalide complex ion $CuCl_2^-$.   Other chloro complexes are formed at higher Cl^- concentrations.   The rate of convective diffusion of the product species away from the surface determines the rate of dissolution of copper.   Nicol investigated the homogeneous oxidation of the cuprous complex to the cupric state in chloride solutions.[105]   It was found that high concentrations of Cl^- inhibited the homogeneous reaction with either O_2 or H_2O_2.   The homogeneous reaction is not important at oxidant concentrations below 5 mM and at concentrations of Cl^- above 0.1 molar.

The anodic dissolution of copper in hydrochloric acid is described by

$$Cu + 2Cl^- \rightarrow CuCl_2^- + e^-$$

The reaction is mass transport controlled and the apparent Tafel slope is 60 mV/decade over a wide range of potential.[101-104,106]   The cathodic reaction is either

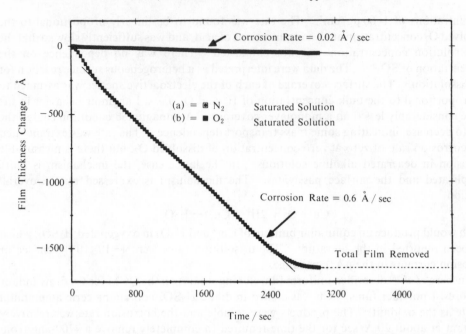

Fig. 5.13 QCM measurement of copper corrosion in oxygenated 0.1N HCl at 25°C. (Reproduced with permission from Chandler *et al.*, Corrosion 89, NACE, New Orleans (April, 1989)).

$$2H^+ + 2e^- \rightarrow H_2 \text{ (deaerated HCl)}$$

or

$$O_2 + 2e^- + 2H^+ \rightarrow H_2O_2 \text{ (oxygenated HCl)}$$

As the film dissolved, the mass changed and the rate of mass loss was monitored as a function of time. A typical plot of the corrosion of copper in deaerated 0.1 N HCl is shown as the upper curve in Fig. 5.13. The corrosion was constant, and very low, between 0.001 and 0.02 Å/sec, as expected for solutions low in oxidant concentration. The original metal film thickness was 1500 Å. Copper corrosion in oxygenated (100% O_2, 1 atm) 0.1 N HCl is shown as the lower curve in Fig. 5.13. The oxygen concentration corresponds to 2 mM. The corrosion rate was constant and equal to 0.6 Å/sec. The monotonic and constant change of film thickness with time indicates that there were only minor changes of surface roughness, nor were any surface films deposited during the corrosion process.

The anodic reaction for Co dissolution in sulfuric acid is given by

$$Co \rightarrow Co^{2+} + 2e^-$$

The reaction is kinetically controlled. The cathodic reaction on Co that produces corrosion in acid solution is either

$$2H^+ + 2e^- \rightarrow H_2 \text{ (deaerated } H_2O_4)$$

or

$$O_2 + 4H^+ + 4e^- \rightarrow 2H_2O \text{ (oxygenated } H_2SO_4)$$

The latter $4e^-$ reaction has been found to dominate for O_2 reduction on Co in sulfuric media,[107] but a $2e^-$ reduction to peroxide is observed in chloride media. The metal film was 1500 Å. Fig. 5.14 shows the corrosion rate in 0.1 N H_2SO_4. The upper curve was

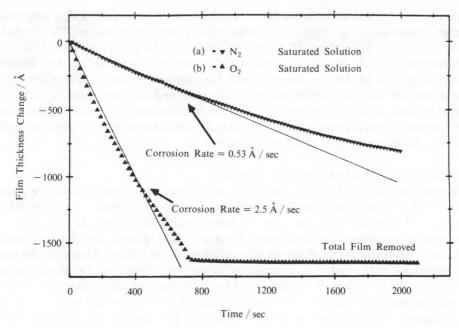

Fig. 5.14 QCM measurement of Co corrosion in oxygenated 0.1N H₂SO₄ at 25°C. (Reproduced with permission from Chandler *et al.,* Corrosion 89, NACE, New Orleans (April, 1989)).

obtained in deaerated solution, and showed an initial corrosion rate of 0.53 Å/sec, but decreased and became slower at longer times.   The initial rate agreed closely with that obtained previously in our laboratories by electrochemical experiments.   The latter results showed a corrosion current density of 0.15 mA/cm², which corresponds to a corrosion rate of 0.52 Å/sec.   In 1 mM oxygenated soluion (100% O₂, 1 atm) in 0.1 N H₂SO₄, the corrosion rate is shown on the lower curve in Fig. 5.13, and is 2.5 Å/sec.   In the latter case, the corrosion rate was observed to be relatively constant during the entire film removal process.   Electrochemical measurements of the corrosion rate has been found to be 2.1 Å/ sec in our laboratory.

In the Co film corrosion studies, different results were observed with quartz crystals obtained from different manufacturers.   For results shown in Figs. 5.12 and 5.13 above, the quartz substrates were highly polished and were supplied by Valpey-Fisher.   The results were very reproducible when these crystals were used.   The smoothness of the Valpey-Fisher crystals was characterized by a 250 Å peak-to-valley roughness.   Quartz crystals from Inficon were also used, and were found to be much rougher.   A characteristic 1 micrometer peak-to-valley roughness was found for these latter materials.   Corrosion rates of Cu agreed closely with those obtained with the Valpey-Fisher materials, but the corrosion rates for Co did not.   Especially in the case of Co corrosion in deaerated solution, the results were unsatisfactory.   The Inficon crystals gave a corrosion rate that continuously changed with time and only approached a rate of 0.53 Å/sec at the earliest times.   In addition, the results varied from sample to sample of Co.   It appears that one should use extremely smooth substrates for all measurements, unless it can be demonstrated (as it was for Cu) that rougher crystals give satisfactory results.

Hager *et al.*[108] studied the corrosion of Fe films on the QCM.   The films were subjected to linear voltammetry in both the active and passive regions in 1N Na₂SO₄ solution.   Instead of integrating the current to obtain the charge and using an assumed stoichiometry to calculate the mass to compare to that measured by the QCM, these studies differentiated the QCM data to compare with the measured current.   The alternative treatment depends on the assumed stoichiometry also, and does not seem to offer an advantage for analysis of QCM results.   Because the electrochemistry is quite complicated for the Fe system in the pH range chosen for study, the results were not definitive but gave qualitative support for QCM study in corrosion systems.

5.4.2   Electrochemical Ion Insertion Reactions

Redox reactions at ion insertion electrodes require the simultaneous insertion (and release) of charge from a current collector and ions from an electrolyte.   Such reversible charge injection processes form the basis for battery electrodes, electrochromic devices, electrochemical switching, electrochemical transistors and diodes, and ion exchange membranes.   Several of the applications take advantage of the change of conductivity and optical properties as the materials undergo redox cycling.   Studies of the fundamental components of the ion insertion reaction have typically used the redox materials as thin films on an inert current collector.   The stoichiometry of the insertion reaction, the rate of electron transfer, diffusion rates in the host material, and determination of the redox capacity has been carried out by electrochemical techniques such as cyclic voltammetry (see Ref. 55 for a review) and impedance analysis.[109–111]

The QCM has recently been introduced to monitor the mass associated with the ion insertion process.   Feldman and Melroy[112] found that electroprecipitated prussian blue (PB) films contained interstitial water that could be reversibly removed in low humidity gas.   Prussian blue is an intercalation material that may be written as

$$Fe_4[Fe(CN)_6]_3 \qquad \text{(insoluble)}$$

or

$$M^+Fe[Fe(CN)_6] \qquad \text{(soluble)}$$

The "solubility" refers to the ease with which the material may be peptized.   Redox cycling between PB and prussian white (PW) would be predicted to involve cation insertion (reduction) and release (oxidation), for either form of the complex.   However, if PB is oxidized to the Berlin Green (BG) state, one predicts that *anions would be inserted* into the "insoluble" form, but *cations would be released* from the "soluble" form.   It was found that only cations were inserted and released in both processes, consistent with the "soluble" form of the electroprecipitated film.   K⁺, Rb⁺, and Cs⁺ were reversibly cycled in the films at pH 4.   There was no evidence for anion participation in the redox process for these systems.   There was qualitative evidence for solvent transport as well during cycling.

Such studies have been extended by Lasky and Buttry[113] who showed reversible cation (Cs⁺) insertion in nickel ferrocyanide films (the nickel analog of PB).   In addition, it was found that solvent transport accompanied the ion movement by comparing mass changes when the films were cycled in D₂O and H₂O.   The physical picture that emerges is that expulsion of each Cs⁺ produces a void in the lattice that becomes partially filled by ~3.2 water molecules on average.   Further, Cs⁺ apparently fills the sites upon insertion in the *unhydrated* form.   Further extension of PB films to analysis for electroinactive cations (such as K^+) was carried out by Deakin and Byrd.[114]   These authors adapted the QCM for use with soluion flow.   Further discussion of PB-type films on the QCM is given elsewhere.[13]

Insertion oxides and chalcogenides are used for reversible Li batteries.   Upon reduction of a material such as V_6O_{13} for example, electrons and Li^+ ions are added simultaneously up to a maximum of 8 moles of Li per mole of V_6O_{13}.   This capacity is primarily due to the open channel structure of V_6O_{13} throuh which cations diffuse to reside on sites within the cavities.[115]   Li,[116,117] Na,[117] Cu,[117] and Zn[117] are reversibly intercalated into V_6O_{13} at low intercalant concentrations, but some loss of capacity and reversibility have been reported for extended cycling in battery applications.[118,119]   Particles of V_6O_{13} have been attached to the QCM and cycled in $LiClO_4$/propylene carbonate, and the results were reported recently.[120]   A typical cyclic voltammogram of polycrystalline V_6O_{13} at a sweep rate of 0.1 mV/sec is shown in Fig. 5.15.   Lithium intercation/release occurs reversibly with a double peak at 2.75 V (vs. Li).   The reversibility and the stoichiometric confirmation is shown in Fig. 5.16 (region A), in the range $0 < x \leq 1$, where x is the number of moles of inserted Li per mole of V_6O_{13}.   The results establish that the lithium ion is inserted into the V_6O_{13} channels in the unsolvated state in this region.   Cycling into regions B and C (see Fig. 5.15), however, cause large deviations from the simple behavior observed in region A, and

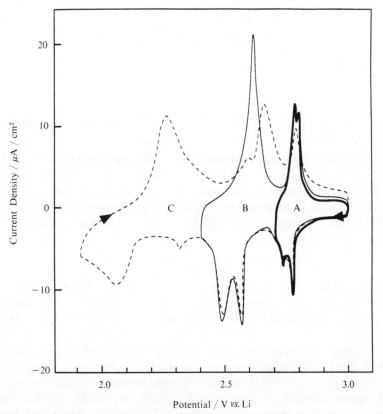

Fig. 5.15 Cyclic voltammogram of V_6O_{13}/Li in $LiClO_4$/propylene carbonate, sweep rate of 0.1 mV/sec at 25°C.   Curves for cycles, A, B, and C, respectively.

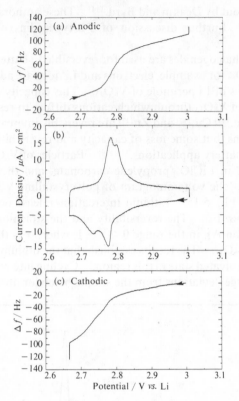

Fig. 5.16 Concurrent QCM and cyclic voltammetry of V_6O_{13} for cycle A: (a) QCM frequency change for anodic
branch of the sweep; (b) Cyclic voltammogram for cycle A; (c) QCM frequency change for cathodic
branch of the sweep.

there is significant loss of capacity upon insertion.   The characteristics of the behavior are
seen most closely by inspection of the frequency change *vs.* charge plotted in Fig. 5.17 for
region A.   The slope is constant in this figure and is equal to 18.7 Hz cm²/mC on reduction
(a) and 18.6 Hz cm²/mC on oxidation (b).   This is to be compared to the theoretical value
of 18.11 Hz cm²/mC assuming unsolvated Li⁺ insertion and calculated from the
relationship

$$\Delta f = \frac{MC_f}{nF} Q$$

derived from Eq. (5.8).   The agreement is quite satisfactory.   Upon cycling in region B
there is significant deviation upon reduction (Fig. 5.18(a)), but subsequent oxidation
appears to yield the theoretical behavior with only small deviation (Fig. 5.18(b)).   The
deviation is accompanied by a net loss of faradaic charge for the entire cycle (region B) of
about 8%.[121]   The deviation and loss of faradaic efficiency is further exaggerated in region
C (Fig. 5.19).   The loss of faradaic charge is about 12% in region C.   The lost charge in
regions B and C is never recovered, even after extended potentiostatic discharge at 3.0 V (*vs.*
Li).   The deviation and loss of capacity in regions B and C have been attributed to a
combination of change of morphology and loss of electrical contact with some of the
particles in the powdered V_6O_{13}.[120,121]   The 12% expansion of the crystal along the *c*-axis

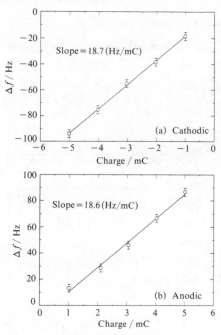

Fig. 5.17 QCM frequency change *vs.* charge for V_6O_{13} in cycle A: (a) Cathodic sweep demonstrates that the experimental data (points) match the theoretical expectation (line) for insertion of unsolvated Li^+; (b) Removal of Li^+ (anodic) also matches theoretical expectation.

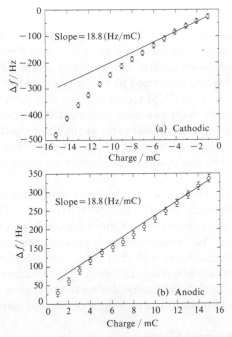

Fig. 5.18 Insertion of unsolvated Li^+ into V_6O_{13} (a) and removal (b) for cycle B is accompanied by a second process on the cathodic sweep which causes the deviation of experimental points from the theoretical line.

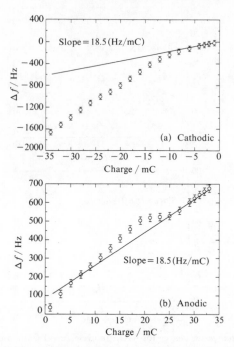

Fig. 5.19 Insertion (a) removal (b) of Li⁺ at the V_6O_{13} electrode for cycle C. Considerable deviation on the cathodic (insertion) sweep is caused by secondary processes, but only the removal process is seen on the anodic sweep.

(137) that attends Li insertion is reversible for single crystals. It may lead, however, to irreversible changes of packing and morphology of the packed particles on cycling. This is being investigated further in our laboratories by quartz crystal impedance techniques. If changes of particle packing are confirmed to be the cause of the deviation, this behavior could limit the application of the QCM techniques to other powdered electrodes.

The insertion behavior of WO_3 has been investigated in several solutions[122,123] with modest success. Several processes appear to occur simultaneously upon intercalation, and the measurement of mass change with the QCM has not enabled research groups to analyze the behavior in detail. The use of other additional techniques are necessary for further clarification.

The QCM was used to investigate the electrochromic character of the nickel oxide electrode as it is cycled between $Ni(OH)_2$ and $NiOOH$.[124–126] The redox cycling is very reversible, accompanied by the insertion of cations (either K⁺ or Li⁺). However, the mass change observed cannot be quantitatively explained by the mass of the ions alone. Apparently H_2O must move with the cations, but whether the water is associated with the cation by solvation could not be established by the measurements. IrO_x films were found to support H_3O^+ injection and release during redox cycling in aqueous H_2SO_4 solutions.[127] Again, the need for additional techniques to be used along with the QCM is clear.

5.4.3 Ion Inserting Polymer Films
Conducting polymers and redox polymers have been studied extensively with

electrochemical techniques. These systems have many of the same properties and applications as for inorganic intercalation materials, but there is more flexibility in fabricating the polymeric materials into thin films, for example. The QCM has been used to establish the nature of the fundamental processes involved in ion insertion and release reactions. Most of the polymers insert and release *anions* with redox cycling, and the QCM has been used to determine whether this is the only process which occurs.

Poly(vinylferrocene) was studied as a model system by several groups.[128-132] Electrodeposited PVF[130-132] has inferior stability as compared to spin coated material,[128,129,133,134] and the latter has been observed to behave reversibly over many cycles and several days. Varineau and Buttry[129] observed that electrodeposited PVF injects PF_6^- on oxidation, and that the mass increase (QCM) agrees exactly with that calculated from the charge passed. There is no evidence for solvent movement in these studies. Recently in our laboratories, we have found that PVF behaves ideally up to the oxidation peak on the cyclic voltammogram (~40% oxidation), and there is some solvent uptake at higher oxidation levels in $LiClO_4$ in acetonitrile.[133,134] In other electrolytes, PVF is unstable and the films are removed from the electrode surface by a combination of mechanical degradation and chemical breakdown.[129,133,134]

Poly(aniline) films are of the second class of electroactive polymers, namely conducting polymers. Orata and Buttry[135] studied the electropolymerization and redox cycling of the material in aqueous solutions. Anions were observed to be inserted on oxidation and removed on reduction. There was some additional insertion of H_3O^+ as a function of pH and voltage. Degradation of the film was observed at high oxidation levels. Other groups have extended these studies[136,137] to nonaqueous solutions. The latter studies demonstrated by QCM that mass continued to increase with oxidation, and that anion doping takes place not by the insertion of the solvated anion but by that of the anion alone. Cordoba-Toriesi, *et al.*[138] combined the QCM with electrochemical impedance measurements, but no advantage over combined QCM cyclic voltammetry was noted. Electrochemical impedance measurements at different levels of oxidation have been carried out for other polymers,[109-111] and in parallel studies[133,134] with the QCM, but not concurrently. At high frequency, the electrochemical impedance measurements reveal the rate of charge injection. At intermediate frequencies, diffusion within the polymer films is dominant, and at lower frequencies the film behaves as a unit (redox capacity region). It is in the latter region that the QCM–CV studies are normally carried out and the time domains where the QCM is most effectively used. The electronic circuitry normally used with the QCM does not have the frequency response that is required to give valid mass readings at high frequencies, so such measurements should be discouraged.

Electropolymerization of poly(pyrrole) has been studied by Baker and Reynolds,[139] who note rigid layer behavior up to several hundred nanometers film thickness. Redox cycling of PPy films has bee studied earlier by Kaufman *et al.*,[140] who noted that anion insertion upon oxidation was apparently accompanied by cation movement in certain voltage ranges.

In earlier papers from this laboratory,[141,142] we presented results for PPy films grown by cycling between 1.5 and +0.8 V *vs.* Ag/AgNO$_3$ (0.01 mol dm^{-3}) in acetonitrile solutions of ClO_4^-, BF_4^-, and TOS$^-$ anions. For the smaller anions, ClO_4^- and BF_4^-, the reduction process (undoping) resulted in a mass decrease, indicating that these ions were removed from the film. For PPy films grown and cycled in ClO_4^- solutions, anions are inserted in stoichiometric quantities up to the peak for oxidation (region I).[133,134] In the capacitive region (region II, more positive potentials), there is positive deviation that was attributed to solvent movement.

Recent experiments of the electropolymerization of PPy in the presence of anions such as poly(vinylsulfonate)(PVS) and poly(4-styrenesulfonate) (PSS) have shown that PPy incorporates the large anion during growth to compensate charge in the pyrrole backbone.[143-147] These large anions are immobilized due to steric hindrance, and during subsequent oxidation/reduction of the film in perchlorate electrolyte, cations must move into the film to maintain charge neutrality. The QCM[141,142,148] has been used to verify that PVS and PSS polypyrrole films insert cations plus solvent species in the initial stages of oxidation.

Fully cycled films were studied in the oxidative portion of the scan (-0.7 to -0.3 V *vs.* SCE) for LiClO$_4$, NaClO$_4$, and MgClO$_4$ and the QCM data are shown in Fig. 5.20. The

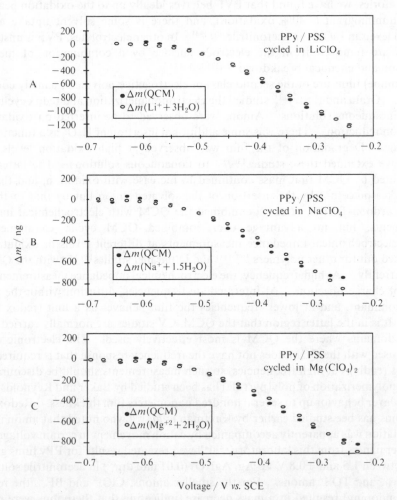

Fig. 5.20 Oxidation in region I for PPy/PSS cycled in (a) LiClO$_4$ (b) NaClO$_4$ (c) Mg(ClO$_4$)$_2$. Comparison of experimental data (Δm (QCM) with mass change calculated from charge (Δm (cation+H$_2$)), assuming the respective cations are solvated.

data show that cations plus associated solvent are removed to compensate the positive oxidative charge in region I. The mass change in this portion of the scan was always negative, indicating removal of species from the film. Lithium is the most highly associated cation with magnesium (divalent) the next highest and sodium the least associated. Association is from 1–3 molecules of water per cation. It should be noted here that there are no definitive data to prove that the water is associated as solvation water. The data only show that there is a *net* movement of water out of the film at the same time that cations are also released.

The behavior in the capacitive region (region II) was investigated by holding the voltage of the film at +0.3 V (*vs.* SCE) until the film was charged to equilibrium and the background current had dropped to a negligible level. The voltage scan from +0.3 V to −0.3 V yielded the concurrent charge and QCM (mass) data shown in Fig. 5.21. The analysis revealed

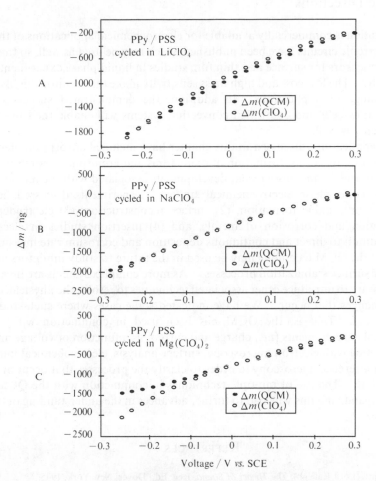

Fig. 5.21 Reduction scan in region II for PPy/PSS cycled in (a) LiClO₄ (b) NaClO₄ (c) Mg(ClO₄)₂. The experimental mass change (Δm (QCM)) is compared to that calculated from charge data (Δm (ClO₄)), assuming that unsolvated ClO₄⁻ anions are released from the film.

that only ClO_4^- was removed from the film with no accompanying solvent.   If the scan was continued into the faradaic region, the mass increased, which indicates that cations began to participate in the process.   A transition area between the two regions occurs in which both cations and anions move.   If the films were cycled only in the capacitive region (from $+0.3$ V to -0.3 V), only ClO_4^- ions were removed during reduction and reinserted upon oxidation.   Zhong and Doblhofer[149] have recently demonstrated by SEM-EDAX analysis that anions are inserted and released in PPy-dodecylsulfonate composite films in the capacitive region, similar to the present findings.

Other polymer systems that have been studied with the electrochemical QCM are poly(tetracyanoquinodimethane),[150]   poly(3-methythiophene),[151]   diheptylviologen bromide,[152]   poly(aniline)/Nafion composite films,[153]   and   poly(pyrrole)/3-(pyrrol-1-yl)propane sulfonate composites.[154]

5.5   Future Directions

Instrumentation is commercially available for electrochemical applications of the QCM, and other electronic circuits have been published which may be used as well, so that the use of gravimetric sensors for surface and thin film studies in liquid phase experiments should expand rapidly.   The low cost and high mass sensitivity make the monitors highly suitable for a wide range of applications.   In addition, the demonstrated success of QCM resonators in flow cells and controlled convection systems will enable their use in many practical systems as well.

Gas phase applications discussed in this chapter have included adsorption, desorption, and decomposition reactions, formation of oxide films and atmospheric corrosion.   This has served to introduce the more recent developments associated with the introduction of the QCM to liquid phase electrochemical studies.   Experiments discussed here have included (1) anodic oxide formation, (2) surface reconstruction, (3) electrodeposition, electrodissolution and corrosion of metals, and (4) insertion studies in electroactive films.   In addition to direct and continuous deposition and corrosion rate measurements, it appears that the QCM technique may be used in the future to study inhibitors and other highly specific surface stabilization processes.   As more complex systems are investigated, it will be necessary to introduce other associated techniques to resolve the physical, chemical and energy changes that occur.   We have indicated some cases where such studies have been carried out.   That is, the QCM has been used in conjunction with standard electrochemical measurements (*i.e.,* charge and current as a function of voltage and time), and supplemented with electron microscopy, surface analysis, electrochemical impedance, and optical interference microscopy in order to clarify the processes that occur at surfaces and in thin films.   The use of multiple techniques in conjunction with the QCM can be expected to expand, and this will lead to further advances in the understanding of the solid-liquid interface.

REFERENCES

1.   J. W. Strutt, (Lord Raleigh), *The Theory of Sound,* Rev. Ed., Dover, New York, 1945.
2.   M. Onoe, *Proc. IRE,* **45**, 94 (1957).
3.   G. Z. Sauerbrey, *Physik Verhandl.,* **8**, 113 (1957); *Z. Phys.,* **155**, 206 (1959).
4.   T. Nomura, *Anal. Chem. Acta,* **124**, 81 (1981).

5.   T. Nomura, T. Nagamune, K. Izutsu and T. S. West, *Bunseki Kagaku,* **30**, 494 (1981).
6.   T .Nomura, and M. Iijima, *Anal. Chem. Acta,* **131**, 97 (1981).
7.   K. K. Kanazawa, and J. G. Gordon II, *Anal. Chem.,* **57**, 1770 (1985).
8.   K. K. Kanazawa, and J. G. Gordon II, *Anal. Chim. Acta,* **175**, 99 (1985).
9.   O. Melroy, K. Kanazawa, J. G. Gordon, D. Buttry, *Langmuir,* **2**, 697 (1986).
10. M. R. Deakin, and O. Melroy, *J. Electroanal. Chem.,* **239**, 321 (1988).
11. M. R. Deakin, T. T. Li and O. Melroy, *J. Electroanal. Chem.,* **243**, 343 (1988).
12. M. D. Ward, and D. A. Buttry, *Science,* **249**, 1000 (1990).
13. D. A. Buttry, *Electroanalytical Chemistry* (A. J. Bard, ed.), Marcel Dekker, New York, 1990.
14. M. R. Deakin, and D. A. Buttry, *Anal. Chem.,* **61**, A1147 (1989).
15. William H. Smyrl, and K. Naoi, in: *Perspectives on Corrosion* (G. Prentice and W. H. Smyrl, eds.), AIChE Symposium Series 278, Vol. 86, New York, 1990.
16. W. G. Cady, *Piezoelectricity*, Vols. I and II, Dover Publications, New York, 1964.
17. R. A. Heising, *Quartz Crystals for Electrical Circuits,* D. Van Nostrand, New York, 1946.
18. W. P. Mason, *Piezoelectric Crystals and Their Applications to Ultrasonics*, Van Nostrad, New York, 1960.
19. C. Lu, in: *Applidations of Piezoelectric Quartz Microbalances* (E. Lu and A. W. Czanderna, eds.), Elsevier, Amsterdam, 1984.
20. R. Beck, U. Pitterman and K. G. Weil, *Ber. Bunsenges. Phys, Chem.,* **92**, 1363 (1988).
21. E. Benes, *J. Appl. Phys.,* **56**, 608 (1984).
22. R. Schumacher, J. J. Pesek, O. Melroy, *J. Phys. Chem.,* **89**, 4338 (1985).
23. M. R. Deakin and O. Melroy, *J. Electrochem. Soc.,* **136**, 349 (1989).
24. R. Schumacher, G. Borges and K. K. Kanazawa, *Surf. Sci. Lett.,* **163**, L621 (1985).
25. R. Schumacher, J. G. Gordon and O. Melroy, *J. Electroanal. Chem.,* **216**, 127 (1987).
26. W. Stoeckel, and R. Schumacher, *Ber. Bunsenges. Phys. Chem.,* **91**, 345 (1987).
27. A. Grzegorzewski and K. E. Heusler, *J. Electroanal. Chem.,* **228**, 455 (1987).
28. P. Lostis, *Rev. Opt.,* **38**, 1 (1959).
29. S. W. Wenzel, and R. M. White, *Appl. Phys. Lett.,* **54**, 1976 (1989).
30. O. Melroy, K. Kanazawa, J. G. Gordon II and D. Buttry, *Langmuir,* **2**, 697 (1986).
31. H. Schlichting, *Boundary Layer Theory*, McGraw-Hill, New York, 1979.
32. S. Bruckenstein and M. Shay, *J. Electroanal. Chem.,* **188**, 131 (1985).
33. S. Bruckenstein and M. Shay, *Electrochim. Acta,* **30**, 1295 (1985).
34. S. Bruckenstein and S. Swathirajan, *Electrochim. Acta,* **30**, 851 (1985).
35. H. Muramatsu, E. Tamiya and I. Karube, *Anal. Chem.,* **60**, 2142 (1988).
36. H. E. Hager, *Chem. Engr. Comm.,* **43**, 25 (1986).
37. H. Bahadur and R. Parshad, in: *Physical Acoustics*, (W. P. Mason and R. N. Thurston, eds.), Academic Press, New York, Vol. 16, (1982), p. 37.
38. H. Pulker, E. Benes, D. Hammer and E. Soellner, *Thin Solid Films,* **32**, 27 (1976).
39. W. P. Mason, *Trans. ASME,* **69**, 359 (1947).
40. W. P. Mason, W. O. Baker, H. J. McSkimm and J. H. Heiss, *Phys. Rev.,* **75**, 936 (1949).
41. A. J. Matheson, *Molecular Acoustics*, John Wiley and Sons, New York, 1971.
42. A. J. Ricco, and S. J. Martin, *Appl. Phys. Lett.,* **50**, 1474 (1987).
43. M. W. Carr, A. R. Hillman, S. D. Lubetkin and M. J. Swann, *J. Electroanal. Chem.,* **267**, 313 (1989).
44. A. Mueller, M. Wicker, R. Schumacher and R. N. Schindler, *Ber. Bunsenges. Phys. Chem.,* **92**, 1395 (1988).
45. C. E. Reed, K. K. Kanazawa and J. H. Kaufman, *J. Appl. Phys.,* **68**, 1993 (1990).
46. C. S. Lu and O. Lewis, *J. Appl. Phys.,* **43**, 4385 (1972).
47. W. Hinsberg, C. Wilson, K. Kanazawa, *J. Electrochem. Soc.,* **133**, 1448 (1986); *Pro. SPIE Int. Soc. Opt. Eng.,* **539**, 6 (1985).
48. E. P. EerNisse, *J. Appl. Phys.,* **43**, 1330 (1972).
49. E. P. EerNisse, *J. Appl. Phys.,* **44**, 4482 (1973).
50. E. P. EerNisse, *J. Vac. Sci. Technol.,* **12**, 564 (1975).
51. G. T. Cheek and W. E. O'Grady, *J. Electroanal. Chem.,* **277**, 341 (1990).
52. K. E. Heusler, A. Grzegorzewski, L. Jaeckel and J. Pietrucha, *Ber. Bunsenges. Phys. Chem.,* **92**, 1218 (1988).
53. D. S. Ballantine, Jr. and H. Wohltjen, *Anal. Chem.,* **61**, 704A (1989).
54. J. G. Brace, T. S. Sanfelippo and S. G. Joshi, *Sens. Actuators,* **14**, 47 (1988).
55. R. W. Murray, W. R. Heineman, J. Janata and W. R. Seitz eds., *Chemical Sensors and Microinstrumentation*, ACS Symposium Series, Vol. 403, Americal Chemical Society, Washington, DC, 1989.
56. S. J. Martin, A. J. Ricco and N. R. Sorenson, Extended Abstract #50, Electrochemical Society, 1987, vol.87-1.
57. J. E. Roederer and G. J. Bastiaans, *Anal. Chem.,* **55**, 2333 (1983).
58. S. W. Wenzel and R. M. White, *IEEE Trans. Electron Devices,* **35**, 735 (1988).
59. S. J. Martin, A. J. Ricco, T. M. Niemczyk and G. C. Frye, *Sens. Actuators,* **20**, 53 (1989).

60. A. J. Ricco, S. J. Martin, T. M. Niemczyk, and G. C. Frye, in: *Chemical Sensors and Microinstrumentation* (R. W. Murray *et al.*, eds.), ACS Symposium Series, Vol. 403, Americal Chemical Society, Washington, DC, 1989.

61. G. C. Frye, S. J. Martn, A. J. Ricco and C. J. Brinker, *ibid.*

62. S. J. Martin, A. J. Ricco and R. C. Hughes, *Proceedings of the 4th International Conference on Solid-State Sensors and Actuators*, Tokyo, (June 1987) (IEEE of Japan, Tokyo, 1987).

63. K. F. Lau, K. H. Yen, J. Z. Wilcox and P. S. Kagiwada, *Proceedings of the Symposium on Frequency Control*, 388 (1979).

64. J. F. Alder, and J. J. McCallum, *Analyst.*, **108**, 1169 (1983).

65. J. Hlavay and G. G. Guilbault, *Anal, Chem.*, **49**, 1890 (1977).

66. R. L. Chuan, *J. Aerosol Sci.*, **1**, 111 (1970).

67. J. G. Olin, G. J. Sem and D. L. Christenson, *Am. Ind. Hyg. Assoc.*, **32**, 209 (1971).

68. J. G. Olin and G. J. Sem, *Atmos. Environ.*, **5**, 653 (1971).

69. A. Chabre, *Nucl. Sci. Abstr.*, **37**, 22601 (1973).

70. T. E. Carpenter and D. L. Bencheley, *Am. Ind. Hyg. Assoc.*, **33**, 503 (1973).

71. P. S. Daley and D. A. Lundgren, *Am. Ind. Hyg. Assoc.*, **36**, 518 (1975).

72. G. J. Sem, and K. Tsurubayashi, *Am. Ind. Hyg. Assoc.*, **36**, 791 (1975).

73. I. Haller and P. White, *J. Phys. Chem.*, **67**, 1784 (1963)

74. W. F. Fisher and W. H. King, Jr., *Anal, Chem.*, **39**, 265 (1967).

75. W. H. King, Jr. and L. W. Corbett, *Anal. Chem.*, **41**, 580 (1969).

76. C. L. Glaves, G. C. Frye, D. M. Smith, C. J. Brinker, A. Datye, A. J. Ricco and S. J. Martin, *Langmuir*, **5**, 459 (1989).

77. W. H. King, Jr., *Anal. Chem.*, **36**, 1735 (1964).

78. W. H. King, Jr., U. S. Patent 3,164,004 (Jan. 5, 1965).

79. W. H. King, Jr., *Res./Dev.*, **20**, 28 (1969).

80. W-Y. Lee, H. C. Siegmann and J. M. Eldridge, *J. Electrochem. Soc.*, **124**, 1744 (1977).

81. D. W. Rice, P. B. P. Phipps and R. Tremoureux, *J. Electrochem. Soc.*, **126**, 1459 (1979).

82. P. Schulze and K. E. Heusler, *Ber. Bunsenges. Phys. Chem.*, **78**, 601 (1974).

83. H. W. Gundlach and K. E. Heusler, *Z. Phys. Chem. NF.*, **119**, 213 (1980).

84. S. Zakipour, C. Leygraf and G. Portnoff, *J. Electrochem. Soc.*, **133**, 873 (1986).

85. P. B. P. Phipps, and D. W. Rice, in: *Atmospheric Chemistry* (G. R. Brukaber and P. B. P. Phipps, eds.), ACS Symposium Series 89, American Chemical Society, Washington, 1979.

86. M. Seo, I. Sawamura, L. Grassjo, Y. Haga and N. Sato, *J. Mater. Sci. (Japan).*, **39**, 357, 1990.

87. S. Bruckenstein and S. Swathirajan, *Electrochem. Acta,* **30**, 851 (1985).

88. S. Bruckenstein and M. Shay, *Electrochem. Acta,* **30**, 1295 (1985).

89. R. Schumacher, *Angew. Chem. Int. Ed. Engl.*, **29**, 329 (1990).

90. W. Stoeckel and R. Schumacher, *Ber. Bernsenges, Phys. Chem.*, **93**, 606 (1989).

91. W. Stoeckel and R. Schumacher, *Ber. Bernsenges. Phys. Chem.*, **93**, 600 (1989).

92. M. Benje, M. Eiermann, U. Pittermann and K. G. Weil, *Ber. Bunsenges. Phys. Chem.*, **90**, 435 (1986).

93. R. Schumacher, J. J. Pesek and O. R. Melroy, *J. Phys. Chem.*, **89**, 4338 (1985).

94. K. K. Kanazawa and Dos, *Plat. Surf. Finish.*, July 1987, p. 52.

95. W. H. Smyrl, in: *Comprehensive Treatise on Electrochemistry*, Vol. 4 (R. White *et al.*, eds.), Plenum Press, New York (1981).

95a). W. J. Bernard and J. W. Cook, *J. Electrochem. Soc.*, **106**, 643 (1959).

96. W. D. Hinsberg, C. G. Willson and K. K. Kanazawa, *J. Electrochem. Soc.*, **133**, 1448 (1986).

96a). M. J. Dignam and P. J. Ryan, *Can. J. Chem.*, **41**, 3108 (1963).

97. L. Grasjo, M. Seo and N. Sato, *Corrosion Science,* **31**, 299 (1990).

97a). J. W. Diggle, T. C. Downie and C. W. Goulding, *Chem. Rev.*, **69**, 365 (1969).

98. R. Schumacher, A. Mueller and W. Stoeckel, *J. Electroanal. Chem.*, **219**, 311 (1987).

99. C. Chandler, MS Thesis, University of Minnesota, (1990).

100. C. Chandler, J-B.Ju, R. Atanasoski and W. H. Smyrl, Paper #37, Corrosion 89, NACE, New Orleans (April 1989).

101. W. H. Smyrl, *J. Electrochem. Soc.*, **132**, 1551 (1985).

102. W. H. Smyrl, *ibid.*, **132**, 1555 (1985).

103. W. H. Smyrl, and L. L. Stephenson, *ibid.*, **132**, 1563 (1985).

104. R. T. Atanasoski, H. S. White and W. H. Smyrl, *J. Electrochem. Soc.*, **133**, 2435 (1985).

105. M. J. Nicol, *S. Afr. J. Chem.*, **35**, 77 (1982).

106. B. T. Bell, MS Thesis, University of Minnesota (1986).

107. J-B.Ju, W. H. Smyrl and R. T. Atanasoski, submitted to the *J. Electrochem. Soc.*

108. R. D. Ruedisueli Hager and M. E. Buehler, *Corrosion,* **42**, 345 (1986).

109. T. B. Hunter, P. S. Tyler, W. H. Smyrl and H. S. White, *J. Electrochem. Soc.*, **134**, 2198 (1987).

110. M. Lien and W. H. Smyrl, in: *Transient Techniques in Corrosion Science and Engineering* (W. H. Smyrl *et al.*, eds.), Electrochemical Society, Pennington, NJ., 1988.

111. W. H. Smyrl and C.-H. Paik, *ibid.*

112. B. J. Felman and O. R. Melroy, *J. Electranal. Chem.*, **234**, 213 (1987).

113. S. J. Lasky and D. A. Buttry, *J. Amer. Chem. Soc.*, **110**, 6258 (1988).

114. M. R. Deakin and H. Byrd, *Anal. Chem.*, **61**, 290 (1989).

115. D. W. Murphy and P. A. Christian, *Science*, **205**, 651 (1979).

116. P. C. Spurdens and B. C. H. Steele, *Solid State Ionics*, **21**, 151 (1986).

117. (a) M. Z. A. Munshi and W. H. Smyrl, *Solid State Ionics*, **45**, 183 (1991); (b) M. Z. A. Munshi and W. H. Smyrl, C. Schmidtke, *Chem. Mater.*, **2**, 530 (1990); (c) M. Z. A. Munshi, W. H. Smyrl and C. Schmidtke, *Solid State Ionics*, **47**, 35 (1991).

118. K. M. Abraham, J. L. Goldman and M. D. Dempsey, *J. Electrochem. Soc.*, **128**, 2493 (1981).

119. D. W. Murphy, P. A. Christian, F. J. DiSalvo, J. N. Carides and J.V.Waszczak, *J. Electrochem. Soc.*, **128**, 2053 (1981).

120. H.-K. Park, K. Podolski, Z. Munshi, W. H. Smyrl and B. B. Owens, *J. Electrochem. Soc.*, **138**, 627 (1991).

121. H.-K. Park, W. H. Smyrl and B. B. Owens, submitted to the *J. Electrochem. Soc.*, 1991.

122. H. Masuda and N. Baba, *Chem. Letters (Japan)*, 1877 (1987).

123. S. J. Babiner, paper presented at the Nov., 1990 meeting of the AIChE (also submitted to *Solar Energy Materials*).

124. S. I. Cordoba-Torresi, C. Gabrielli, A. Hugot-LeGoff and R. Torresi, *J. Electrochem. Soc.*, **138**, 1548 (1991).

125. P. Bernard, C. Gabrielli, M. Reddam, H. Takenouti, J. Leonard and P. Blanchard, *Electrochem. Acta.*, **36**, 3 (1991).

126. G. T. Cheek and W. E. O'Grady, in: *The Application of Surface Analysis Methods to Environmental/Material Interactions* (D. R. Baer, C. R. Clayton and G. D. Davis, eds.), The Electrochemical Society, Pennington, NJ, 1991.

127. T. Yoshino, N. Baba, H. Masuda and K. Arai, in *Electrochromic Materials* (M. K. Carpenter and D. A. Corrigan, eds.), Electrochemical Society, Pennington, NJ, 1990.

128. M. D. Ward, *J. Phys. Chem.*, **92**, 2049 (1988).

129. P. T. Varineau and D. A. Buttry, *J. Phys. Chem.*, **91**, 1291 (1987).

130. S. Bruckenstein, C. P. Wilde, M. Shay, A. R. Hillman and D. C. Loveday, *J. Electroanal. Chem.*, **258**, 457 (1989).

131. A. R. Hillman, D. C. Loveday and S. Bruckenstein, *J. Electoanal. Chem.*, **274**, 157, (1989).

132. A. R. Hillman, D. C. Loveday and S. Bruckenstein, *Langmuir*, **7**, 191 (1991).

133. M. Lien, Ph. D. Thesis, University of Minnesota, 1991.

134. M. Lien and W. H. Smyrl, manuscript in preparation.

135. D. Orata and D. A. Buttry, *J. Amer. Chem. Soc.*, **109**, 3574 (1987).

136. H. Daifuku, T. Kawagoe, N. Yamamoto, T. Ohsaka and N. Oyama, *J. Electroanal. Chem.*, **274**, 313 (1989).

137. H. Daifuku, T. Kawagoe, T. Matsunaga, N. Yamamoto, T. Osaka and N. Oyama (accepted in *Syn. Metals* 1991).

138. S. Cordoba-Torresi, C. Gabrielli, M. Keddam, H. Takenouti and R. Torresi, *J. Electroanal. Chem.*, **290**, 269 (1990).

139. C. K. Baker and J. H. Reynolds, *J. Electroanal. Chem.*, **251**, 307 (1988).

140. J. N. Kaufman, K. K. Kanazawa and G. B. Street, *Phys. Rev. Lett.*, **53**, 2461 (1984).

141. K. Naoi, M. M. Lien and W. H. Smyrl, *J. Electroanal. Chem.*, **272**, 273 (1989).

142. K. Naoi, M. Lien and W. H. Smyrl, *J. Electrochem. Soc.*, **138**, 440 (1991).

143. T. Schmidzu, A. Ohtani, T. Iyoda and K. Honda, *J. Chem. Soc., Chem. Comm.*, **1986**, 1415.

144. T. Iyoda, A. Ohtani, T. Shimidzu and K. Honda, *Chem. Lett.*, **1986**, 687.

145. T. Shimidzu, A. Ohtani, T. Iyoda and K. Honda, *J. Electroanal. Chem.*, **224**, 123 (1987).

146. (a) L. L. Miller and Q. X. Zhou, *Macromolecules*, **20**, 1594 (1987).
      (b) B. Zinger and L. L. Miller, *J. Am. Chem. Soc.*, **106**, 6891 (1984).

147. O. X. Zhou, L. L. Miller and J. R. Valentine, *J. Electroanal. Chem.*, **261**, 147 (1989).

148. M. Lien, W. H. Smyrl and M. Morita, *J. Electroanal. Chem.*, **309**, 333 (1991).

149. C. Zhong and K. Doblhofer, *Electrochim. Acta*, **35**, 1971 (1990).

150. G. Inzelt, *J. Electroanal. Chem.*, **287**, 171 (1990).

151. S. Servagent and E. Vieil, *J. Electroanal. Chem.*, **280**, 222 (1990).

152. G. O. Ostrom and D. A. Buttry, *J. Electroanal. Chem.*, **256**, 411 (1988).

153. D. Orata and D. A. Buttry, *J. Electroanal. Chem.*, **257**, 71 (1988).

154. J. R. Reynolds, N. S. Sundaresan, M. Pomerantz, S. Basak and C. K. Baker, *J. Electroanal. Chem.*, **250**, 355 (1988).

155. R. T. Atanasoski, C. Shmidtke and W. H. Smyrl, paper #206 presented at the Phoenix Meeting of the Electrochemical Society, October 1991.

6

Multichannel Spectroscopic Ellipsometry for Real Time Analysis of Electrochemical and Plasma Deposition of Thin Films

R.W. COLLINS

Materials Research Laboratory and Department of Physics, The Pennsylvania State University, University Park, PA 16802, U.S.A.

6.1 Introduction

The demands on thin films deposited by electrochemical and plasma methods have become more stringent as their applications have become more advanced. Thus, non-invasive real time probes are helpful for process monitoring and control so that the desired specifications can be ensured. Although each application requires specialized thin film characteristics, the following information is of general interest in many applications: thickness, void volume fraction, film continuity, microstructural uniformity, grain size, surface morphology, optical properties, electronic band structure, composition, and doping. If the data collected in real time can also be interpreted in real time, then the resulting information can be used to control the material properties through automatic feedback which adjusts preparation variables such as electrode potentials, gas flows, etc. Even if real time data interpretation is not possible, real time measurement may provide the best opportunity to characterize the growing film owing to the complexity of the final structure which often arises from the need to deposit sequential layers of different properties. Real time monitoring is also important to assess reproducibility and stability, to troubleshoot when problems arise, and to design new processes and quickly arrive at the desired preparation variables.

Because of the adverse liquid and high pressure gaseous environments of electrochemical and plasma deposition, a non-perturbing and non-invasive real time probe must be based on photons. Optical ellipsometry is one of the most powerful probes as it provides measures of both the amplitude (ψ) and the phase change (Δ) that the electric field of a monochromatic, polarized light wave undergoes when it reflects from a specular material.[1] When the material presents a single, atomically-smooth and abrupt surface to the ambient, then the two angles (ψ,Δ) can provide a complete description of the optical properties of the material, *i.e.* the index of refraction and extinction coefficient (n,k), or the real and imaginary parts of the dielectric function ($\varepsilon_1,\varepsilon_2$), as long as the corresponding information for the ambient gas or liquid is known. The complete optical properties are inaccessible to a routine reflectance measurement because only a single value is obtained in the experiment, the ratio of the reflected-to-incident irradiances.

Real time ellipsometry became a reality after the development of automatic ellipsometers in the mid-1960's and their associated fast data collection rates [from 10 μs to about 1 s per (ψ,Δ, depending on instrument design].[2-6] Since then, most real time ellipsometry studies of electrochemical and plasma deposition of thin films have been performed at fixed wavelength and have been used to determine the film thickness, optical properties at the single wavelength, and rudimentary microstructural information.[7-10]

There are two main limitations to the single wavelength approach. First, it is very difficult to identify materials and impossible to characterize their electronic band structure based on the available information.   Second, it is difficult to characterize deviations in the single wavelength (ψ,Δ) data, collected during film growth, from model calculations assuming a perfect layer-by-layer process.   Such deviations are usually associated with complex nucleation, coalescence, and interfacial phenomena, which are of great interest because they lend insights into film growth processes.   For example, in the simplest optical model for nucleation, two parameters, the film thickness and void (or liquid) volume fraction, are required in addition to the optical functions of the bulk film.[11]   Only when the latter are known, e.g. from literature results or from a measurement of the thick opaque film, can the microstructural parameters be determined by numerical inversion of (ψ,Δ).   Unfortunately, experimental errors, errors in the bulk optical functions, and deviations from the assumed model often combine to render the numerical inversion approach ineffective.   It may then be possible to fit (ψ,Δ) data using geometric models of microstructural evolution which connect void fraction and thickness.   However, it is difficult to judge whether such models are correct or unique.   Clearly, the additional information provided by a spectroscopic capability is required to overcome these limitations, but the technical barriers to real time spectroscopic ellipsometry are high.

Manual ellipsometry has been applied widely over the years to determine the optical properties of materials at discrete wavelengths, thus providing insights into electronic structure and processes.[12]   In this application, a true spectroscopic capability of the manual instruments is limited by the patience and endurance of the operator, as the time required to collect a single accurate (ψ,Δ) pair at a given wavelength is about 10 min.   Thus, the development of automatic ellipsometers not only provided the real time capability but also led to a dramatic expansion in the application of spectroscopic ellipsometry.   First, it was demonstrated that $(\varepsilon_1,\varepsilon_2)$ derived from (ψ,Δ) spectra can be multiply-differentiated so that the electronic transitions in the reflecting material can be identified accurately.[13]   Second, it was demonstrated that (ψ,Δ) spectra collected on complex multilayered materials can be interpreted to provide layer thicknesses and microstructural information, along with optical properties, in analyses that would be unthinkable to apply to discrete wavelength data.[14,15]

Automatic spectroscopic ellipsometry, as originally developed in the rotating analyzer configuration,[13] requires ~30 min to collect one pair of (ψ,Δ) spectra, depending on the desired signal/noise ratio, the number of spectral points acquired, and the stepping speed of the spectrometer used for wavelength scanning.   Thus, such an instrument is restricted to studies of static samples.   In recent pioneering work, however, Muller and coworkers have developed a spectroscopic ellipsometer with real time capability based on the self-compensating principle.   This instrument can provide high precision, high accuracy spectra consisting of 400 (ψ,Δ) pairs from 1.8 to 3.1 eV in 3 s.[16]   Single (ψ,Δ) measurements are obtained in 1 ms using high-speed Faraday cells[17]; rapid spectral scanning is achieved through a rotating interference filter; and the detection system employs a conventional photomultiplier tube for sequential acquisition of (ψ,Δ) pairs across the full visible spectrum.   For a 100-point spectrum, the ultimate speed of such a system is 100 ms, but this limit depends on the nature, spectral dependence, and rate of change of the surface under study.   This unique instrument has provided information of unprecedented detail on the microstructural aspects of Pb underpotential deposition on Cu,[18] and electrochemical oxidation of Ag.[19]

More recently, a second real time spectroscopic ellipsometer has been developed.[20]   This new instrument is based on the rotating polarizer principle and can provide high precision, high accuracy spectra consisting of 128 (ψ,Δ) pairs from 1.5 to 4.5 eV, also in a time of 3 s.   In contrast to the self-compensating ellipsometer, this instrument employs a conventional broadband light source, but the unique aspect is a multichannel detection system consisting of a spectrograph and integrating photodiode array for parallel acquisition of spectra from four successive detector read-outs.   The ultimate speed of this instrument is closely linked to the technology of commercial multichannel detection system; with the current state of the art, a 128-point spectrum can be acquired in about 5 ms, albeit at relatively low precision.

In this article, development details of the new multichannel spectroscopic ellipsometer will be described (Sect. 6.2) as well as its applications in diverse areas of electrochemistry.   The applications will concentrate on electronically active films for which real time information on the electronic structure as well as the microstructure is of great interest.   The first application involves electrochemical deposition of the conducting polymer polypyrrole on a Au electrode (Sect. 6.3).   For this material, information on the doping-induced electronic states below the band gap are deduced, and the associated transition oscillator strengths provide information on doping.   The second application involves plasma-enhanced chemical vapor deposition of hydrogenated amorphous silicon (Sect. 6.4).   For this material, the optical gap can be obtained during different stages of the growth of ultrathin films.   Through these applications, the power of the real time spectroscopic ellipsometry technique is clearly demonstrated, and the limitations of the earlier single wavelength approach have been overcome.

6.2   Instrumentation Development

6.2.1   Description of the Ideal Rotating Polarizer Multichannel Ellipsometer

As shown in Fig. 6.1, the rapid scanning spectroscopic ellipsometer applied in this work consists of a Xe arc lamp, collimator, rotating polarizer assembly with Rochon element (P_{rot}), sample (S) in an electrochemical cell or vacuum chamber, fixed analyzer assembly (A) with Glan-Taylor element, single prism spectrograph, and a 1024-pixel photodiode array detector.[20-22]   The detector is a component of a commercially-available optical multichannel analyzer system that includes a versatile detector controller.   In all our work, we have sacrificed spectral resolution for signal-to-noise ratio and employed the pixel grouping capability of the detector controller to collect 128 spectral positions.   Each eight-pixel group intercepts a photon energy band 0.05 eV wide at 1.5 eV and 0.025 eV wide at 3.2 eV.   A single pixel group can be read in 35 μs, and the entire array in 4.5 ms.   The array is an integrating detector; thus, these read-outs are proportional to the integrated irradiance intercepted by the pixel group over the time interval starting from the previous read-out.   The rotation frequency, $\omega/2\pi$, for the polarizer is 12.5 Hz.   This is sufficiently slow so that the array can be read every 45° of polarizer rotation (triggered by an optical encoder attached to the polarizer shaft), as required for the data collection procedures described in the following paragraphs.

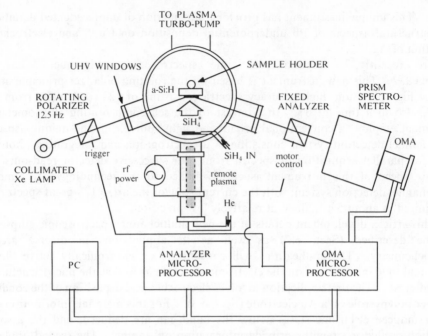

Fig. 6.1 Optical configuration of the rotating polarizer ellipsometer with multichannel detection system.   In this schematic, the sample is shown mounted in the vacuum chamber used for plasma-enhanced CVD of a-Si:H; (PC, personal computer; OMA, optical multichannel analyzer).

First, we define the ellipsometric angles, $\{\psi, \Delta\}$, by:

$$\tan\psi \exp(i\Delta) = (|r_p|/|r_s|)\exp\{i(\delta_p - \delta_s)\}, \tag{6.1}$$

where r_p and r_s are the complex amplitude reflection coefficients for the electric field directions parallel (p) and perpendicular (s) to the plane of incidence, and $|r_p|$, $|r_s|$, δ_p, and δ_s are the respective magnitudes and phases.[1]   The reflection coefficients are defined in turn by:

$$r_p = E_{rp}/E_{ip}; \qquad r_s = E_{rs}/E_{is}, \tag{6.2}$$

where E_{ip}, E_{is}, E_{rp}, and E_{rs} are the complex amplitudes of the electric field components in the p- and s-directions for the incident and reflected waves.

Next, we will describe the procedures to relate the irradiance spectra collected over four successive quadrants of the optical cycle, $\{S_{jk}; j=1,...,4; k=1,...,128\}$, to the $\{\psi(h\nu), \Delta(h\nu)\}$ spectra.   Here, we designate j as the quadrant index and k as the pixel group index, the latter covering the maximum spectral range from 1.5 to 4.5 eV.   For an ideal rotating element multichannel ellipsometer in the $P_{rot}SA$ configuration, the irradiance at the kth pixel group of the detector, I_k, exhibits the following waveform[23]:

$$I_k(t) = I_{0k}(1 + \alpha_k'\cos2\omega t + \beta_k'\sin2\omega t), \tag{6.3}$$

where α_k' and β_k' are experimentally determined Fourier coefficients for pixel group k.   Thus, the experimental spectra $\{S_{jk}; j=1,4; k=1,128\}$ are given by:

$$S_{jk} = \int_{(j-1)\pi/4\omega}^{j\pi/4\omega} I_{0k}(1 + \alpha_k'\cos2\omega t + \beta_k'\sin2\omega t)\mathrm{d}t. \tag{6.4}$$

The resulting equations for $j=1,...,4$ can be solved for each pixel group k to obtain the three unknowns I_{0k}, α_k' and β_k' and one consistency check.[24]   The latter three results are of greatest interest here:

$$\alpha_k' = (\pi/2)(S_{1k} - S_{2k} - S_{3k} + S_{4k})/(S_{1k} + S_{2k} + S_{3k} + S_{4k}) \tag{6.5a}$$

$$\beta_k' = (\pi/2)(S_{1k} + S_{2k} - S_{3k} - S_{4k})/(S_{1k} + S_{2k} + S_{3k} + S_{4k}) \tag{6.5b}$$

$$0 = S_{1k} - S_{2k} + S_{3k} - S_{4k}. \tag{6.5c}$$

Thus, from the measured $\{S_{jk}, j=1,4; k=1,128\}$, the experimental $\{\alpha_k', \beta_k'\}$ spectra can be obtained.   Equation (6.5c) is used to check for system errors as described in Section 6.2.2.   In deriving Eqs. (6.5a–c), we define $t=0$ by the start of the S_{1k} integration.   Because each pixel group is read successively, the time origin is a linearly increasing function of k with a slope of 35 μs.

To obtain $\{\psi(h\nu), \Delta(h\nu)\}$, we use the standard theoretical equations for the rotating polarizer system[9,23]

$$I_k(t) = I_{0k}\{1 + \alpha_k\cos2(\omega t - P_{Sk}) + \beta_k\sin2(\omega t - P_{Sk})\}, \tag{6.6a}$$

$$\tan\psi(h\nu_k) = [(1 + \alpha_k)/(1 - \alpha_k)]^{1/2}\tan(A - A_S) \tag{6.6b}$$

$$\cos\Delta(h\nu_k) = \beta_k/[(1 - \alpha_k^2)^{1/2}], \tag{6.6c}$$

where the theoretical and experimental 2ω Fourier coefficients are related through a $2P_{Sk}$ rotation transformation:

$$\alpha_k = \alpha_k'\cos2P_{Sk} + \beta_k'\sin2P_{Sk} \tag{6.7a}$$

$$\beta_k = -\alpha_k'\sin2P_{Sk} + \beta_k'\cos2P_{Sk}. \tag{6.7b}$$

In Eq. (6.6b), A is the fixed polarizer scale reading, and A_S is the offset needed to convert this reading to the true analyzer angle measured in a counterclockwise sense with respect to the plane of incidence (when looking into the beam).   The angle $-P_{Sk}$ is the true angle of the rotating polarizer at the time origin for the kth pixel group.   This angle is a linear function of k with a slope of $0.16°$, which is the angle that the polarizer rotates during the 35 μs pixel group read time.   Equations (6.6a–c) and (6.7a–b) are identical to those for the more conventional rotating analyzer system but with all analyzer and polarizer angular variables interchanged.[25]

Two calibrations are needed to apply Eqs. (6.6a–c) and (6.7a–b) to the experimental Fourier coefficients $\{\alpha_k', \beta_k'\}$.   The first is a standard photon energy calibration of the spectrograph/detector (e.g. performed with a Hg lamp) that relates $h\nu$ and k.   The second is an angular calibration to obtain the offset A_S and the phase spectrum P_{Sk} and is performed on the static substrate mounted in the $P_{rot}SA$ configuration prior to deposition and real time measurement.   The angular calibration is performed by the residual function approach for samples or photon energy ranges such that $30° < |\Delta| < 150°$, or by the zone-difference phase function approach otherwise.   These methods are described in detail in the literature and rely on the fact that when linearly polarized light reflects from an isotropic surface with $\Delta \neq 0°$ or $180°$, it remains linearly polarized if and only if the incident field direction is along the p or s axes.[26,27]

In summary, a measurement which neglects all system errors first requires collecting

$\{S_{jk}\ j=1,4;\ k=1,128\}$ as a function of time during film growth.   Equations (6.5a–b) are then applied to calculate the experimental Fourier coefficients $\{\alpha_k',\ \beta_k'\}$.   Using the calibration information deduced prior to real time measurement, Eqs. (6.7a–b) and then Eqs. (6.6b–c) are applied to deduce $\{\psi(h\nu),\Delta(h\nu)\}$ vs. time for the evolving surface.   At the polarizer rotation frequency of 12.5 Hz, repetitive spectra can be collected from successive single optical cycles of 40 ms.   In the work presented here, the film deposition rates were low enough that we could sacrifice time resolution for precision.   Thus, sub-monolayer sensitivity was achieved by accumulating and averaging data collected over 80 successive optical cycles, or 3.2 s of total acquisition time.   With this scheme, standard deviations in (ψ,Δ) of $(0.01°,\ 0.02°)$ at 2.0 eV and $(0.03°,\ 0.04°)$ at 3.0 eV have been obtained for a Au surface.[20]   Recent improvements have yielded similar sensitivity using a 10 optical cycle average with an acquisition time of 0.8 s.

6.2.2   Errors in the Rotating Polarizer Multichannel Ellipsometer

Throughout the course of our ellipsometer development, various experimental errors were encountered and corrections were incorporated into expanded calibration and data reduction procedures as needed for high accuracy.   In general, the errors are relatively small when the sample converts the incident light to near-circularly polarized light (*i.e.* when $\alpha\sim 0;\ \beta\sim 0$, and $|\Delta|=90°;\ \psi\sim|A-A_S|$).[28]   This is best approximated, for example, in real time measurements of thin film growth on metallic substrates, as in our studies of polypyrrole electrodeposition on Au.   However, when the light reflected from the sample is near-linearly polarized, for example in the red part of the spectrum for the c-Si substrates used in our plasma-enhanced chemical vapor deposition studies, then errors such as non-linearity and image persistence can be considerable.   In this case the procedures described in Section 6.2.1 are not sufficient to extract monolayer-level growth characteristics (see, for example, Section. 6.4.3).   In this section, the major errors in the system are outlined.

The first error, common to all photometric ellipsometers, is detector non-linearity.[22]   Non-linearity of the Si photodiode array was characterized by measuring the observed count rate (total observed counts per unit exposure time) vs. pixel group for a cw source at different irradiance levels.   For a given irradiance level and pixel group, we found that the observed count rate was a function of the exposure time, rather than being constant as would be required for linearity.   Fortunately, however, a detailed study of the full data set led to a single correction factor, depending only on the total observed counts (and not explicitly on the exposure time, count rate, or pixel group number), that could be used to divide the observed counts and obtain values strictly proportional to the incident irradiance integrated over the exposure time.   This correction factor for our detector is shown in Fig. 6.2.   In order to correct the ellipsometric data for this effect, we apply the relationship: $S_{jk,c}=S_{jk,r}/\,C_{NL}(S_{jk,r})$, where the 'c' and 'r' denote corrected and observed (raw) counts and $C_{NL}(S_{jk,r})$ represents the functional relationship in Fig. 6.2.

A second detector error that influences the data is image persistence, which is characterized by blocking a cw source with a fast shutter during a series of sequential read-outs of the detector.[22]   The detector exposure time is chosen to be longer than the full open-close time of the shutter.   After correction for background and dark level, pixel exposures commencing after the full close time of the shutter should read zero counts.   In practice, such exposures give a weak count level which is 0.55% of the observed counts recorded in the previous read-out.   Consideration of the persistence effect suggests a

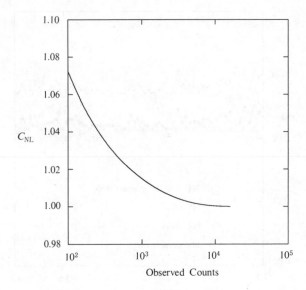

Fig. 6.2 Non-linearity correction factor, C_{NL}, as a function of observed photon counts for the photodiode array detector. This correction factor is used to divide the observed counts to obtain values strictly proportional to the irradiance integrated over the exposure time. (After Ref. 22)

correction to the raw S_{jk} values of the form: $S_{jk,c}=S_{jk,r}+C_{IP}(S_{jk,r})-C_{IP}(S_{(j-1)k,r})$, where $C_{IP}(x)=0.0055x$. The first correction term on the right represents unread counts which remain and affect $S_{(j+1)k}$; the second term represents the residual counts from $S_{(j-1)k}$.

Figure 6.3 shows the effects of non-linearity and image persistence corrections on the quantity $1-(\alpha_k'^2+\beta_k'^2)^{1/2}$, measured in the straight-through configuration ($P_{rot}A$) with the sample removed. This quantity represents the deviation from unity in the effective experimental ac/dc gain of the instrument; for a system free of errors it should be zero.[25] Note that the effects of non-linearity and image persistence are to suppress the ac component with respect to the dc component. An order of magnitude improvement in effective linearity is achieved by applying both corrections.

The third error results when photons are detected at pixel group k having an energy outside the narrow band centered at $h\nu_k$. Stray light occurs at three levels: (1) scattering within the spectrometer/detector enclosure, (2) multiple-reflections from the detector window, and (3) cross-talk between pixel groups. Stray light is a serious error, influencing the data most strongly at high photon energies where the output of the Xe lamp is low, and at photon energies corresponding to minima in sample reflectivity (e.g. in the interference patterns of spectra obtained on transparent films >500 Å thick). In these situations, the stray light contributes a larger percentage of the observed counts. Sources (2) and (3) are identifiable by features in the stray light distribution observed when a high energy-blocking filter is inserted at the entrance to the spectrgraph. These sources are best minimized by system design, specifically by limiting the number of interfaces that the beam encounters before it is absorbed by the detector. Stray light source (1) can be corrected at the raw data level because it is nearly uniform over the blocked pixels and is roughly proportional to the

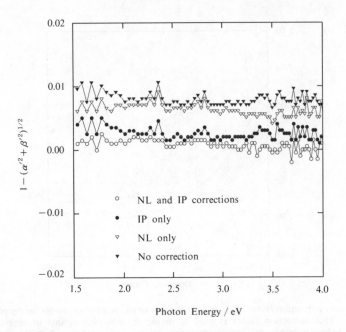

Fig. 6.3 Experimental deviation of the ac/dc gain ratio from unity, $[1-(\alpha'^2+\beta'^2)^{1/2}]$, measured in the straight-
       through configuration ($P_{rot}A$), demonstrating the efficacy of the non-linearity (NL) and image
       persistence (IP) corrections.   In the absence of errors, the gain deviation should vanish.   [After Ref. 22]

observed counts summed over the entire array.   The exact procedure will not be reviewed
here as it is too complex, owing to the linear phase relationship among the S_{jk} measurements
versus k. (See Reference 22 for details.)

The previous three errors are specific to the detection system; however, the source and
polarizer system also introduces errors, even when alignment is perfect.[21]   In our system,
residual source polarization, which is modulated by the rotating polarizer, influences the 2ω
Fourier coefficients and generates weak 4ω coefficients in the detected output.   A non-zero
consistency relationship [Eq. (6.5c)] is one indication of this error.   In addition, for the
quartz Rochon rotating polarizer element, the transmitted light has a slight
ellipticity.[26]   This effect, related to the optical activity of quartz, also influences the 2ω
Fourier coefficients.   Both errors can be included in expanded theoretical equations,
analogous to Eqs. (6.6a–c), with photon-energy dependent parameters which characterize
the errors.   These parameters can be obtained experimentally using a two-step calibration
procedure in which the residual function approach is applied in both p- and s-directions to
overdetermine A_s and P_{Sk}.   Once these error parameters are known, the error terms can be
included to first order in the calibration equations to obtain corrected values of A_s and
P_{Sk}.   Finally, the errors can be included to all orders in the data reduction equations to
obtain corrected values of (ψ,Δ).

As an example of the potential errors that could arise in calibration, Fig. 6.4(a) shows the
analyzer offset angle for a c-Si sample covered by a 590 Å thermally-grown oxide, before
(A_1) and after (A_s) the source polarization and optical activity corrections.   The spurious

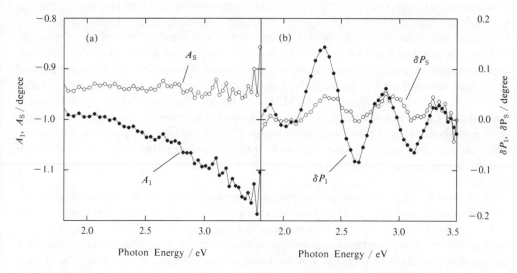

Fig. 6.4 Calibration data obtained as a function of photon energy for a c-Si substrate covered with a 590 Å
thermally-grown oxide.   (a) Analyzer azimuth offset uncorrected (A_1) and corrected (A_S) for errors
associated with source polarization and polarizer optical activity; (b) Deviation from linearity (as a
function of pixel group number) in the polarizer phase angle uncorrected (δP_1) and corrected (δP_S) for
the same errors as in (a).   In the absence of errors, A_S should be independent of photon energy, and δP_S
should vanish.   [Adapted from Ref. 21]

photon energy dependence in A_1 is eliminated, demonstrating the validity of the correction
procedure.   Fig. 6.4(b) shows the deviation from linearity in the phase calibration angle
before (δP_1) and after (δP_{Sk}) the same corrections.   In the absence of errors, this quantity
should vanish for a constant motor speed and pixel group read-out time.   Note that the
oscillations are reduced by a factor of 3–4 in the correction procedure.   The oscillations
appear to arise from wavelength-dependent rotation of the source polarization by the
Rochon polarizer.   A future improvement in this system involves adding a second fixed
polarizer in the beam path before the rotating polarizer so that the source polarization error
would be eliminated completely.[29]

6.3   Applications in Electrochemical Deposition of Thin Films

6.3.1   Introduction: Polypyrrole Electropolymerization and Properties

The electrochemical deposition and properties of the thin film conducting polymer
polypyrrole (PPy) have been studied in detail over the last decade.[30]   There are a number
of applications for these films, including batteries, corrosion-resistant coatings for
photoanodes, electrochemically controlled membranes, electrochromic displays, and
memory devices.   The display applications, for example, take advantage of the color
change that occurs upon oxidation from the undoped insulating phase to the doped
conducting phase.[31]   As a result, the optoelectronic characteristics of PPy as well as the
influence of processing procedures on these characteristics are of interest for both scientific
and technological reasons.

The mechanisms of PPy film growth, its bonding, and structural characteristics have been studied using a number of electrochemical techniques as well as infrared absorption, nuclear magnetic resonance, scanning electron microscopy, electron diffraction, small angle x-ray scattering, real time single wavelength ellipsometry, and scanning tunneling microscopy (STM).   It has been proposed that the polymer consists of linear chains of coplanar monomer units connected by α–α' bonds with preferential orientation of the rings parallel to the substrate surface.[32]   In the early stage of growth, however, individual helical chains have been directly observed by STM.[33]   Although the material is predominantly amorphous, diffraction studies have been interpreted in terms of 20–50 Å microcrystalline regions embedded in the amorphous network.[34,35]   Although the polymer nucleation, coalescence, and layer-by-layer growth have been inferred by electrochemical measurements and ellipsometry, the presence of islands has been directly observed by STM.[33]

In particular, single wavelength ellipsometry appears very promising for eliciting the microstructural evolution.   The most advanced results to date were performed during nitrate- and ferricyanide-doped PPy preparation in an aqueous solution, using a He–Ne laser probe.[36]   The reflectance was measured along with (ψ, Δ) during growth, allowing a unique determination of $(\varepsilon_1, \varepsilon_2)$ at 1.96 eV along with thickness, d, as a function of time during film growth.   The results were interpreted qualitatively in terms of a three-step, nucleation-coalescence-growth sequence in the first 500 Å.   As noted earlier, the disadvantage of this approach is that there is no redundancy built into the analysis, even with the measurement of the additional reflectance parameter, and any deviations from the three-phase model or any diffuse laser light scattering in the liquid or at the film surface can lead to spurious solutions.   As will be described in Sect. 6.3.3, the real time spectroscopic capability overcomes these limitations because the solution is overdetermined.   The resulting statistical information provides a measure of the quality of the best fit to the data.   Thus, the validity of the model and its assumptions can be assessed, and complexities can be introduced and justified from a statistical standpoint.

Earlier studies of PPy prepared in organic and aqueous solutions have revealed the key role of anion incorporation in the doping process.   For PPy oxidized in dry acetonitrile in the presence of ClO_4^- or BF_4^-, up to one anion is trapped in the film for every three monomers.[32]   On the other hand, for PPy oxidized in aqueous nitrate solution the maximum doping level appears higher; approximately one NO_3^- anion can be incorporated for every two monomers.[37]   The incorporated anions have been proposed to induce polaron and bipolaron defects along neighboring polymer chains.[38]   In this case, a polaron is a radical-cation C-bonding defect and its associated chain distortion.[39]   It is energetically more favorable to ionize this defect to form a bipolaron than it is to generate a second polaron.   For films prepared in organic solutions at moderate and high doping levels, the lack of a correlation between the electrical conductivity and the spin density from electron paramagnetic resonance measurements was explained by invoking mobile bipolarons which carry a charge of +2e but no spin.   Only at the lowest doping levels, however, did such a correlation appear, and it was attributed to transport along the chains via singly-charged, spin-1/2 polarons.

Optical measurements, coupled with electronic structure calculations, have provided additional support for the bipolaron model.   The calculations for a single, isolated bipolaron predict two unoccupied states in the gap and three optical transitions: (valence band)-to-(conduction band), (valence band)-to-(lower lying bipolaron level), and (valence band)-to-(higher-lying bipolaron level).[39] The corresponding transition energies are 4.0 eV, 0.46 eV and 3.1 eV, respectively. In comparison, optical density measurements obtained *in situ* from the transmittance of films lightly-doped with ClO_4^- show weak features at 0.7 eV, 2.1 eV, and 3.2 eV, all of which shift to higher energy with increased doping concentration.[40] At all concentrations the defect levels are closer to the center of the gap than predicted in the theoretical calculations.

Prior to the study reported here, the most advanced measurements of the optical properties of PPy were obtained by *ex situ* spectroscopic ellipsometry. Both real and imaginary parts of the dielectric function, $(\varepsilon_1, \varepsilon_2)$, were obtained from 1.5 to 6.0 eV for air-stabilized BF_4^--doped films deposited in a solution of acetonitrile and water.[41] An ellipsometric approach is desired in comparison with transmittance for two reasons. First, both parts of the optical functions are helpful for an unambiguous identification of electronic transition energies obtained by fitting the data to predicted absorption and dispersion behavior. Although Kramers-Kronig analysis has been applied to transmittance data,[42] spectroscopic ellipsometry provides a more direct and reliable alternative method. Second, a reflection-based measurement can be used with the opaque metallic working electrodes traditionally used in electrodeposition. The spectroscopic ellipsometry measurements must be performed *in situ*, however, to minimize the complicating effects of the ambient. In fact, polypyrrole has been the focus of the first real time spectroscopic ellipsometry investigation of an electropolymerization process. Analysis of these results in terms of the optical properties and doping are presented in the next section.

6.3.2 Determination of the Optical Properties of Polypyrrole from Real Time Observations

The real time spectroscopic ellipsometry was performed during chronoamperometric deposition using a conventional three-electrode configuration, including an opaque polycrystalline Au film working electrode, a Au sheet counter electrode, and a saturated calomel reference electrode (SCE). The Au working electrode was deposited on glass to a thickness of 1000–1500 Å by thermal evaporation under optimized conditions that ensured a smooth surface and high bulk density. This was important in order to minimize the complexity of the optical model required in the ellipsometric analysis described in Section 6.3.3. The working electrode potential was fixed at 0.62 V during deposition, well below the peak anodic potential of the pyrrole (0.9 V). As a result, the bulk film thickness deposition rate was slowed to 0.8 Å/s (as determined from the ellipsometric analysis), so that monolayer resolution could be achieved with an acquisition time of 3.2 s for a single pair of (ψ, Δ) spectra. The aqueous solution was prepared with 5 mM and 0.1 M concentrations of the monomer and the KNO_3 supporting electrolyte, respectively. The pH of the solution was adjusted to 3 using HNO_3, in order to prevent oxidation of the Au electrode itself. Other details concerning the experimental procedure appear in the original publications.[43,44]

Figure 6.5 shows the chronoamperometry result obtained during film growth. In the initial 40 s, a sharp decrease in the current is characteristic of diffusion-controlled transport. The subsequent increase and stabilization has been discussed qualitatively in terms of an initial nucleation process, followed by coalescence of the resulting clusters.[37,45] The ellipsometry results can be explained similarly but, in contrast, can be

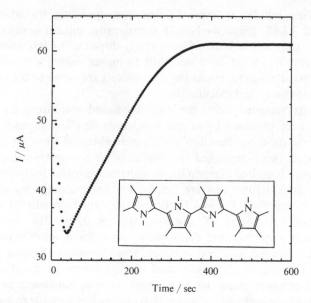

Fig. 6.5 Chronoamperometric response obtained during polypyrrole (inset) electrodeposition. In this experiment, an aqueous solution of 5 mM pyrrole in 0.1 M KNO₃ was used, and the applied potential was 0.62 V *vs.* SCE. [Adapted from Ref. 44]

analyzed to extract quantitative information on water volume fraction and film thickness (see Section 6.3.3).

The real time spectroscopic ellipsometry data were collected at an angle of incidence of 74° with optical access to the sample surface through fused silica windows suitably mounted in the walls of a teflon cell to minimize stress-induced birefringence. The experimental results, expressed in terms of the angles (ψ,Δ), appear in the 3D graph of Fig. 6.6. In this experiment, a total of ~80 pairs of (ψ,Δ) spectra were collected over the deposition time of 600 s, each consisting of 49 spectral points from 1.5 to 3.3 eV. The data acquisition time for a single pair of (ψ,Δ) spectra was 3.2 s, and such spectra were collected every 7.5 s. Although the potential photon energy range of the instrument is 1.5–4.5 eV, we did not use the high energy data in the analysis of PPy owing to the reduced precision.

If the film was deposited to opacity, in theory the PPy optical functions could be determined directly from (ψ,Δ), as long as the film surface was smooth and abrupt on an atomic scale. In practice, however, the surface quality degraded significantly during the growth of thicker films as could be seen both visually and by the fact that (ψ,Δ) spectra continued to evolve even after such films became opaque. This behavior is an indication of continuous surface roughening, and the resulting apparent dielectric function is not a true characteristic of the bulk material. Thus, our optical study was confined to relatively thin films which were semitransparent at the end of the deposition, as can be seen by the residual feature at the back of the 3D plot of Fig. 6.6 near 2.5 eV. This feature is associated with the Au electrode d-band-to-Fermi-level transition.

As a first approximation in the overall interpretation of the data set in Fig. 6.6, we neglect any possible surface roughness and assume that the PPy can be represented as a single

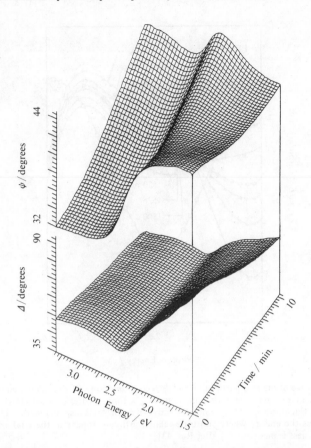

Fig. 6.6 Evolution of (ψ, Δ) spectra as a function of time during electrodeposition of NO_3^--doped polypyrrole. Approximately 80 pairs of spectra were collected, each one consisting of 49 values from 1.5 to 3.3 eV. [After Ref. 43]

uniform film in a perfect three-medium model (solution/PPy/Au).   The optical functions of the ambient solution and substrate must be obtained as an initial step in any analysis procedure.   The dielectric function of H_2O was used for the solution because the change caused by the addition of the electrolyte and monomer were below our instrument precision.   The Au dielectric function was measured in 0.1 M KNO_3 aqueous solution using the same ellipsometer and electrochemical cell.   The only remaining unknowns in the optical problem are the PPy film thickness, d, which depends on time and the dielectric function, $(\varepsilon_1, \varepsilon_2)$, which depends on photon energy.   To obtain $(\varepsilon_1, \varepsilon_2)$, we concentrate on the last (ψ, Δ) spectra in Fig. 6.6; however, an accurate value of d at this time is required before a solution can be obtained by direct mathematical inversion (e.g. by Newton's method[46]).

There are a number of approaches to solve this classic problem in ellipsometry.   The first approach applied here exploits the continuous spectroscopic information available.[47]   The PPy film thickness value is chosen as that which eliminates the Au

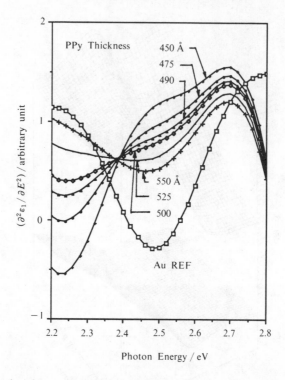

Fig. 6.7 Second derivative of the real part of the trial dielectric function of PPy, calculated from the last pair of (ψ, Δ) spectra in Fig. 6.6 (at ~10 min), assuming a three-medium model (H_2O/PPy/Au) with the indicated film thicknesses. The second derivative of ε_1 for Au is also included. The minimum for the latter identifies the energy where substrate-related artifacts appear in the trial ε_1 for PPy when the assumed thickness is incorrect. [After Ref. 43]

substrate-related feature at 2.5 eV in the PPy dielectric function. This feature is coupled into the PPy dielectric function when the numerical inversion of the (ψ, Δ) spectra is performed with the improper thickness. This technique will be successful only if (1) the film optical properties are smooth in the vicinity of this feature, and (2) the three-medium model is a close approximation to the actual sample structure. If the latter condition is not satisfied, then the substrate-related artifacts in the film dielectric function will not be eliminated for any reasonable choice of film thickness.

In practice, mathematical inversion of the final (ψ, Δ) spectra in Fig. 6.6 to obtain the PPy dielectric function is performed for a number of trial thicknesses. Each resulting trial dielectric function is smoothed using Fourier techniques and then differentiated twice to enhance the substrate-related artifact. Fig. 6.7 shows results for the real part ε_1, after narrowing the proper thickness range to 450–550 Å. Also shown is the second derivative of the real part of the Au dielectric function which identifies the exact position of the artifact. From Fig. 6.7, we can identify the correct thickness as 490 Å with an uncertainty of about ±5–10 Å. For thicknesses 30–40 Å below and above this value, well-defined maxima and minima appear in the derivative spectra near 2.5 eV that originate from the substrate. The fact that the artifact can be completely eliminated suggests that

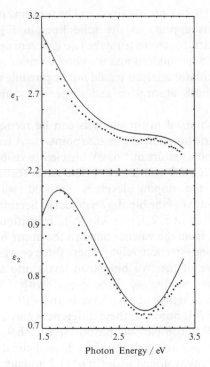

Fig. 6.8 Comparison of the real and imaginary parts of the dielectric function of NO_3^--doped PPy obtained by the method of Fig. 6.7 (points), and by linear regression analysis using three Lorentz oscillators to simulate the electronic transitions. [After Ref. 43]

the three-medium optical model is close to reality.   Fig. 6.8 (points) presents the dielectric function for the PPy obtained by inversion with the correct thickness of 490 Å.

A second, completely different method to determine $(\varepsilon_1,\varepsilon_2)$ and d from the last pair of spectra in Fig. 6.6, requires expressing the PPy optical functions in terms of wavelength independent parameters.   If this can be done, then *all* unknowns in the problem are wavelength independent, and can be determined in a linear regression analysis (LRA) of the (ψ,Δ) spectra.[14]   Here, we express $(\varepsilon_1,\varepsilon_2)$ as a sum of classical Lorentz oscillators:

$$\varepsilon = \varepsilon_\infty + \sum_{m=1}^{N_o} F_m(E_m^2 - E^2 - iE\Gamma_m)^{-1},\tag{6.8}$$

where ε_∞ is the infinite photon energy limit of the dielectric function, and E_m, Γ_m and F_m are the resonance energy, damping coefficient, and strength for the mth harmonic oscillator.[48]   For N_o oscillators, the number of free parameters in the LRA is $3N_o+2$.   Thus, the solution to this problem provides not only $(\varepsilon_1,\varepsilon_2)$ and d, but also a description of the electronic transitions that give rise to the optical properties.   From the LRA, the thickness is determined to be 475 ± 20 Å, in good agreement with the inversion approach.   The deduced ε_∞ value corresponds to an index of refraction of 1.5 ± 0.08, a reasonable value for a polymer film.   Three transitions with resonance energies at

1.65±0.15, 2.3±0.9, and 3.8±0.2 eV are obtained.   The resulting $(\varepsilon_1, \varepsilon_2)$ calculated from the best-fit oscillator parameters appears as the solid lines in Fig. 6.8.   The monotonic difference between the dielectric functions from the two different approaches arises from the 15 Å difference in thickness in the analysis and is a good estimate of the overall error due to thickness.   The Lorentz oscillator analysis would not be possible without the ellipsometric capability of determining both absorptive and dispersive components of the optical functions independently.

The transition energies obtained in the analysis can be recognized as features in the imaginary part of the dielectric function in Fig. 6.8 (points).   A feature just above the high energy limit of the spectra and a feature at 1.65 eV are clearly visible, whereas only the hint of a shoulder appears between 2.0 and 2.5 eV.   The latter feature becomes more easily identifiable at 2.4 eV as the doping level is reduced with potential (see next paragraph).   Within the context of the bipolaron model of Section 6.3.1, it is reasonable to assign the electronic features at 1.65, 2.3, and 3.8 eV, to transitions from the valence band to the lower bipolaron level, from the valence band to the upper bipolaron level, and from the valence to conduction bands, respectively.   These three energies suggest a blue shift of the band gap and a collapse of the two bipolaron levels into the center of the gap in comparison with the earlier studies of PPy doped with ClO_4^-.   Both effects are qualitatively consistent with a higher doping level in the $PPy:NO_3^-$ films in light of the trends discussed in Section 6.3.1; however, these differences may also be a characteristic of the dopant anion itself.   For comparison purposes, Fig. 6.9 shows the energy level positions (a) for an isolated bipolaron, calculated for hypothetical n-type doping by Na^+;[39] (b) for defect states in PPy heavily doped with ClO_4^- (1:3 dopant:monomer);[40] and (c) for the transitions detected in NO_3^--doped PPy of this study.

In a second identical deposition at 0.62 V (vs. SCE), ellipsometric spectra were collected in real time as the potential was decreased at 20 mVs⁻¹.   Selected dielectric functions obtained by the inversion approach are presented in Fig. 6.10.   At an applied potential of 0.5 V, the 2.3 eV transition becomes more pronounced and evolves into a clear feature at 2.4 eV as the 1.65 eV transition is suppressed with reduced doping.   At −0.3 eV, both features have disappeared and a broad absorption tail associated with a stronger red-shifted band-to-band transition remains.   A detailed interpretation of these results is hindered by

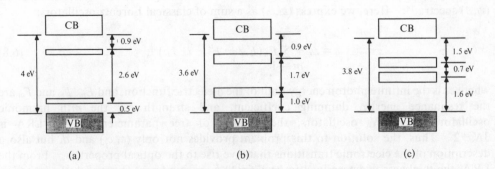

Fig. 6.9 Electronic states on a diagram depicting energy versus spatial coordinate for (a) an isolated bipolaron in PPy, calculated theoretically [Ref. 39]; (b) ClO_4^--doped PPy (1:3 ClO_4^-:monomer), obtained experimentally [Ref. 40]; and (c) NO_3^--doped PPy, from this study.

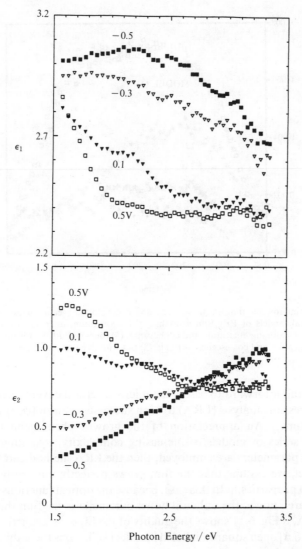

Fig. 6.10 Dielectric functions of NO_3^--doped PPy electrodeposited at 0.62 V *vs.* SCE and then subjected to successively lower reducing potentials as indicated to lower the doping level.   [After Ref. 43]

the fact that polarons having electronic transitions in the 1.5–3.0 eV range may remain after the bipolarons are reduced below the optical detection limit.   More generally, however, the results of Fig. 6.10 show that the relative dopant-induced defect density can be assessed from real time observations over a wide range of electrode potential.

6.3.3   Determination of the Microstructural Evolution of Polypyrrole from Real Time Observations

Once the real and imaginary parts of the optical functions of the bulk polypyrrole film are

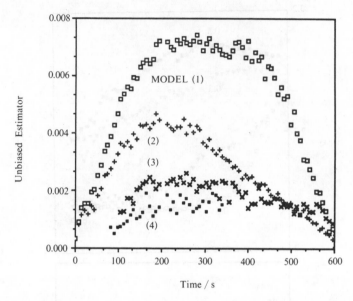

Fig. 6.11 Unbiased estimator of the mean square deviation plotted versus deposition time for four microstructural models of PPy film growth: (1) three-medium, uniform growth model; (2) three-medium model assuming nucleation and coalescence; (3) four-medium, (static interface)/(bulk) model assuming nucleation and coalescence; (4) as in (3) but with dynamic interface layer.   [After Ref. 43]

known, then it is straightforward to assess the microstructural development of the film by applying linear regression analysis (LRA) to each successive pair of (ψ,Δ) spectra obtained as a function of time.   An appreciation of the growth phenomena is developed by consideration of a series of models of increasing complexity.   As long as wavelength-independent fitting parameters are employed, then the LRA method can be applied.[14]

In the first model, we assume that the film grows perfectly uniformly, with thickness independent optical properties.   In this case, because the optical functions of the substrate, film, and ambient are known, the only unknown parameter is the film thickness, which is deduced in the LRA.   Fig. 6.11 shows the quality of the fit, σ, as a function of time for the ~80 spectra of Fig. 6.6 [open squares, labeled "model (1)"]. σ is the unbiased estimator of the mean square deviation, given by:

$$\sigma = (N-p-1)^{-1/2}(\sum_{i=1}^{N}|\tan\psi_e(h\nu_i) - \tan\psi_c(h\nu_i)|^2 + |\cos\Delta_e(h\nu_i) - \cos\Delta_c(h\nu_i)|^2)^{1/2} \qquad (6.9)$$

where the subscripts 'e' and 'c' denote experimental and best fit calculated results.[14]   In Eq. (6.9), N is the number of spectral positions, forty-nine for the data set of Fig. 6.6, and p is the number of independent free parameters, unity for the simplest model with variable d.   The inverted-U shaped behavior in Fig. 6.11 is expected for an inadequate model.   A low value of σ is obtained near $t=0$ because the data here are dominated by the known substrate properties, and any difference in the film from bulk characteristics has little influence on the optical data and the fit.   In addition, σ must drop to zero for the final (ψ,Δ)

pair since the PPy optical functions were derived by numerical inversion of these spectra.

At the next highest level of complexity, we introduce a second photon energy-independent free parameter, the electrolyte volume fraction in the film (assumed to be H_2O).   We expect that such a refinement is needed based on previous microstructural studies of static PPy films by SEM and STM.[33,49]   The H_2O fills the void spaces in the microstructure that are present in the initial nucleation process but is gradually displaced by PPy as coalescence proceeds.

In order to model microstructure within the framework of the LRA, we need an effective medium theory (EMT) which allows us to calculate the dielectric function of the PPy/H_2O mixture from the dielectric functions of the two components.[50,51]   Among a number of possible EMT's, that of Bruggeman works best in modeling the microstructure of amorphous semiconductors such as a-Si (see Section 6.4).[52]   We use it here in view of the similarities between the PPy and a-Si with respect to their disordered structure and electronic transport behavior.   The Bruggeman EMT is expressed mathematically by:

$$0 = \sum_{i=1}^{N_c} f_i \frac{\varepsilon_i - \varepsilon}{\varepsilon_i + 2\varepsilon},$$

(6.10)

where ε is the effective medium dielectric function to be determined, f_i and ε_i are the volume fraction and dielectric function of the ith component of the composite material, respectively.   In the specific case here, $N_c = 2$, and $i = 1,2$ correspond to the PPy and H_2O components.   The assumption implicit in Eq. (6.10) is that the geometry of the inclusions is spherical and that only dipole interactions are involved.   Furthermore, application of an EMT in general is based on the assumption that the microstructural scale is much smaller than the wavelength of light but large enough so that the components retain their bulk dielectric properties.   The former assumption is reasonable given the thickness range explored here (0–500 Å); the latter is reasonable given the disordered structure of PPy and short electron mean free path, as indicated by large damping coefficients obtained in the fit to Eq. (6.8).

The crosses in Fig. 6.11, labeled (2), show the σ value versus time using the two parameter fit to the data of Fig. 6.6.   The resulting independent free parameters, H_2O content and film thickness are presented in Fig. 6.12.   The improvement in the fit is more significant for the thicker films, for which a given H_2O volume fraction addition has a relatively larger effect on the (ψ,Δ) spectra.   The data in Fig. 6.12 can be interpreted in terms of a sparse distribution of nucleation centers covering ~10% of the substrate surface in the early stage of growth.   These clusters tend to grow outward into the solution in the first 150 Å of growth, maintaining a H_2O volume fraction between 0.85 and 0.90.   Above 150 Å, such a low density microstructure is unstable, and rapid densification of the PPy film occurs over a relatively narrow range of thickness, as the initial fiberous clusters coalesce.   Above 250 Å, further densification is gradual and the film grows in a near layer-by-layer fashion at a constant rate.   The results demonstrate the importance of the real time capability; not only is the thickness obtained but also the expected microstructural integrity of the deposit.   It is clear that a microstructurally continuous film is not obtained until after 200 s (H_2O fraction <50%).   The results are relatively immune to experimental artifacts in comparison to single wavelength ellipsometry because a pair of spectra having a total of 98 points is analyzed at each time to obtain 2 free parameters.

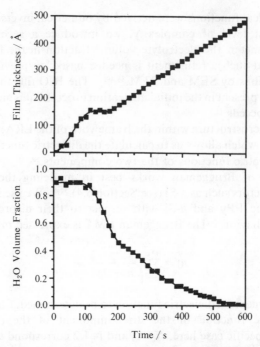

Fig. 6.12 Evolution of film thickness (top) and water volume fraction in the PPy film during the electrodeposition of Fig. 6.6, derived from a three-medium microstructural model [labeled (2) in Fig. 6.11]

However, it is important to consider additional complexities in our model since the variation in σ with time, being well outside experimental error, indicates that the two-parameter model does not provide a complete picture.   Because of the relatively poor contrast between the optical properties of the ambient H_2O and the PPy (in comparison, for example, to a semiconductor material, a-Si:H, see Section 6.4), the desired further improvements in σ cannot be obtained by splitting the film into two layers in an attempt to simulate a graded water content in the film.   The fact that the σ values for the one- and two-parameter models increase strongly from the very beginning of the growth suggest that these simple models are not properly simulating the initial phenomena occurring at the Au/PPy interface. (Consult corresponding results for a-Si:H in Section 6.4.3).   In fact, here the optical contrast between the Au and the PPy is very high and any interface roughening or smoothening is expected to have a significant impact on the evolution of the (ψ, Δ) spectra.

Further analysis of the (ψ, Δ) spectra of Fig. 6.6 in the neighborhood of 300 s where the two parameter fit shows a σ of 0.0035 (see Fig. 6.11), results in nearly a factor two improvement in σ when a second, dense absorbing layer is incorporated at the electrode interface, consisting of a Au/PPy physical mixture with optical properties determined by the Bruggeman EMT.   The Au content of this layer simulates roughness at the Au/PPy interface, and its thickness and Au fraction at 300 s are found to be 20±2 Å and 0.10±0.02, respectively.   If such a layer is assumed to form immediately as the first 20 Å of the film, and then to remain at the interface with fixed composition throughout, then the resulting time dependence of σ is shown in Fig. 6.11 [curve labeled (3)].   This appears to account for the previous difficulties of the single film models for the PPy.   In order to obtain fully consistent results for the thickness evolution of the top PPy film, however, we must apply a model in which the interface layer thickness and Au fraction evolves along with that of the growing PPy. This model gives the σ versus time variation labeled (4) in Fig. 6.11 and provides evidence of Au reordering, PPy consolidation, and gradual roughening at the electrode interface over the time range from 0–400 s. After the overlying PPy/H_2O film has densified near 400 s, the interface structure appears to stabilize. With the exception of the earliest time regime $t < 40$ s, the overlying PPy/H_2O layer thickness and void fraction in this final model, including the thin interface layer, are the same as those in Fig. 6.12 within the confidence limits. A quantitative presentation of the interface phenomena is beyond the scope of this review and appears elsewhere.[44]

Further slight improvements in the fit in the earliest stages of growth ($t < 40$ s) are obtained by assuming the film grows as a Au/dielectric film mixture in the first 10 Å. Although the improvement in σ is not large, such a result appears to suggest monomer adsorption in this stage, proceeding in parallel with the Au surface reordering.[44] Thus, in summary, the structural models required to explain the data conform to our intuition concerning the electropolymerization process, and the data supply considerable quantitative detail concerning the processes of nucleation, coalescence and continuous film growth.

6.4 Applications in Plasma Deposition of Thin Films

6.4.1 Introduction: Hydrogenated Amorphous Silicon Preparation and Properties

The preparation and properties of thin film hydrogenated amorphous silicon (a-Si:H) have been studied in great detail since 1969, when attention was first drawn to it as a product of plasma decomposition of SiH_4.[53] In the succeeding years, numerous applications of a-Si:H and related materials deposited by plasma-enhanced chemical vapor deposition (PECVD) have been developed, including photovoltaic cells, thin film transistors, image sensors, electroluminescent displays, and detectors.[54,55] Among these applications many have been competitive in the marketplace. One of the primary advantages of the PECVD technique for a-Si:H, particularly in photovoltaic applications, is the ability to deposit the material inexpensively over very large areas.

These technological successes have stimulated extensive research on the growth and structure of a-Si:H and its alloys with Ge and C, along with alternative methods of preparation.[56] The most widely accepted model for the growth of PECVD Si:H proposes that under optimum conditions, deposition occurs from SiH_3 radicals.[57,58] These radicals require a free bond on the surface for incorporation, and thus, on hydrogen-covered a-Si:H they have a relatively low sticking coefficient and a long surface diffusion length. They bond at a site from which H has been extracted either by another H or SiH_3 radical. The optimum substrate temperature for electronic device quality material is in the range of 225°C to 275°C, leading to a H content of about 5–10 at. %. Interconnection, cross-linking, and H-elimination reactions are insufficient at lower temperatures, and the resulting material is porous, containing extensive microstructural defects and $(SiH_2)_n$ polymeric units. For higher temperatures, H-elimination during growth is too efficient, and a higher density of Si coordination defects (*i.e.* dangling bonds) which act as efficient charge carrier recombination centers are present.

By alloying a-Si:H with Ge and C, achieved in practice with gas mixtures of SiH_4 and

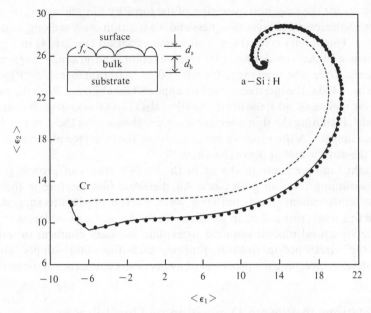

Fig. 6.13 Experimental pseudo-dielectric function trajectory at 3.4 eV for the growth of a-Si:H on Cr at 250°C by parallel-plate PECVD [points, 0.9 s (or 2.7 Å) intervals in the initial growth stages].   Broken and solid trajectories were calculated assuming perfect atomic layer-by-layer growth and a model for nucleation and coalescence, respectively.   For the latter, a two-layer model for a-Si:H film growth is assumed: hemispherical clusters on a 45 Å square grid increase in radius and coalesce, leaving 9 Å of residual surface roughness atop the bulk material.   [After Ref. 66]

GeH₄ or CH₄, the optical band gap of the semiconductor can be varied from 1.2 to 2.5 eV. As a result, photovoltaic performance can be enhanced by using stacked cells, each in the conventional p-i-n configuration, in which the top cell has the widest gap, and the gap is graded to lower energies for the progressively deeper cells.[59]   In this way, a greater fraction of the solar spectrum can be collected.   Thus, the optical properties of the amorphous semiconductor materials are of great interest, and any technique whereby the optical properties can be obtained in real time is important for growth monitoring and potential control applications in photovoltaic production.

The microstructural development of PECVD a-Si:H has been studied in greatest detail by electron microscopy techniques[60,61] and single wavelength ellipsometry.[62-65]   Because of the extreme uniformity which characterizes optimum a-Si:H growth, only the ellipsometric measurements have provided detailed insights into the microstructural evolution in the early nucleation stages.   As an example, Fig. 6.13 shows the 3.4 eV pseudo-dielectric function trajectory, $(<\varepsilon_1>,<\varepsilon_2>)$, swept out as a function of time during conventional parallel-plate PECVD of a-Si:H from pure SiH₄, onto a 250°C c-Si wafer which had been previously coated with a smooth, opaque layer of ion-beam sputtered Cr.[66]   Ellipsometric data were collected every 0.9 s, representing an average accumulation of 2.7 Å, based on the best fit growth model presented in the next paragraph.   The pseudo-dielectric function can be calculated directly from (ψ, Δ) using the following transformation:

$$<\varepsilon> = <\varepsilon_1> + i<\varepsilon_2> = \varepsilon_a \sin^2\theta\{1 + [(\rho-1)/(\rho+1)]^2 \tan^2\theta\}, \qquad (6.11)$$

where ε_a is the dielectric function of the ambient, θ is the angle of incidence (70° in this case), and $\rho = \tan\psi \exp(i\Delta)$. This is the same transformation that converts (ψ,Δ) to $(\varepsilon_1,\varepsilon_2)$ for a single ideal interface between an ambient (ε_a) and an opaque material (ε).[1] Thus, the two stable points of the trajectory in Fig. 6.13, the starting point of the opaque Cr surface at lower left, and the opaque a-Si:H (~600 Å thick) at upper right, are close to the true 3.4 eV dielectric functions of these materials, differing only by the fact that the two surfaces may not be ideal and exhibit some roughness (or for the Cr, a native oxide). In fact, in contrast to the electrodeposition process for PPy, the a-Si:H endpoint is quite stable under optimum PECVD conditions, showing only slight shifts throughout the growth of a thick film, indicating that no more than 3 Å of additional microscopic roughness develops from opacity (600 Å at 3.4 eV) to 40,000 Å![67]

The broken line in Fig. 6.13 is calculated assuming perfect growth within a three-medium model (ambient/a-Si:H/Cr) with a thickness independent dielectric function for the a-Si:H given by the final stable endpoint where the film is opaque. The deviation from this model is greatest at the very beginning of the trajectory and becomes gradually less as the spiral converges to the endpoint. In order to understand this behavior, a model of nucleation was developed whereby hemispheres form on a square grid, increase in radius, make contact and coalesce.[66] The Bruggeman EMT [Eq. (6.10)] was applied to calculate the optical properties of the density-deficient material as in the PPy application of Section 6.3.3. This model provides as excellent fit to the data (solid line in Fig. 6.13) using an initial grid size of 45 Å; thus, the nuclei make contact at a thickness of ~23 Å. After contact, the modulations of the surface are assumed to relax through continued increase in the radii of the contacted hemispheres as the a-Si:H thickness increases, until a peak-to-valley roughness of 9 Å is reached. A stable residual roughness layer of 9 Å is required to fit the convergence behavior of the spiral near its opaque endpoint. Owing to the large optical contrast between the a-Si:H and ambient vacuum, the ellipsometric data are extremely sensitive to surface roughness, in contrast to the situation for PPy growth for which the greatest optical contrast appears at the PPy/Au interface.

The simple nucleation model for a-Si:H has been very useful in providing microstructural information, allowing an assessment of the process/property relationships in a-Si:H materials. In fact, it has been found that the nucleation-coalescence-relaxation sequence is only clearly observed under optimum PECVD conditions.[62] Under other conditions, such as low or high substrate temperature or SiH$_4$:diluent gas flow ratios of less than 1:10, two alternative growth modes have been proposed to explain the ellipsometry data. In the first mode, nuclei form but do not make contact or coalesce. As a result, voids remain at the substrate interface and propagate with continued growth throughout the entire film, resulting in columnar morphology also observed in electron microscopy.[60] In the second, nuclei form and make contact, but the surface does not relax and progressively roughens atop a dense film. Because of the complexity of these processes, it is impossible to develop a unique model based on the single wavelength ellipsometry data.

In spite of the extremely useful information that single wavelength real time ellipsometry provides, the two limitations noted in Section 6.1 are especially relevant in the a-Si:H application. First, the most important optical parameter for photovoltaic applications, the band gap, is inaccessible because the only optical information available is the dielectric function at the single wavelength of measurement. Second, it is also important to be able to quantify the microstructural evolution without assuming a particular geometrical model as was done in the analysis of the data of Fig. 6.13.   More specifically, given the sensitivity of the ellipsometry data to the surface morphology for a-Si:H, the simplest microstructural model suitable for a-Si:H nucleation and coalescence must now include three parameters: d_s and d_b, the surface roughness and bulk layer thicknesses and f_v, the surface layer void volume fraction (see inset Fig. 6.13; this is called the "two-layer" model in the following). In the more complex situations when the PECVD conditions are not optimal, the bulk layer may also exhibit a time-dependent void volume fraction as well, and even a three-layer model may be required.   Thus, in order to obtain an unambiguous picture of microstructural evolution, at least three parameters (possibly more) must be deduced versus time.   This is not possible from single wavelength (ψ,Δ) data without making assumptions or sacrificing full quantification.

To address these limitations, we have applied the multichannel spectroscopic ellipsometer described in Section 6.2 to characterize the optical functions and band gap from real time measurements during the growth of a-Si:H by PECVD.   In fact, the technique is so sensitive in this application that such information can be obtained on films as thin as 20 Å.   The procedures we have developed to accomplish this are described in Section 6.4.2.   With the optical functions in hand, a complete monolayer-sensitive quantification of the nucleation and coalescence behavior has been performed.   These results are described in Section 6.4.3.   Because of the greater optical contrast between void and a-Si:H in comparison to that between H_2O and PPy, significantly greater sensitivity to this behavior has been achieved in the a-Si:H study.

6.4.2 Determination of the Optical Properties of a-Si:H from Real Time Observations

Figure 6.14 shows typical real time pseudo-dielectric function data obtained during PECVD of a-Si:H onto a native oxide-covered c-Si substrate held at 250°C.   In this case, 94 points were collected over the photon energy range from 1.5 to 4.2 eV.   The acquisition time for a single pair of spectra was 3.2 s, and the repetition time was ~12 s.   The extra delay between spectra in comparison to the PPy study occurred as a result of a background correction for the plasma glow.   The PECVD process employed a remote He discharge to dissociate down-stream injected SiH_4 (see Fig. 6.1).   This technique provides a more easily controllable deposition rate in comparison to the conventional parallel-plate method, without any apparent degradation of material properties.   The bulk film deposition rate in these studies was 0.08 Å/s; as a result submonolayer resolution (1 Å/measurement) is obtained.

Before modeling such pseudo-dielectric function data, we need information on the structure and optical functions of the substrate.   For oxide/c-Si, we perform LRA on spectra collected from the substrate at 25°C (prior to heating it to the deposition temperature), in order to deduce the oxide thickness.   This analysis employs literature dielectric functions of c-Si and SiO_2 also collected at room temperature.[68,69] We assume that the oxide thickness and optical properties remain unchanged upon heating the substrate under vacuum to the deposition temperature.   Thus, with its thickness known, the oxide can be analytically extracted from the spectra collected from the substrate at the elevated temperature.   The outcome is the dielectric function of the c-Si at the deposition temperature.   For Cr, the surface is etched prior to insertion into the vacuum chamber. In this case, the pseudo-dielectric function collected at the deposition temperature is

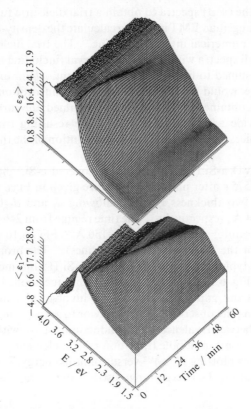

Fig. 6.14 Evolution of pseudo-dielectric function spectra versus time during remote He PECVD of a-Si:H on
native oxide-covered c-Si at 250°C.   Approximately 300 pairs of spectra are shown here, each one
consisting of 94 points from 1.5 to 4.2 eV.

assumed to be the true dielectric function.   With the optical functions of the major
components of the substrates measured at the deposition temperature, we can now proceed
to characterize the a-Si:H optical functions.

Neither of the two techniques applied to obtain the bulk PPy dielectric function, linear
regression analysis (with Lorentz oscillators) and substrate artifact minimization, are
optimum for the a-Si:H application.   First, we have had little success in expressing the
dielectric function of a-Si:H (which is dominated by valence-to-conduction band electronic
transitions) in terms of wavelength-independent parameters.   More importantly, however,
because of the strong influence that surface roughness has on the (ψ,Δ) [or $(<\varepsilon_1>,<\varepsilon_2>)$]
spectra for a-Si:H, a two-layer model for the growing film (see Fig. 6.13, inset) with three
wavelength independent parameters $\{d_s, d_b, f_v\}$ is required as noted in Section 6.4.1.   The
substrate artifact minimization procedure is not sufficiently sensitive, however, to extract
any more than one thickness in this case.

As an alternative approach, we exploit information contained in the complete time
dependence of the (ψ,Δ) spectra, assuming that over some time interval during growth, the
bulk a-Si:H dielectric function is independent of thickness.[70]   The approach involves
guessing $\{d_s, d_b, f_v\}$ values associated with a particular pair of (ψ,Δ) spectra of interest, say

at $t = t_o$, and inverting the (ψ, Δ) spectra to obtain a trial dielectric function appropriate at $t = t_o$.   As usual the Bruggeman EMT is used to calculate the density-deficient surface layer optical functions in the numerical inversion routine.   The trial dielectric function is then applied in LRA fits to all spectra within the time interval (including t_o) over which the film dielectric function is assumed to be thickness-independent.   [For example, in the case of PPy (Section 6.3.3) we would exclude the monolayer adsorption and Au reordering regimes.]   The σ values obtained for all such fits are summed; the correct guesses for $\{d_s, d_b, f_v\}$ are those that provide a minimum in $\sum_t \sigma$.   The resulting trial dielectric function obtained with these choices is correct, and the time evolution of the three parameters is also correct.

The results for PECVD a-Si:H on native oxide-covered c-Si, obtained from a pair of (ψ, Δ) spectra collected 575 s after plasma ignition are given in Figs. 6.15–6.17.   Fig. 6.15 shows $\sum_t \sigma$ versus the two thickness guesses, allowing d_s and d_b to be unambiguously identified as 12 Å and 34 Å , respectively.   The time regime from 240 to 1800 s was used for the minimization procedure; after 1800 s, $d_b \sim 150$ Å.   Fig. 6.16 shows the dielectric function appropriate for the 34 Å bulk film (solid lines).   The broad absorption feature centered near 3.75 eV is typical of results obtained on a-Si:H films more than two orders of magnitude thicker.[62]   Fig. 6.17 shows the analysis technique applied to obtain the onset of optical absorption, or band gap (open points).   It involves plotting $\varepsilon_2^{1/2}$ versus photon energy, and extrapolating the observed linear behavior to zero-ordinate.[71]   This provides the energy difference between valence and conduction bands with assumed parabolic densities of states and a constant dipole transition matrix element.   The alternative Tauc approach, which involves plotting $(E^2 \varepsilon_2)^{1/2}$ versus photon energy,[72] provides a gap whose value depends somewhat on the energy range used in the extrapolation, and thus is less suitable.

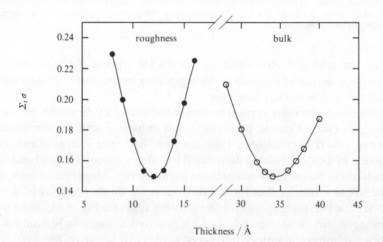

Fig. 6.15 A plot of the two-layer analysis applied to determine the bulk and surface roughness thicknesses and bulk dielectric function for ultrathin PECVD a-Si:H (at $t = 575$ s) from pseudo-dielectric function spectra vs. time.   The ordinate depicts the sum of unbiased estimators of the mean square deviation obtained in LRA fits of the spectra from 240 to 1800 s.   A trial dielectric function used in the LRA was determined from the spectra at $t = 575$ s using a guess for one thickness (plotted on the abscissa) and a value for the other at the minimum (34 or 12 Å).

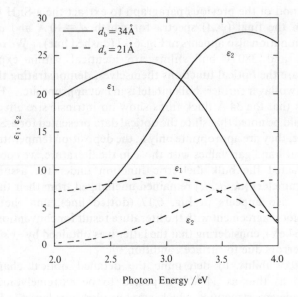

Fig. 6.16 Dielectric functions for ultrathin PECVD a-Si:H deduced from real time observations using the procedure of Fig. 6.15.   Solid lines: 34 Å thick continuous bulk film on a native oxide-covered c-Si substrate; broken lines: 21 Å thick clusters on Cr in the nucleation stage ($d_b = 0$).

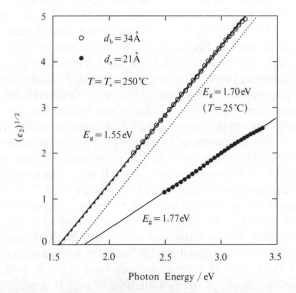

Fig. 6.17 Optical gap determinations for PECVD a-Si:H from real time data.   Open circles: 34 Å bulk film on native oxide-covered c-Si at 250°C (band gap of 1.55 eV); solid circles 21 Å thick clusters on Cr at 250°C (band gap at 1.77 eV).   The solid lines are fits to these data.   The broken line (band gap at 1.55 eV) and dotted line (band gap at 1.70 eV) represent fits to data obtained for the final film (380 Å) on oxide/c-Si at 250°C and 25°C, respectively.

We used the method of the previous paragraph to extract the a-Si:H optical functions independently from the final (ψ, Δ) spectra for which $d_s = 10$ Å and $d_b = 380$ Å. The resulting gap determination also appears in Fig. 6.17 (dashed line). We find that the band gap for the 34 Å and 380 Å bulk films are identical within experimental error $(1.55 \pm 0.01$ eV), as are the optical functions themselves, demonstrating that our films are uniform and that a two-layer surface/bulk model is in fact appropriate. Furthermore, this result demonstrates that the 34 Å thick films show no intrinsic size effects in the optical properties. It should be noted that since the optical data presented for a-Si:H thus far were obtained in real time, they are appropriate only at the deposition temperature (250°C). In order to compare our band gap values with those in the literature, we cooled the final film to 25°C and extracted the bulk dielectric function under the assumption that the microstructural parameters $\{d_s, d_b, f_v\}$ remained unchanged from their final values. The gap determination also appears in Fig. 6.17 (dotted line), and the resulting value, 1.70 ± 0.01 eV, is in good agreement with the literature result for conventional parallel-plate PECVD a-Si:H (1.64 eV), considering that the latter was obtained by *ex situ* measurement, which is subject to errors due to surface condition.[71]

The unprecedented ability to determine the detailed optical characteristics of a semiconductor film as thin as 34 Å is expected to be extremely important for the characterization of device structures which employ ultrathin layers. Furthermore, an accurate band gap value is expected since the problem of unaccounted for surface oxides and roughness are avoided. These plague *ex situ* transmittance and reflectance determinations of band gap for a material such as a-Si:H.

The dielectric function of a-Si:H can be extracted for even thinner layers prepared on Cr metal substrates. When the total a-Si:H thickness is less than 23 Å, however, d_b is less than a single monolayer. This result, having been established from a spectroscopic analysis similar to that described later in Section 6.4.3, is in agreement with the earlier single wavelength studies which also revealed a thickness of 23 Å upon cluster contact. Thus, d_b should be set to zero, meaning that the film consists of isolated clusters, and the single-layer model for the film is appropriate here. Fig. 6.16 shows the dielectric function determined in this regime (broken lines) and Fig. 6.17 shows the optical gap determination (solid points). In this case the cluster thickness ($d_s = 21$ Å) was determined by trial-and-error on the condition that ε_2 drop smoothly to zero for photon energies below the gap (<1.75 eV). The weak absorption strength in ε_2 compared to the 34 Å bulk film is attributed to the high volume fraction of voids (*i.e.* $f_v \sim 0.48$). The interesting aspect of this result, however, is the blue-shifted peak energy of ε_2 (4.0 eV *vs.* 3.75 eV for the 34 Å thick bulk film), which cannot be understood in terms of voids. The effect most likely arises from the high fraction of SiH$_n$ ($1 \le n \le 3$) bonds lining the surface of the clusters.[73] This proposal is also consistent with a band gap which is 0.22 eV wider than for bulk a-Si:H.[74] Finally, we conclude that this dielectric function is a better approximation to the optical properties of the high void fraction surface layer on bulk a-Si:H, owing to the presence of SiH$_n$ bonding there. A refined analysis of a-Si:H deposition on oxide/c-Si using this improved surface layer dielectric function, however, leads to a bulk dielectric function and microstructural evolution (see Section 6.4.3) that differ negligibly from that of the conventional Bruggeman EMT bulk/void optical model for the surface layer.

6.4.3   Determination of the Microstructural Evolution of a-Si:H from Real Time Observations

The microstructural evolution is represented by the time dependences of the parameters $\{d_s, d_b, f_v\}$, which can be extracted over the full deposition as part of the same overall analysis of Section 6.4.2 which led to the optical functions.   In this section, we will concentrate on the evolution of the two thicknesses, d_s and d_b, as they exhibit the most interesting behavior at least with regard to the deposition process dependence.   In Fig. 6.18, we show results for the same PECVD a-Si:H deposition on oxide/c-Si that was analyzed in Figs. 6.15–17.   In contrast to the single wavelength interpretation, no assumptions have been made regarding the geometry of nucleation, coalescence, and surface relaxation.

In the earliest stages of film growth in Fig. 6.18, $d_b < 2$ Å, indicating that the first bulk monolayer has not yet formed; in this regime the surface layer simulates nucleating clusters. Thus, the two-layer model of the film is an over-interpretation of the data and, strictly, the one-layer model should be applied.   The open circles in Fig. 6.18, denote results for d_s obtained with the one-layer model in which $d_b \equiv 0$.   Thus, the differences between the one- and two-layer interpretations in this regime are negligible.   When $d_b \sim 2$–3 Å, d_s reaches a maximum thickness.   At this time ($t = t_b$), the first bulk monolayer has formed and subsequent flux is incorporated predominantly in the bulk layer.   The presence of a transition from a one- to two-layer model can even be observed in the statistical parameter, σ, as shown in Fig. 6.19.   Here σ for the one- and two-layer models overlap for $t < t_b$; however, the one-layer σ increases abruptly above the two-layer σ for times greater than t_b. Thus, the second layer is statistically meaningful only for $t > t_b$, providing additional support for the formation of the first bulk monolayer at time t_b.   Finally, the near constant

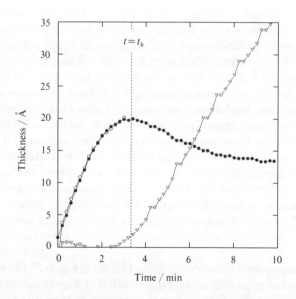

Fig. 6.18   Time evolution of the surface (d_s, solid circles) and bulk (d_b, open triangles) layer thicknesses in a two-layer model for a-Si:H growth by remote He PECVD on a native oxide-covered c-Si substrate at 250°C.   The open circles denote the evolution of the surface layer in a one-layer model in which $d_b \equiv 0$.

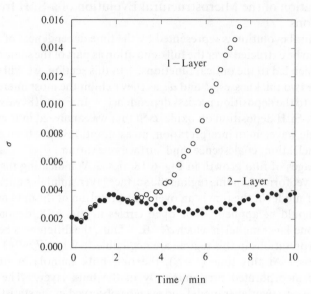

Fig. 6.19 The unbiased estimator of the mean square deviation as a function of time for the one- and two-layer
models of Fig. 6.18 for the growth of a-Si:H by remote He PECVD on a native oxide-covered c-Si
substrate at 250°C.

$\sigma(t)$ for the two-layer model indicates that additional layers are not required to characterize the growth process.

For $t > t_b$, the time evolution of the surface layer in Fig. 6.18 reveals the ability of subsequent deposit to smoothen the nucleation-related surface morphology. Thus, for PECVD a-Si:H on native oxide-covered c-Si, initial nuclei reach a thickness of 20 Å just prior to contact, and for $t > t_b$ the surface smoothens by 8 Å on the time scale of Fig. 6.18. Further smoothening by 2 Å occurs beyond the depicted time scale until the deposition is terminated after $d_b = 380$ Å.   The 10 Å surface layer at the end of the deposition most likely includes contibutions not only from roughness, but also from surface SiH_n bonding. Earlier single wavelength real time ellipsometry studies in which the SiH_n bonding layer is removed in a low power Ar glow suggest that the SiH_n contribution to d_s is ∼6±2 Å.[75]

It should also be noted that the thickness at which the a-Si:H clusters make contact, 20 Å for the native oxide-covered c-Si substrate, provides a measure of the average nucleation density at this time.   The value we obtain is somewhat model-dependent because an analysis of f_v is required to estimate the shape of the nuclei upon contact.   Because f_v ∼0.5 at this point, however, it is reasonable to suggest that the clusters are hemispherical.   If this geometry is assumed, then a nucleation density of 6×10^{12} cm^{-2} is obtained for the deposition of Fig. 6.18.

To highlight the importance of the behaivor in Fig. 6.18, Fig. 6.20 shows corresponding data for amorphous silicon growth using a much different deposition method, magnetron sputtering.[76]   In this case, the film precursor is atomic Si from the solid target and no hydrogen is incorporated during the growth process.   The substrate used in the sputter-deposition was c-Si covered with an 87 Å , thermally grown oxide.   For this substrate,

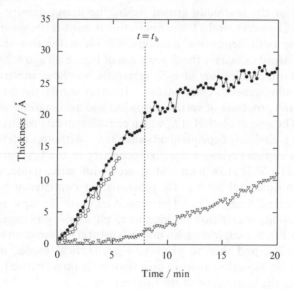

Fig. 6.20 Time evolution of the surface (d_s, solid circles) and bulk (d_b, open triangles) layer thicknesses in a two-layer model for a-Si growth by magnetron sputtering onto a 300°C c-Si substrate covered with a 87 Å thermally-grown oxide. The open circles denote the evolution of the surface layer in the one-layer model in which $d_b \equiv 0$. [After Ref. 76]

initial nuclei also reach a thickness of ~20 Å prior to contact, suggesting a similar nucleation density as in the case of PECVD a-Si:H on native oxide-covered c-Si. In contrast to the PECVD a-Si:H, however, the surface exhibits strong roughening behavior for $t > t_b$.

The differences between the growth behavior for PECVD and sputter-depositions stem simply from the differences between chemical and physical vapor deposition processes. It is helpful to consider theoretical studies of film growth for further insights into the mechanisms involved.[77,78] In continuum models of growth, the stability of advancing one-dimensional surface profiles have been studied in response to imposed sinusoidal perturbations of wavelength, λ_r. Effects of finite atomic size and shadowing have been proposed to enhance the surface perturbations whereas adatom surface diffusion damps them. A smooth profile is regained for an adatom diffusion length, $\lambda_0 > \lambda_r$. In our experimental work, the perturbation is the nucleation-generated surface microstructure. The smoothening behavior for PECVD most likely arises from an adatom diffusion length much greater than 40 Å (the dominant roughness wavelength for hemispherical nuclei making contact at $d_s = 20$ Å). This is reasonable given the nature of growth from SiH₃ precursors on a H-terminated surface as described in Section 6.4.1. In contrast, for the sputtered a-Si, the precursors tend to stick where they land; any surface diffusion originates from the energy of the incoming Si atoms and is probably much less than 40 Å. This lack of diffusion explains the roughening behavior in Fig. 6.20.

Final remarks on the initial nucleation behavior for these two depositions processes are in order before concluding. For similarly-prepared native oxide-covered c-Si substrates, the nucleation density for sputtered a-Si is found to be a factor of two higher than that for PECVD a-Si:H. For the thermally grown oxide, the defect density on the surface is expected to be lower, however, and a lower nucleation density is obtained in comparison to the native oxide for both deposition methods.[76,79] It is for this reason that similar nucleation densities are obtained for the depositions of Figs. 6.18 and 6.20. The combined results suggest that the nucleation of a-Si materials on these substrates exhibit both heterogeneous and homogeneous components. In other words, the nucleation density is influenced both by the processes of surface diffusion and aggregation, and also by defects on the substrate. The time evolution of f_v, which provides direct insights into the geometry of the initial clusters is similarly dependent on substrate. Although a detailed presentation is beyond the scope of this review, a disc-like geometry in the first monolayer is clearly apparent for PECVD a-Si:H growth on c-Si covered with native oxide, whereas the shape is more closely hemispherical on the Cr substrate, in consistency with earlier single wavelength ellipsometric analysis.[66] The importance of the spectroscopic analysis, however, lies in the ability to establish the number of physical layers required to explain the data (through Fig. 6.19), to extract detailed microstructural information with this model (as in Figs. 6.18 and 6.20), and then to propose a geometrical model, *a posteriori*. This procedure places the ellipsometric analysis on a rigorously quantitative footing and dispels questions concerning the uniqueness of the final model.

6.5 Summary and Future Work

A novel, rapid scanning real time spectroscopic ellipsometer has been developed for monitoring the plasma and electrochemical preparation of thin films on the monolayer scale. This instrument is designed in the rotating polarizer-sample-analyzer ($P_{rot}SA$) configuration and employs a multichannel detection system, based on a Si photodiode array, which can be read in <5 ms. Complete (ψ,Δ) spectra over a maximum photon energy range from 1.5 to 4.5 eV can be computed from four successive read-outs of the array, each of which represents the irradiance striking the detector surface integrated over a 45° quadrant of the 180° optical cycle. For our system, the four read-outs require 40 ms, and this represents the minimum acquisition time for a pair of (ψ,Δ) spectra. In this work submonolayer-level precision is achieved with an 80 optical cycle average, requiring a 3.2 s data acquisition time. Improvements are being made continually on the system, and similar performance on the 100 ms time scale is soon to be expected. Likewise, improvements in accuracy are also being made, and procedures have been developed to correct for source polarization, polarizer optical activity, detector nonlinearity, image persistence, and spectrograph/detector stray light. These corrections are performed at both instrument calibration and data reduction levels, and are very important when the modulated light reflected from the surface is near-linearly polarized, e.g. for crystalline semiconductors below the onset of direct absorption.

Throughout this work, we have stressed the two primary advantages of the spectroscopic approach over previous single wavelength studies. First, both the real and imaginary parts of the dielectric function (or the index of refraction and extinction coefficient) of the growing film can be obtained, in some cases at different stages in the growth process. Thus, the technique can be employed for materials identification, and the electronic structure (e.g. energy levels and band gap) of the deposited materials can be determined.

This capability is extremely important for preparation of electronically active materials, but less so for electrochemical studies of oxidation and corrosion.   Second, once the optical properties of the substrate or electrode, the ambient, and all the material components of the surface film are known as a function of photon energy, linear regression analysis (LRA) can be applied to characterize the time evolution of the microstructure using simple models having wavelength-independent free parameters of thickness and material volume fraction. The time evolution of the statistical information derived from the best fits to the spectra within a given microstructural model can be used to establish the required degree of complexity for the correct model.

We have applied this overall experimental approach to characterize the growth process and resulting properties of electronically active thin films, including polypyrrole by electrochemical deposition and hydrogenated amorphous silicon (a-Si:H) by plasma enhanced chemical vapor deposition.   As noted, the deduced information falls into two categories: optical and microstructural.

For polypyrrole deposited in the oxidized conducting state onto a thin film Au electrode, the bulk material dielectric function from 1.5 to 3.3 eV has been determined from real time observations at a film thickness of 490 Å.   The results have been interpreted to provide the energies associated with band-to-band and band-to-defect transitions. The latter originate from doping-induced defects, and these transitions are observed to disappear gradually as the electrochemical potential is reduced.   An analysis of the microstructure reveals a nucleation and growth sequence in which relatively sparsely distributed clusters form in the early stage of growth and increase in size, making contact to form a continuous film after a thickness of 150 Å.   The ellipsometry data are extremely sensitive to the dielectric discontinuity at the polypyrrole/Au interface, and a Au reordering/roughening phenomenon is observed in the early stages of film growth.   Future studies of polypyrrole and other conducting polymers will concentrate on the origin of the electronic transitions, the influence of the defect density on their energies, as well as the development of a capability to determine electronically-active doping density from real time observations.

For a-Si:H deposited on native oxide-covered c-Si, the bulk material dielectric function from 2.0 to 4.0 eV has been obtained from real time observations on continuous films as thin as 34 Å.   Corresponding data have also been obtained for a-Si:H clusters 21 Å thick on a metallic substrate, revealing the effects of surface SiH_n bonding in shifting the oscillator strength for absorption to higher energies.   From these dielectric functions, accurate results for the band gap have been deduced, which are free of surface-related artifacts that influence all *ex situ* measurements.   The sensitivity of the ellipsometric data to the dielectric discontinuity at the ambient/film interface in turn provides unprecedented sensitivity to microstructural coalescence.   The results suggest a uniformity of deposition and nucleation density much higher than that of the PPy.   For optimum PECVD conditions and oxide/c-Si substrates, clusters make contact after ~20 Å thickness and the resulting nucleation-induced surface morphology smoothens by a total of 10 Å with subsequent growth.   It is notable that such a smoothening phenomenon does not occur for a-Si prepared by physical vapor deposition.   Thus, we conclude that it is driven by the higher surface diffusion length of film precursors in PECVD.   Future applications in amorphous semiconductor growth involve further development of these general techniques to obtain the band gap on ultrathin layers in electronic device configurations, in an attempt to correlate device performance with interface characteristics.

In summary real time spectroscopic ellipsometry is a powerful new probe of film growth in electrochemical and plasma environments.   In addition to our studies of polypyrrole and a-Si:H, the technique has led us to important insights into the growth of hydrogenated amorphous carbon by ion beam deposition, diamond by filament-enhanced CVD, Al by evaporation, as well as Au oxidation, and the etching of III–V semiconductor heterostructures.   We expect it to play an important role in the future in understanding complex processes of film growth, etching, and surface modification, as well as the evolution of the optical properties of the materials as they progress from monolayer clusters to the bulk film stage.

ACKNOWLEDGMENTS

We would like to thank Dr. Y.-T.Kim, Prof. D.L. Allara, and Prof. K. Vedam for their contributions to the study of PPy, Dr. N.V. Nguyen, Mr. Ilsin An, and Mr. Brian Pudliner for their work on the perfection of the ellipsometer, and Mr. Y.M. Li, Mr. Ilsin An, Mr. H.V. Nguyen, and Prof. C.R. Wronski for their contributions to the study of a-Si:H.   The encouragement of Profs. K. Vedam and R. Messier is especially appreciated.   We gratefully acknowledge financial support from the National Science Foundation under Grant Nos. DMR-8901031 and DMR-8957159, the latter of the Presidential Young Investigator Program.   Assistance was also provided by the Electric Power Research Institute, the Solar Energy Research Institute (subcontract No.XG-1-10063-10), and the State of Pennsylvania under the Ben Franklin Centers of Excellence Program.

REFERENCES

1. R.M.A. Azzam and N.M. Bashara, *Ellipsometry and Polarized Light*, North-Holland, Amsterdam (1977).
2. H. Takasaki, *J. Opt. Soc. Am.*, **51**, 463 (1961); H. Takasaki, *Appl. Opt.*, **3**, 345 (1964); H. Takasaki, *Appl. Opt.*, **5**, 759 (1966).
3. A.B. Winterbottom, in: *Ellipsometry in the Measurement of Surfaces and Thin Films, Symposium Proceedings*, Washington 1963 (ed. E. Passaglia, R.R. Stromberg and J. Kruger), (Natl. Bureau of Standards Misc. Publication 256, Washington D.C., September 15, 1964), p. 97.
4. J.L. Ord and B.L. Wills, *Appl. Opt.*, **6**, 1673 (1967)
5. B.D. Cahan and R.F. Spanier, *Surf. Sci.*, **16**, 166 (1969).
6. S.N. Jasperson and S.E. Schnatterly, *Rev. Sci. Instrum.*, **40**, 761 (1969).
7. J.B. Theeten and D.E. Aspnes, *Ann. Rev. Mater. Sci.*, **11**, 97 (1981).
8. D.E. Aspnes, *Proc. Soc. Photo-Opt. Instrum. Eng.*, **946**, 84 (1988).
9. R.W. Collins, *Rev. Sci. Instrum.*, **61**, 2029 (1990).
10. S. Gottesfeld, in: *Electroanalytical Chemistry: A Series of Advances*, Volume 15 (ed. A.J. Bard), p. 143, Marcel Dekker, New York, 1989.
11. F. Hottier and R. Cadoret, *J. Cryst. Growth*, **56**, 304 (1982).
12. In Ref. 1, p. 417.
13. D.E. Aspnes, *Opt. Commun.*, **8**, 222 (1973).
14. D.E. Aspnes, *Proc. Soc. Photo-Opt. Instrum. Eng.*, **276**, 188 (1981).
15. K. Vedam, P.J. McMarr and J. Narayan, *Appl. Phys. Lett.*, **47**, 339 (1985).
16. R.H. Muller and J.C. Farmer, *Rev. Sci. Instrum.*, **55**, 371 (1984).
17. H.J. Mathieu, D.E. McClure and R.H. Muller, *Rev. Sci. Instrum.*, **45**, 798 (1974).
18. J.C. Farmer and R.H. Muller, *J. Electrochem. Soc.*, **132**, 313 (1985).
19. S.T. Mayer and R.H. Muller, *J. Electrochem. Soc.*, **135**, 2133 (1988).
20. Y.-T. Kim, R.W. Collins and K. Vedam, *Surf. Sci.*, **223**, 341 (1990).
21. N.V. Nguyen, B.S. Pudliner, I. An and R.W. Collins, *J. Opt. Soc. Am. A*, **8**, 919 (1991).
22. I. An and R.W. Collins, *Rev. Sci. Instrum.*, **62**, 1904 (1991).

23. J.B. Theeten, R.P.H. Chang, D.E. Aspnes and T.E. Adams, *J. Electrochem. Soc.*, **127**, 378 (1980).
24. G. Laurence, F. Hottier and J. Hallais, *Rev. Phys. Appl.* (*Paris*), **16**, 579 (1981).
25. D.E. Aspnes and A.A. Studna, *Appl. Opt.*, **14**, 220 (1975).
26. D.E. Aspnes, *J. Opt. Soc. Am.*, **64**, 812 (1974).
27. J.M.M. de Nijs, A.H.M. Holtslag, A. Hoeksta and A. van Silfhout, *J. Opt. Soc. Am. A*, **5**, 1466 (1988).
28. D.E. Aspnes, *J. Opt. Soc. Am.*, **64**, 639 (1974).
29. R.W. Stobie, B. Rao and M.J. Dignam, *J. Opt. Soc. Am.*, **65**, 25 (1975).
30. G.B. Street, in: *Handbook of Conducting Polymers*, Volume 1 (ed. T.A. Skotheim), p. 265, Marcel Dekker, New York, 1986.
31. A.F. Diaz, J.I. Castillo, J.A. Logan and W.-Y. Lee, *J. Electroanal. Chem.*, **129**, 115 (1981).
32. G.B. Street, T.C. Clarke, M. Krounbi, K. Kanazawa, V. Lee, P. Pfluger, J.C. Scott and G. Weiser, *Mol. Crys. Liq. Cryst.*, **83**, 253 (1982).
33. R. Yang, K.M. Dalsin, D.F. Evans, L. Christensen and W.A. Hendrickson, *J. Phys. Chem.*, **93**, 511 (1989).
34. K.K. Kanazawa, A.F. Diaz, W.D. Gill, P.M. Grant, G.B. Street, G.P. Gardini and J.F. Kwak, *Synth. Met.*, **1**, 329 (1980).
35. R.H. Geiss, G.B. Street, W. Volksen and J. Economy, *IBM J. Res. Dev.*, **27**, 321 (1983).
36. A. Hamnett, S.J. Higgins, P.R. Fisk and W.J. Albery, *J. Electroanal. Chem.*, **270**, 479 (1988).
37. A. Asavapiriyanont, G.K. Chandler, G.A. Gunawardena and D. Pletcher, *J. Electroanal. Chem.*, **177**, 229 (1984).
38. J.C. Scott, P. Pfluger, M.T. Krounbi and G.B. Street, *Phys. Rev. B*, **28**, 2140 (1983).
39. J.L. Bredas, B. Themans and J.M. Andre, *Phys. Rev. B*, **27**, 7827 (1983).
40. J.C. Scott, J.L. Bredas, K. Yakushi, P. Pfluger and G.B. Street, *Synth. Met.*, **9**, 165 (1984).
41. H. Arwin, D.E. Aspnes, R. Bjorklund and I. Lundstrom, *Synth. Met.*, **6**, 309 (1983).
42. K. Yakushi, L.J. Lauchlan, G.B. Street and J.L. Bredas, *J. Chem. Phys.*, **81**, 4133 (1984).
43. Y.-T. Kim, D.L. Allara, R.W. Collins and K. Vedam, *Thin. Solid Films*, **193/194**, 350 (1990).
44. Y.-T. Kim, R.W. Collins, K. Vedam and D.L. Allara, *J. Electrochem. Soc.*, **138**, 3266 (1991).
45. R.E. Noftle and D. Pletcher, *J. Electroanal. Chem.*, **227**, 229 (1987).
46. W.G. Oldham, *Surf. Sci.*, **16**, 97 (1969).
47. H. Arwin and D.E. Aspnes, *Thin Solid Films*, **113**, 101 (1984).
48. F. Wooten, *Optical Properties of Solids*, Chapter 3, Academic Press, New York, 1972.
49. A.F. Diaz, *Chem. Scripta*, **17**, 145 (1981).
50. D.E. Aspnes, *Thin Solid Films*, **89**, 249 (1982).
51. G.A. Niklasson, C.G. Granqvist and O. Hunderi, *Appl. Opt.*, **20**, 26 (1981).
52. D.E. Aspnes, J.B. Theeten and F. Hottier, *Phys, Rev. B*, **20**, 3292 (1979).
53. R.C. Chittick, J.H. Alexander and H.F. Sterling, *J. Electrochem. Soc.*, **116**, 77 (1969).
54. J.I. Pankove (ed.), *Semiconductors and Semimetals*, Volume 21D, Academic Press, New York, 1984.
55. M.J. Thompson and D.E. Carlson (ed.), *Amorphous Silicon Technology*, (North Holland, Amsterdam, 1989), published as *J. Non-Cryst. Solids*, **115** (1989).
56. R.A. Street, *Hydrogenated Amorphous Silicon*, Cambridge University, Cambridge, England, 1991.
57. R. Robertson and A. Gallagher, *J. Appl. Phys.*, **59**, 3402 (1986).
58. A. Gallagher, *Mater. Res. Soc. Symp. Proc.*, **70**, 3 (1986).
59. Y. Kuwano, H. Nishiwaki, S. Tsuda, T. Fukatsu, K. Enomoto, Y. Nakashima and H. Tarui, *16th IEEE Photovoltaic Specialists Conference*, p. 1338, IEEE, New York (1982).
60. J.C. Knights and R.A. Lujan, *Appl. Phys. Lett.*, **35**, 244 (1979).
61. R.C. Ross, A.G. Johncock and A.R. Chan, *J. Non-Cryst. Solids*, **66**, 81 (1984).
62. R.W. Collins, in: *Amorphous Silicon and Related Materials*, (ed. H.Fritzsche), p. 1003, World Scientific Singapore, 1989.
63. B. Drevillon, *J. Non-Cryst. Solids*, **114**, 139 (1989).
64. Y. Hayashi, H. Izumi, M. Matsuura and A. Itoh, in: *Technical Digest, Conference on Lasers and Electro-Optics*, paper THK 14, Optical Society of America, Washington DC (1986).
65. A. Canillas, E. Bertran, J.L. Andujar and B. Drevillon, *J. Appl. Phys.*, **68**, 2752 (1990).
66. R.W. Collins and B.Y. Yang, *J. Vac. Sci. Technol. B*, **7**, 1155 (1989).
67. R.W. Collins and J.M. Cavese, *J. Appl. Phys.*, **61**, 1662 (1987).
68. D.E. Aspnes and A.A. Studna, *Phys. Rev. B*, **27**, 985 (1983).
69. I.H. Malitson, *J. Opt. Soc. Am.*, **55**, 1205 (1965).
70. Y. Cong, I. An, K. Vedam and R.W. Collins, *Appl. Opt.*, **30**, 2692 (1991).
71. G.D. Cody, B.G. Brooks and B. Abeles, *Solar Energy Mater.*, **4**, 231 (1982).
72. J. Tauc, R. Grigorovici and A. Vancu, *Phys. Status Solidi*, **15**, 627 (1966).
73. D. Ewald, M. Milleville and G. Weiser, *Philos. Mag. B*, **40**, 291 (1979).
74. W. Paul and D.A. Anderson, *Solar Energy Mater.*, **5**, 229 (1980).
75. R.W. Collins and J.M. Cavese, *J. Non-Cryst. Solids*, **97/98**, 1439 (1987).

76. I. An, H.V. Nguyen, N.V. Nguyen and R.W. Collins, *J. Vac. Sci. Technol. A*, **9**, 622 (1991).
77. A. Mazor, D.J. Srolovitz, P.S. Hagan and B.G. Bukiet, *Phys, Rev. Lett.*, **60**, 424 (1988).
78. R.P.U. Karunasiri, R. Bruinsma and J. Rudnick, *Phys. Rev. Lett.*, **62**, 788 (1989).
79. I. An, H.V. Nguyen, N.V. Nguyen and R.W. Collins, *Phys. Rev. Lett.*, **65**, 2274 (1990).

7

Real-Time, Submonolayer Monitoring of Electrochemical Processes Using Acoustic Plate Mode Devices

Antonio J. Ricco and Stephen J. Martin

Microsensor Department 1315, Sandia National Laboratories, Albuquerque, New Mexico 87185, U.S.A.

7.1 Introduction

The ability to measure electrode surface mass changes corresponding to a small fraction of a monolayer during an electrochemical process is useful in elucidating a range of electrochemical mechanisms and monitoring many processes. A variety of piezoelectric devices are candidates for making such measurements.

Rayleigh or surface acoustic wave (SAW) devices have been used effectively to sense mass changes at solid/gas interfaces[1-5] with mass resolution as high as[6] 100 pg/cm^2. Unfortunately, high-frequency (>30 MHz) SAW devices are impractical for use in liquids: they possess a substantial surface-normal displacement component that generates compressional waves in any liquid contacting the surface, resulting in severe damping of the wave.[7] Because attenuation of a SAW by a contacting liquid is proportional to frequency, a low-frequency (<20 MHz) SAW device can function as a sensor in liquid environments[8]; since sensitivity is also proportional to frequency, however, such a device has diminished sensitivity.

The bulk crystal oscillator, commonly referred to as a quartz crystal microbalance (QCM), is commonly used to monitor metal deposition processes *in vacuo*. These devices, more accurately described as thickness-shear mode (TSM) resonators, can also function as mass detectors when a liquid contacts one surface of the crystal[9-12]; their sensitivities approach that of the acoustic plate mode devices discussed in detail in this chapter. Because TSM resonators have electrodes on both substrate surfaces, however, they are somewhat difficult to include in an electrochemical cell: the face of the crystal that serves as the working electrode/mass sensitive surface must simultaneously function as one of the rf transduction electrodes. In addition, the opposite crystal face must be electrically insulated from the solution as well as being mechanically unconstrained. Finally, TSM resonators are one-port devices, as compared to SAW and APM devices, which have two ports. The single-port configuration of TSM devices can, in some cases, make instrumentation of a highly stable oscillator circuit less straightforward than for SAW and APM devices. In particular, excessive parasitic capacitance renders the device ineffective as an oscillator-frequency-control element. This necessitates locating the oscillator circuitry very close to the TSM resonator.

The planar interdigital electrode patterns commonly used to excite SAWs can excite various bulk waves as well.[13] Thus, a new type of electrode monitor has been constructed from monolithic acoustic wave (AW) devices utilizing acoustic plate modes (APMs) with shear-horizontal (SH) displacement components.   These devices, which typically operate in the 25–200 MHz frequency range, provide a highly accurate means of measuring mass changes (resolution *ca.* 1 ng/cm²) accompanying electrochemical processes.   SH–APMs have negligible surface-normal particle displacement and therefore work well for liquid sensing applications,[7,13] allowing operation at high as well as low frequencies.   Though mass sensitivity depends only on the thickness of the substrate, the ability to operate at high (as well as low) frequencies has two advantages: frequency-dependent phenomena, such as relaxation in liquids and polymer films, can be examined; the area of the device diminishes roughly in proportion to $1/f^2$, thus high frequency APM devices are smaller.

The two faces of the piezoelectric substrate must be parallel and smooth, so that the bulk waves are multiply reflected between these surfaces, forming plate modes; it is often helpful to think of the substrate as an acoustic waveguide.   One interdigital transducer launches the SH–APMs, which are detected by a second interdigital transducer at some distance along the crystal face from the launching electrodes, as shown in Fig. 7.1.   The electro-chemical reaction is typically carried out using a thin-film electrode on the opposite face of the substrate and in the path of the wave.   Changes in mass at the substrate/electrolyte interface affect the acoustic wave velocity, which is monitored with high accuracy by utilizing the device as the feedback element of an oscillator circuit.

The desirability of utilizing plate mode devices as gas-phase sensors has been pointed out by White: the sensing surface of the crystal can be opposite that bearing the trans-ducers.[14]   This advantage is even more significant for liquid-phase measurements, where the substrate itself serves as the means to isolate the interdigital transducers from the electrolyte.

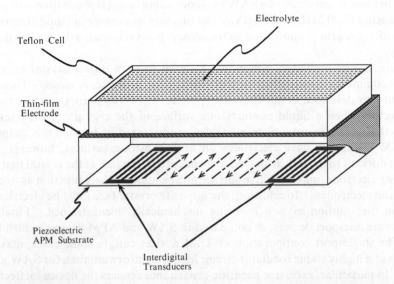

Fig. 7.1 Schematic diagram of acoustic plate mode device for monitoring thin-film electrode processes.   APMs are generated and received by 50 or 75 finger-pair interdigital transducers.   Liquid may contact either side of the substrate.   The dashed arrows show the shear-horizontal (in-plane) nature of the surface displacement, which allows these devices to function in contact with an electrolyte without excessive attenuation.

The electrodeposition of silver and copper, the electroless deposition of copper, the etching of aluminum, and the cyclic voltammetry of gold electrodes have been examined as proof-of-concept experiments.   These applications, along with a brief examination of the theory of SH acoustic plate mode devices, will be discussed in this chapter.

7.2   Theory of Acoustic Plate Mode Devices

7.2.1   Fundamentals

Full details of the propagation and interactions of SH–APMs can be found else-where.[13]   A cursory treatment will be given here to familiarize the reader with some of the basic concepts.

An alternating voltage is applied to an interdigital transducer on a piezoelectric substrate, in this case quartz, generating an alternating strain field that in turn launches an acoustic wave.[15]   In the case of an APM, the wave energy propagates through the bulk of the substrate, in contrast to the SAW, for which the energy is concentrated near the surface.   In general, the propagation characteristics of any acoustic mode having significant amplitude at the substrate surface are affected by changes in the nature and/or quantity of a material in intimate contact with the device surface.   The effects of such interactions are changes in AW amplitude and velocity.

An SH plate mode may be thought of as a superposition of SH plane waves multiply reflected at some angle between the upper and lower faces of the plate.   A series of modes having n nodes ($n = 0, 1, 2, ...$) between substrate faces can propagate, each mode having a slightly different velocity.   The frequency f_n of most efficient coupling for the nth mode is approximately

$$f_n = \frac{v_0}{d}\left(1 + \left[\frac{nd}{2b}\right]^2\right), \tag{7.1}$$

where v_0 is the unperturbed wave velocity, d is the transducer periodicity, b is the substrate thickness, and $n = 0, 1, 2, ...$.

Interpretation of APM sensor results is simplified by exciting only a single mode, accomplished by using a transducer with a bandwidth less than the frequency separation between modes.   Transducer bandwidth is proportional to the factor $1/N$, where N is the number of finger pairs comprising the transducer.   Thus, increasing the number of transducer fingers and decreasing plate thickness (relative to transducer periodicity d) enhance mode resolution.   Note that the wavelength (Λ) along the surface at which the APM is most efficiently excited is equal to the transducer periodicity d (which is twice the center-to-center spacing of adjacent transducer fingers).

7.2.2   Mass Sensitivity

Extreme sensitivity to changes in surface mass set AW devices apart from all other types of sensors.   When mass is bound strongly to the surface of an APM device, it oscillates synchronously with the surface.   A simple and highly accurate way to measure wave velocity is to utilize the APM device as the feedback element of an oscillator loop.[13]   For the nth mode, the frequency shift Δf_n caused by a change in surface mass/area of magnitude ρ_s is approximated by

$$\frac{\Delta f_n}{f_n} \equiv -c_m \rho_s = \frac{j_n}{\rho_q b}\rho_s, \tag{7.2}$$

in which c_m is the mass sensitivity factor, ρ_q is the density of the substrate, $j_0 \equiv 1/2$, and $j_n \equiv 1$ for $n \geq 1$.   Eq. 7.2 reveals that frequency *decreases* linearly with accumulated mass density and that sensitivity depends inversely on plate thickness.   Eq. 7.2 also reveals a subtlety of the APMs: the lowest order ($n = 0$) mode has only half the sensitivity of higher order modes.   This has been verified experimentally[13] and is a consequence of the diminished surface amplitude, in relation to total power flow, of the $n = 0$ mode.

7.2.3   Liquid Entrainment

Because of its shear-horizontal surface particle displacement (in the plane of the device surface and normal to the wave propagation direction), the SH–APM is not excessively attenuated by a contacting liquid.   The in-plane oscillation of the device surface does lead, however, to entrainment of a thin liquid layer at the solid/liquid interface.[7]   The main effect of this viscous coupling is to alter the propagation characteristics (velocity and attenuation) of the APM.[13]   For an angular frequency of oscillation ω_n, the decay length δ of the entrained liquid layer is approximated by

$$\delta = \sqrt{\frac{2\eta}{\rho_l \omega_n}},$$

in which ρ_l and η are liquid density and shear viscosity, respectively.   The coupled liquid layer is about 50 nm thick in water at 158 MHz; note that this is far in excess of the typical thickness of an electrical double layer.

The high frequency at which the APM operates necessitates consideration of viscoelastic response by the liquid.[7,13]   Modeling simple liquids as Maxwellian fluids with a single relaxation time, τ, gives good agreement with experimental data.[7]   When a Maxwellian fluid is driven at a frequency such that $\omega_n\tau \ll 1$, it responds as a Newtonia (ideal) fluid characterized by a shear viscosity η; this is the case for all the aqueous electrolyte solutions considered in this chapter.   In the case of $\omega_n\tau \gg 1$, the oscillation rate exceeds the rate of molecular motion in the liquid and energy ceases to be dissipated in viscous flow, being stored elastically isntead.[16]   Glycerol/water mixtures, for example, have been shown to exhibit significant viscoelastic effects.[7,13]

7.2.4   Acoustoelectric Coupling

Propagation of an APM through a piezoelectric waveguide generates a layer of bound charge at the device surface, and the evanescent electric field associated with this charge extends into the adjacent liquid, coupling to ions and dipoles in solution.[17]   At typical APM frequencies, the transit distance of ions per wave period is much less than the acoustic wavelength Λ.   Therefore, the electrical double layer does not screen the evanescent electric field from the adjacent solution, and this field extends several micrometers from the surface with a decay length of $\Lambda/2\pi$.   Acoustoelectric coupling between the APM-generated electric field and ions in solution leads to perturbations in plate mode velocity and attenuation α that vary with solution conductivity σ_l and dielectric coefficient ε_l as[17]

$$\frac{\Delta v_n}{v_n} = -\frac{K^2}{2}\left(\frac{\varepsilon_s + \varepsilon_0}{\varepsilon_s + \varepsilon_l}\right)\frac{\sigma_l^2}{\sigma_l^2 + \omega_n^2(\varepsilon_s + \varepsilon_l)^2} \tag{7.4}$$

and

$$\frac{\Delta \alpha_n}{k_n} = \frac{K^2}{2}\left(\frac{\varepsilon_s + \varepsilon_0}{\varepsilon_s + \varepsilon_l}\right)\frac{\omega_n\sigma_l(\varepsilon_s + \varepsilon_l)}{\sigma_l^2 + \omega_n^2(\varepsilon_s + \varepsilon_l)^2} \tag{7.5}$$

in which K^2 is the electromechanical coupling coefficient (a measure of the piezoelectric strength of the substrate), $k_n = 2\pi/\Lambda$ is the wavenumber, and ε_s and ε_0 are the dielectric coefficients of the substrate and free space, respectively. It should be noted that if a metal film thicker than *ca.* 10 nm is deposited on the device surface, charge carriers redistribute in this film to oppose the layer of bound charge that is generated at the surface of the substrate by the APM. This "shunts" the evanescent electric field and the values of σ_l and ε_l then affect neither the velocity nor the attenuation of the APM.

7.3 Experimental Details

SH–APM devices were designed at Sandia National Laboratories (SNL) and fabricated by Crystal Technologies, Inc. (Palo Alto, CA), Sawtek, Inc. (Orlando, FL) and at SNL. The ST cut of quartz was used, with propagation along the X direction of the crystal; substrates measured $22.9 \times 7.6 \times 0.5$ mm thick before lapping.

Two different designs were examined: $d = 32$ μm, $f_0 = 158$ MHz, $N = 50$, finger length $= 50d$, center-to-center separation between transducers $= 7.36$ mm; $d = 50$ μm, $f_0 = 102$ MHz, $N = 75$, finger length $= 75d$, center-to-center separation between transducers $= 7.28$ mm. Because the nature of the plate mode spectrum (power transmitted as a function of frequency) and the sensitivity to mass changes both depend upon plate thickness,[13] some devices were thinned to 0.18 mm, by lapping and polishing the face of the device without transducers, to enhance the mass sensitivity and mode separation.

Because the SH–APM is a bulk acoustic mode, either surface (the one bearing the IDTs or the one opposite the IDTs, hereafter referred to as the "front" and "back" surfaces, respectively) can be utilized for detection, with no significant difference in mass sensitivity. In either configuration, the IDTs must be isolated from the contacting electrolyte. The advantage of utilizing the back surface is thus two-fold: the IDTs are isolated from the liquid by the substrate itself, and the edges of the cell that must seal against the device surface can lie outside the acoustic wave path as defined by the area bounded by the IDTs.

Measurements were made with electrolyte contacting either the front or back surface. For front-surface measurements, devices were mounted in stainless-steel flatpacks (Isotronics) and a miniature cell machined from Teflon, with an internal volume of approximately 50 μl, was clamped against the device surface, confining the electrolyte to the region between IDTs. The remainder of the device configuration was the same as described below for back-surface measurements.

For back-surface measurements, each device was mounted in a 25.5 mm × 12.7 mm gold-plated steel flatpack (Isotronics) with a 20.5 mm × 3.7 mm opening, allowing liquid to contact the device as shown schematically by Fig. 7.1. The back face of the device was bonded (in the region surrounding the acoustic wave path) to the opening in the flatpack using a bead of RTV elastomer; the device thus contacts liquid only in the APM propagation path. Electrical contact was made between transducer bonding pads and flatpack feed-throughs by 76-μm diameter Au or Al leads attached with an ultrasonic bonder (Westbond). The flatpack was mounted in a brass test fixture containing impedance matching networks (Integrated Chemical Sensors, Newton, MA). Wires were soldered to the flatpack feed-throughs to make contact to the matching networks in the body of the fixture below. Liquid was held in contact with the sensing surface by a Teflon cell sealed

SH-APM Device

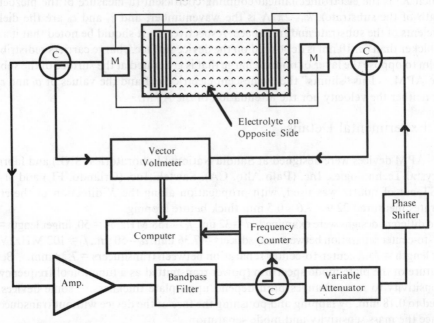

Fig. 7.2 Block diagram of the instrumentation utilized for APM device measurements of electrochemical processes. "C" denotes a directional coupler and "M" an impedance matching network. Changes in the frequency of oscillation of the circuit are proportional to perturbations in the velocity of the acoustic wave; changes in the insertion loss of the device, measured by the vector voltmeter, are proportional to changes in wave attenuation.

by compression to the metal flatpack. The open cell represented in Fig. 7.1, having an approximate internal volume of 1 ml, was used for most experiments, with liquids being added and withdrawn by means of a pipet.

Instrumentation for the oscillator measurements, arranged as shown in Fig. 7.2, included two cascaded wide-band amplifiers (Hewlett-Packard 8447D), a band-pass filter (K&L Microwave 5BT-95/190-5N), two variable attenuators in series (Hewlett-Packard 8494A and 8495A), a tunable phase shifter (Merrimac PSL-4-160B or PSL-4-100B), a 10-dB directional coupler (Anzac DCG-10-4), a frequency counter (Hewlett-Packard 5384A), a vector voltmeter (Hewlett-Packard 8508A), impedance matching networks (Integrated Chemical Sensors, Newton, MA) and a computer for data acquisition (Hewlett-Packard 9816).

With sufficient external gain (provided by the amplifiers), the loop containing the APM device will oscillate. Because the round-trip phase change of the loop must be a multiple of 2π to sustain oscillation, the phase shifter is adjusted until the frequency of oscillation precisely matches the frequency of minimum loss for highest stability. The variable attenuators are then adjusted until there is just enough gain for stable oscillation. Several dB of excess gain are then added (by reducing the attenuation) to allow for increases in loss that may occur as the electrochemical reaction proceeds.

Electrochemical measurements were made by metallizing either the region of the front surface between the IDTs or the entire back surface with a thin film of the working electrode metal.   Electrical contact was made to this thin-film electrode by means of an ultrasonic wire bond or an epoxy-insulated silver paint contact.   The counter electrode was immersed in the electrolyte contained in the Teflon cell.   A three-electrode potentiostat/galvanostat/ programmer (PAR 173/175, PAR 362, or Pine RDE4) was utilized to control and measure applied potentials and/or currents.

Water was doubly distilled.   Electrolytes and solvents were commercially available reagent grade, used as received.   Palladium, silver, copper, and gold shot, as well as chromium chips, (Aesar, 99.99% or better) were thermally evaporated from a resistively heated tungsten basket at a rate of 0.5–2 Å/s; base pressure in the cryo-pumped vacuum system was 2×10^{-8} Torr.   Evaporation was monitored with a commercial TSM device (Inficon XTC Quartz Crystal Microbalance) operating at 6 MHz.

7.4   Results and Discussion

7.4.1   Mass Calibration

The mass sensitivity of a number of SH–APM devices was calibrated by vacuum deposition of silver onto the (unmetallized) quartz surface.   The resulting frequency shift was compared to the film thickness measured by the commercial TSM device; a mass sensitivity factor was then extracted using the density of silver.   The APM frequency shift is plotted vs. the thickness of deposited silver in Fig. 7.3 for the $n = 1$ mode.   The "jog" in the curve between metal thicknesses of 8 and 10 nm is a result of the acoustoelectric effect; this experiment illustrates the relatively narrow range of conductivity over which this effect

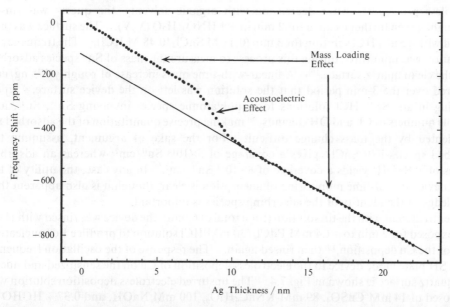

Fig. 7.3   Frequency shift as a function of the thickness of a silver layer vacuum-evaporated onto the surface of a 158 MHz APM device.   A one-ppm frequency shift is equivalent to a change of 158 Hz, and negative frequency shifts correspond to increasing surface mass.   With a short-term frequency stability of the order of 5 Hz, this device can resolve mass changes smaller than 1 ng/cm². A linear least-squares fit to the data from 10 to 22 nm of Ag yields a mass sensitivity of $c_m = 32$ cm²/g in Eq. 7.2.

is significant. The calculated mass sensitivity from the experiment of Fig. 7.3 is $c_m = 32$ cm^2/g. With our present test system, stability of the frequency of oscillation of 0.03 ppm (5 Hz) is typically obtained for 158 MHz devices, indicating a limit of mass resolution of 1 ng/cm^2. With further refinement, stability of 1 Hz is anticipated, equivalent to a mass resolution of 180 pg/cm^2.

The accuracy with which the mass sensitivity measured *in vacuo* reflects that when the device is in contact with liquid was investigated. After evaporating an 81 nm-thick silver film onto an APM device, the test fixture with device was removed from the vacuum system, then an open cell was affixed to the device surface and filled with 1.0 ml of water. After stable oscillation of the $n=1$ mode was achieved, 0.1 ml of a 2:2:1 $H_2O:H_2SO_4:HNO_3$ (V:V:V) etchant was added to the cell. The frequency shift measured as the film dissolved over a 15-min period yielded a mass sensitivity approximately 6% less than the value measured in vacuum, a discrepancy that lies within our estimates of experimental uncertainty.

Mass calibration of a "wet" APM device was also made by comparing the total frequency shift recorded during the process of depositing an electroless copper film (described below) with the film thickness measured using a surface profilimeter (Dektak). The results were consistent with those obtained from the other experiments.

7.4.2 Electroless Deposition of Copper

The electroless deposition of copper is of major commercial importance, e.g., in the fabrication of printed circuit boards. Cu deposition was therefore chosen as a test process for the APM sensor. Pretreatment of the quartz substrate is necessary to catalyze the electroless process.[18] After degreasing with organic solvents, the quartz was rinsed thoroughly, then further cleaned for 2 min in 3:1 $HNO_3:H_2O$ (V:V). The surface was then treated with a Sn^{2+}/HCl solution for 3 min (0.11 M $SnCl_2$/0.48 M HCl). The frequency of oscillation was monitored during this process to measure the mass of Sn^{II} species adsorbed onto the clean quartz surface.[19] A linear-with-time mass increase of roughly 175 ng/cm^2 occurred over the 3-min period that the solution was left on the device surface. Upon standing in air, Sn^{2+}/HCl solutions form polyatomic species involving Sn^{2+}, Sn^{4+}, and variable numbers of Cl$^-$ and OH$^-$ ligands,[20] making precise quantitation of the adsorbed tin represented by the mass change difficult. For the sake of argument, assuming the adsorbed species is[21] $SnCl_3^-$ gives a coverage of 5×10^{14} Sn^{II}/cm^2, whereas an adsorbed species of[21] $SnOH^+$ yields a coverage of 8×10^{14} Sn^{II}/cm^2. In any case, the utility of the APM device in real-time monitoring of adsorption is clear, though it is also apparent that knowledge of the identity of the adsorbing species is important.

After treatment with the tin solution (for a total of 6 min), the device was rinsed with H_2O, then exposed for 2 min to a 1.4 mM $PdCl_2$/30 mM HCl solution to produce Pd^0 nucleation sites for the Cu deposition,[18] then rinsed again. The response of the oscillation frequency of the SH plate mode device to the electroless deposition of Cu on the sensitized and nucleated quartz surface is shown in Fig. 7.4. The unstirred electroless deposition solution was composed of 14 mM $CuSO_4$, 89 mM $KNaC_4H_4O_6$, 100 mM NaOH, and 0.37% HCHO.[18] Fig. 7.4 shows the fractional frequency shift *vs.* time for the deposition experiment. A sudden frequency decrease results when the distilled water used to rinse the substrate is removed at time t_1; the addition of the deposition solution to the surface then results in an increase in frequency to near the original value at time t_2. The acoustic wave deposition

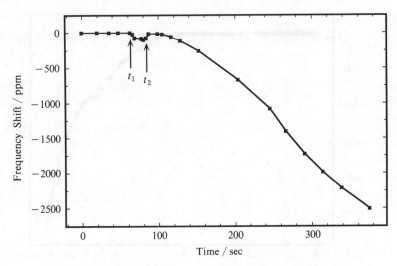

Fig. 7.4 Response of the APM electrode monitor to the electroless deposition of a copper film onto the Sn^{II}/Pd-sensitized quartz surface.   Pure distilled water is present on the surface until time t_1, at which point it is removed; the Cu^{2+}/formaldehyde-based solution is added to the surface at time t_2.   Following an induction period lasting approximately 25 s, deposition commences at a rate of roughly 3 Å/s, continuing until H$_2$ bubble formation on the surface disrupts the process at $t = 380$ s.

monitor reveals a short induction period, during which the rate of change in surface mass accelerates gradually.   This may indicate a slow rate of initial Cu growth on the Pd nucleation sites and/or a relatively low number/area of such sites.   The steady-state deposition rate is *ca.* 2.8 Å/s.   A similar experiment was carried out for which the pretreatments with Sn and Pd were only half as long, *i.e.* 3 min and 1 min, respectively.   In that case, an induction period lasting over 200 s was recorded, during which no observable mass change at all occurred, supporting the hypothesis that a marginal number of Pd sites are available for nucleation.   The steady-state rate of deposition in this case was similar: 2.4 Å/s. Thus, the efficacy of the nucleation process can be readily determined using the SH–APM device to monitor induction periods.

7.4.3   Electrodeposition of Silver

The electrodeposition of silver onto a palladium electrode previously vacuum evaporated onto the quartz substrate was examined.   Deposition was carried out under galvanostatic control.   A silver plating solution reported to have current efficiency near unity[22] was selected: the aqueous electrolyte contained 0.3 M [Ag(CN)$_2$]$^-$ and 0.3 M free CN$^-$ in a basic solution.[23]   The plating solution was added to the electrochemical cell.   A Ag wire served as counter electrode; current density was ~0.3 mA/cm^2.   Fig. 7.5 shows the fractional frequency change *vs.* the charge passed.   The APM electrode monitor reveals an induction period, during which no significant change in surface mass occurs although current is already flowing.   This may be due to reductive dissolution of surface impurities, including the weakly bound oxide that forms when Pd is exposed to air, and/or Pd hydride formation.   Following the induction period, the frequency changes initially at a rate of *ca.* 1.5 ppm/μC, then accelerates to over 15 ppm/μC, indicating a further increase in current

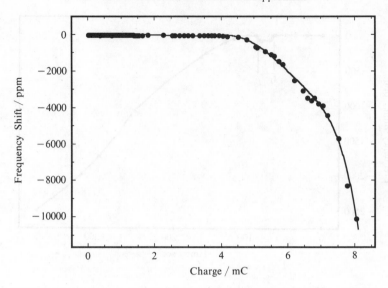

Fig. 7.5 Frequency shift of the APM device as function of charge passed during the electrodeposition of silver onto a thin Pd film; the active electrode area is 0.12 cm². The data reveal a substantial induction period. The smooth line is simply a guide to the eye. An increase in slope near 7 mC of integrated charge indicates an increase in current efficiency for the plating process.

efficiency.   Changes of a small fraction of a monolayer of Ag are readily resolvable.

7.4.4   Electrodeposition of Copper

The electrodeposition of copper from an acid copper solution (0.75 M CuSO$_4$/0.75 M H$_2$SO$_4$) onto an Au film electrode was monitored.   A copper wire anode was utilized. Fig. 7.6 reveals the effect of variations in the current density (J) on changes in surface mass (solid line; decreasing frequency corresponds to increasing mass/area).   While a cathodic current density of 14 µA/cm² causes no measurable response, imposition of $J = 140$ µA/cm² leads to a very linear change in frequency with time following an induction period of about 30 s.   Return of J to 14 µA/cm² causes an instantaneous decrease in the rate of mass increase, with a gradual, further decline to nearly zero mass change/time.   Increasing J again to 140 µA/cm² again leads to a near-linear change in mass with time, though with a somewhat smaller slope (*i.e.* diminished current efficiency) than before.   Changing J to 280 µA/cm² nearly doubles the rate of change of mass with time, as expected.

Shown along with the frequency shift *vs.* time in Fig. 7.6 is the change in insertion loss (dots), which is proportional to APM attenuation, during the Cu plating process.   Interestingly, the insertion loss actually decreases by a small amount as the Cu film thickens.   This indicates that the deposition process is leading to less attenuation of the acoustic wave, suggesting that the copper is smoothing the gold surface or otherwise reducing acoustic losses in the gold layer upon which it is plated.

Figure 7.7 shows the continuation of the electrodeposition experiment started in Fig. 7.6.   At $t = 70$ min, a current density of 140 µA is no longer sufficient to cause deposition of copper, indicating increased overpotential for Cu deposition as a result of changes in surface conditions and/or depletion of the plating solution.   Increasing J to 1.4 mA/cm²

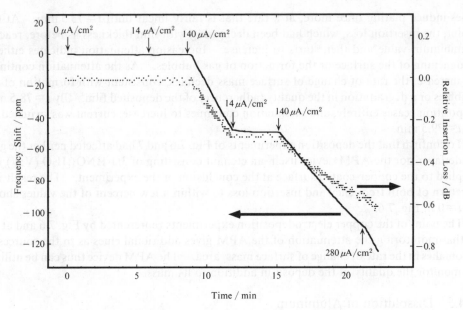

Fig. 7.6 Frequency shift (solid line, left axis) and change in insertion loss (dots, right axis) for a 102 MHz APM electrode monitor during the electrodeposition of copper onto a thin gold film on the device surface. Current densities are indicated. An acid copper plating solution and a copper wire counter electrode were utilized.

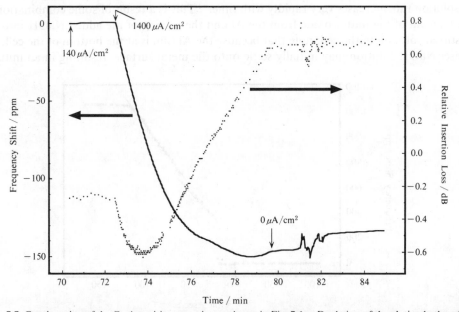

Fig. 7.7 Continuation of the Cu deposition experiment shown in Fig. 7.6. Depletion of the plating bath and/or changes in surface conditions have made it necessary to impose a greater current density in order to observe an increase in surface mass. Note the increase in insertion loss beginning at $t = 73.5$ min accompanied by a diminution in the rate of mass deposition; together, these features suggest evolution of gas on the electrode surface and/or a significant change in deposited film morphology that results in a non-adherent deposit.

does induce plating once more, at a rate that is fairly linear until $t = 73.5$ min.   At this point, the insertion loss, which had been decreasing with film thickness as before, reaches a minimum value and then starts to increase.   Increasing attenuation indicates either a roughening of the surface or the formation of gas bubbles.   As the attenuation continues to increase, the rate of change of surface mass declines, consistent with formation of gas bubbles or a degradation in the quality (adherence) of the deposited film.   By $t = 78.5$ min, deposition ceases entirely, and attenuation continues to increase; current was switched off at $t = 79.5$ min.

To confirm that the deposition experiments of Fig. 7.6 and 7 had affected neither the gold underlayer nor the APM device itself, an etchant consisting of 3:1 $HNO_3 : H_2O$ (V : V) was applied to the copper-coated surface at the conclusion of the experiment.   The result was a return of both frequency and insertion loss to within a few percent of the values shown at $t = 0$ in Fig. 7.6.

The point of the copper electrodeposition experiments represented by Fig. 7.6 and at 7.7 is that monitoring the attenuation of the APM gives additional clues as to the sources of anomalies in the rate of change of surface mass/area.   The APM device thus can be utilized to monitor the quality of the deposit in addition to its mass.

7.4.5   Dissolution of Aluminum

To demonstrate the monitoring of an etching process, the dissolution of a 420 nm-thick aluminum film in 0.3% NaOH solution was followed as a function of time.   Fig. 7.8 reveals that addition of the NaOH to the cell is followed by a short period during which the dissolution rate increases very rapidly with time.   This is a result of some combination of the removal of the native oxide from the Al and the mixing of the added NaOH into the unstirred solution in the cell: note that because the Al film is at the bottom of the cell, the denser NaOH solution may initially settle onto the metal surface, resulting in an initially

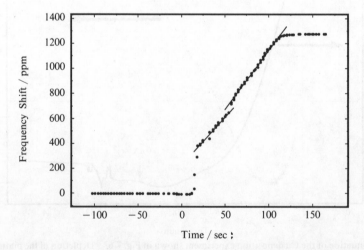

Fig. 7.8 The etching of a 420 nm-thick evaportated aluminum film.   Sufficient NaOH is added to the pure distilled water on the device surface at $t = 0$ to bring the concentration in the (unstirred) cell to 0.3% (w/w).   After a rapid initial dissolution of the first one-third of the film, the etch rate is relatively constant for about 1 min, then increases to a slightly higher rate as the last one-half of the film is dissolved.   The straight lines are linear least-squares fits.

high concentration of OH⁻ at the surface. The last two-thirds of the film is removed at two relatively constant rates between 1 and 2 nm/s, suggesting that the etching process is limited either by diffusion of OH⁻ to the surface or diffusion of the dissolved product away from the surface. The total frequency shift of 1280 ppm leads to a calculated mass sensitivity of 28 cm²/g for this particular 158 MHz device.

7.4.6 Cyclic Voltammetry of Gold

Another illustration of electrode monitoring is provided by cyclic voltammetry. The results of this experiment, which has previously been reported using TSM devices[9,12)] are shown in Fig. 7.9. The working electrode is a vacuum-evaporated gold film deposited on the quartz surface with an intervening Cr adhesion layer. Both current-potential and frequency shift-potential curves are shown for two potential cycles, taken in 0.5 M H₂SO₄ at a scan rate of 10 mV/s. At approximately +0.66 V applied potential, an anodic current peak results from the formation of a layer of oxide/hydroxide on the Au surface. Con-

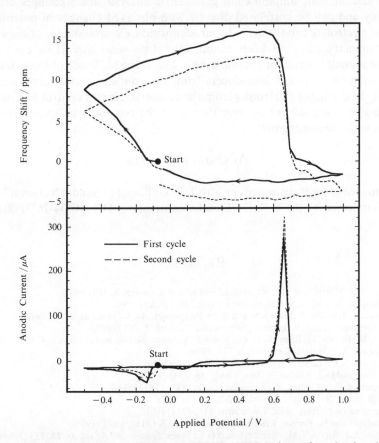

Fig. 7.9 Cyclic voltammetry of a thin Au film on a 158 MHz APM device surface showing changes in the frequency of oscillation (top) and current through the two-electrode cell (bottom) during two potential cycles at a sweep rate of 10 mV/s. The electrolyte is 0.5 M H₂SO₄. Note that oxide/hydroxide formation at +0.66 V applied potential is indicated by an anodic current peak and a simultaneous, rapid frequency decrease of 15 ppm; this corresponds to a mass increase of 5×10¹⁵ oxygen atoms/cm².

comitant with this oxide formation, a sudden decrease in frequency corresponding to the mass of the oxide layer is registered by the APM device. The electrode monitor shows that the oxide gradually dissolves at less positive applied potentials. The 18 ppm frequency excursion corresponds to an increase in surface coverage of 5×10^{15} oxygen atoms/cm². The noise level is on the order of 0.2 ppm, so resolution is a small fraction of a monolayer. Because this experiment used a two-electrode cell, the features of the voltammogram differ markedly from those of the more usual three-electrode voltammogram.[24] The main point, however, is that the monolayer mass changes in adsorption often associated with cyclic voltammetry are readily detected with the APM electrode monitor.

7.5 Conclusions

Real-time monitoring of the mass change accompanying electrode processes provides far more information than simple *ex-situ* gravimetric analysis: mass changes are measured continuously and can be correlated directly with observed changes in potential, current density, and electrolyte conditions. Electrodeposition, electroless deposition, etching, and cyclic voltammetry have all been examined. High sensitivity (1 ng/cm²) allows the detection of a small fraction of a monolayer. Use of the back side of these devices allows complete isolation of the rf transducers from the contacting electrolyte and complete isolation of the oscillator electronics from the potential/current control and measurement circuitry, a significant advantage over the use of the conventional quartz crystal microbalance for such measurements.

ACKNOWLEDGMENTS

We acknowledge helpful discussions with T.R. Guilinger of Sandia National Labs. This work was supported by the U.S. DOE under contract no. DE-ACO4-76DP00789.

REFERENCES

1. A.J. Ricco, S.J. Martin and T.E. Zipperian, *Sensors and Actuators*, **8**, 319 (1985).
2. D.S. Ballantine, Jr. and H. Wohltjen, *Anal. Chem.*, **61**, 704A (1989).
3. E.T. Zellers, N. Hassold, R.M. White and S.M. Rappaport, *Anal. Chem.*, **62**, 1227 (1990).
4. M.S. Nieuwenhuizen and A. Venema, *Sensors and Materials*, **5**, 261 (1989).
5. A. Bryant, M. Poirier, G. Riley, D.L. Lee and J.F. Vetelino, *Sensors and Actuators*, **4**, 105 (1983).
6. A.J. Ricco and S.J. Martin, *Langmuir*, **5**, 273 (1989).
7. A.J. Ricco and S.J. Martin, *Appl. Phys. Lett.*, **50**, 1474, (1989).
8. J.E. Roederer and G.J. Bastiaans, *Anal. Chem.*, **55**, 2333 (1983).
9. S. Bruckenstein and M. Shay, *J. Electroanal. Chem.*, **188**, 131 (1985).
10. H. Masuda and B. Nobuyoshi, *Chemistry Lett.*, 1877 (1987).
11. T. Nomura and O. Hattori, *Anal. Chim. Acta*, **115**, 323 (1980).
12. R. Schumacher and G. Borges, K.K. Kanazawa, *Surface Sci.*, **163**, L621 (1985).
13. S.J. Martin, A.J. Ricco, T.M. Niemczyk and G.C. Fryes, *Sensors and Actuators*, **20**, 253 (1989).
14. C.T. Chuang and R.M. White, in: *1981 Ultrasonic Symp.*, IEEE, New York, 1981, pp. 159–62.
15. B.A. Auld, *Acoustic Waves and Fields in Solids*, Vol. 2, John Wiley & Sons, New York, 1973.
16. A.J. Matheson, in: *Molecular Acoustics*, John Wiley & Sons, New York, pp. 82–83.
17. T.M. Niemczyk, S.J. Martin, G.C. Frye and A.J. Ricco, *J. Appl. Phys.*, **64**, 5002 (1988).
18. F.A. Lowenheim, in: *Electroplating*, McGraw-Hill, New York, 1978, pp. 404–408, 422–423.

19. A.J. Ricco and S.J. Martin, *Proc. Symp. on Electroless Depn. of Metals and Alloys,* Vol. 88–12, The Electro-chemical Society, Pennington, NJ, 1988, pp. 142–153.
20. J. Kisel and M. Schlesinger, *Proc. Symp. on Electroless Depn. of Metals and Alloys,* Vol. 88–12, The Electro-chemical Society, Pennington, NJ, 1988, pp. 100–112.
21. F.A. Cotton, G. Wilkinson, in: *Advanced Inorganic Chemistry,* 4th Edn., John Wiley & Sons, New York, 1980, p. 296.
22. Ref. 18, pp. 257–263.
23. D.P. Shoemaker, C.W. Garland and J.I. Steinfeld, in: *Experiments in Physical Chemistry,* 3rd edition, McGraw-Hill, New York, 1974, p. 677.
24. D.T. Sawyer and J.L. Roberts, Jr., in: *Experimental Electrochemistry for Chemists,* John Wiley & Sons, New York, 1974, p. 67.

8

Photoacoustic Applications to the Solid/Liquid Interface

A. Fujishima*[1] and S. Yoshihara*[2]

*[1] Department of Synthetic Chemistry, Faculty of Engineering, The University of Tokyo, 7-3-1 Hongo, Bunkyo-ku, Tokyo 113, Japan
*[2] Department of Applied Chemistry, Faculty of Engineering, Utsunomiya University, 2753 Ishii-cho, Utsunomiya, Tochigi 321, Japan

8.1 Introduction

There have been several important new developments in the field of *in situ* surface analysis; these include Scanning Tunneling Microscope (STM), Quartz Crystal Microbalance (QCM), among others.   One of these, photoacoustic technique, has been used to characterize the electrode surface immersed in a electrolyte.   In the 1880s Alexander Graham Bell studied the "optoacoustic" effect.[1]   He discovered that by illuminating the sample in a bell jar with chopped sunlight, a sound at the chopping frequency could be heard through a hearing tube.   From then he began to study the absorption of light in solid using this effect.   Later he renamed this effect the "photoacoustic effect" to distinguish it from the "acousto-optic effect."

An early target of this photoacoustic method was gas samples.[2]   The use of this technique for monophase samples is reviewed in the cited literature.[3-4]   Recently photoacoustic devices are being used to study the electrochemical reaction at the interface between the electrode (metal or semiconductor, etc.) and electrolyte.   This article focuses on the application of the photoacoustic method to the solid/liquid interface.

8.2 Principle of Photoacoustic Spectroscopy (PAS)

In photoacoustic spectroscopy, the sample is illuminated by a modulated light source.   The incident light is absorbed and through nonradiative processes heats the sample.   Because the light is chopped, the temperature rise is periodic at the chopping frequency.   It is this periodic temperature rise ($<10^{-3}$ K) at the surface of the sample which causes the generation of elastic waves in the sample.   This elastic wave can be detected by a piezoelectric transducer attached to the back of the sample.   However, this signal is rather small and thus the background noise hides this "photoacoustic" signal.   To overcome this problem, the signal can more easily be detected through a "lock in" technique.   Other PAS methods using microphone as detector are reviewed in the literature.[5-8]   This article focuses on the PAS method using the piezoelectric transducer.

8.3 Experimental Setup for PAS

The experimental setup for PAS is shown in Fig. 8.1.[9]   The light source in this case is an Ar ion laser.   This type of laser has the advantage of emitting a coherent source of high

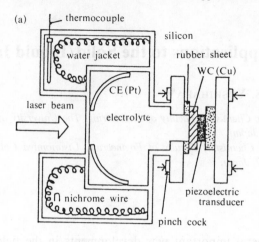

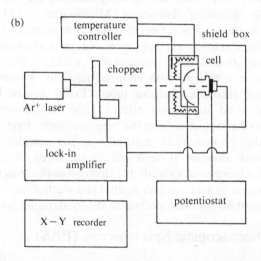

Fig. 8.1 Schematic diagram of the photoacoustic cell (a) and the experimental arrangement (b).

intensity monochromatic light. However if we are performing spectrometric investigation, we need another optical source such as a dye laser. The most common light
source for this spectrometric measurement is a Xe lamp, because of its high intensity of light
as a wide variety of wavelengths. With the aid of a monochromater or interference filter,
we can obtain monochromatic light.

The incident light is chopped by a mechanical chopped for low frequency use (<1 kHz)
or an acousto-optic modulator for high frequency use (>10 kHz). This chopped light
illuminates the electrode surface through an electrolyte. Generated elastic wave can be
detected by a piezoelectric transducer that converts the elastic wave to a voltage
signal. This voltage signal at the chopping frequency is attenuated by a "lock in" amplifier,
so through this process the signal-to-noise ratio can be enlarged.

In most cases, the cell is placed in a shielded box made of steel or lead. In our case we
can also control the cell temperature through a water jacket surrounding the electrolytic

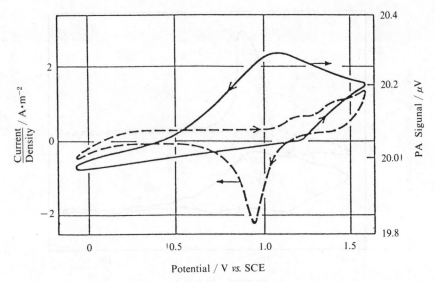

Fig. 8.2 Dependence of photoacoustic signal (−) and current density (−−−) on electrode potential, WE; Au, Electrolyte; 1 kmol/m³ HClO₄, Sweep rate; 40 s/V, Wavelength; 514.5 nm.

cell, as shown in Fig. 8.1.

8.4 New Photoacoustic Applications to the Solid/Liquid Interface

8.4.1 *In situ* Investigation of Metal Electrode Surface

Our earlier work is shown in Fig. 8.2.[10] The working electrode was gold and the electrolyte was HClO₄ aqueous solution. Under anodic polarization, an oxide film is formed on the Au electrode and the corresponding PA signal shows an increase. But continuous cathodic polarization reduces the oxide film so the corresponding photoacoustic signal returns to the initial level.

Next we applied this technique to electroplating, especially copper deposition on gold.[11] The current-potential curve and PA signal for this system are shown in Fig. 8.3. The dotted line represents the current-potential curve. Under cathodic polarization at 0 V *vs.* SCE, copper deposition begins to take place, at the same time the PA signal begins to increase. Under continuous anodic polarization, the deposited copper begins to dissolve at the same time the PA signal begins to decrease, concluding with the PA signal returning to its initial level.

Another early application of PAS to electrode/electrolyte surface is shown in Fig. 8.4.[12] The working electrode was an Fe electrode. Under anodic polarization the current-potential curve shows two anodic peaks at −0.6 V and at −0.2 V, respectively, and the *in situ* PA signal also shows a two-step increase. Under cathodic polarization, the current-potential curve shows one cathodic peak at −0.5 V; the corresponding PA signal shows a two-step decrease at −0.2 V and −1.0 V *vs.* SCE, respectively. This data implies the formation of a passivating double layer structure on iron. Under anodic polarization, the first oxide layer is formed on the iron surface at −0.8 V *vs.* SCE, and the second oxide layer

170

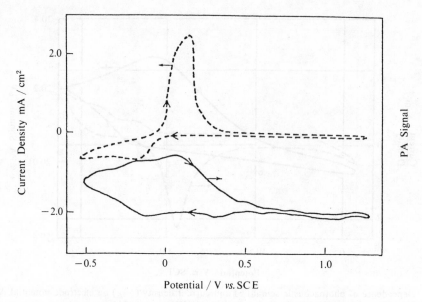

Fig. 8.3 Acoustic signal-potential (—) and current-potential (---) curves of an Au electrode in the presence of Cu^{2+}, 1 mol/dm^3 HClO$_4$, Potential sweep rate 40 s/V, $\lambda = 514$ nm.

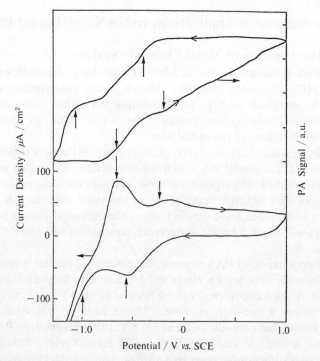

Fig. 8.4 Acoustic signal-potential and current-potential curves of the iron electrode in the 0.1 mol/dm^3 potassium phosphate +0.05 mol/dm^3 sodium borate solution of pH 8.0: Potential scanning rate, 10 mV/s; $\lambda = 514.5$ nm (Ar Ion Laser).

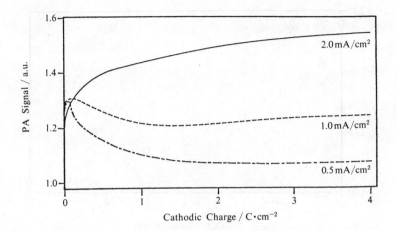

Fig. 8.5 PA signal (amplitude)-cathodic charge curves [gold plating on copper], electrolyte; $3 \times$ dm^3 Na$_3$Au(SO$_3$)$_2$ +
1.4$\times$10^{-1} mol/dm^3 EDTA + 3.3$\times$10^{-1} mol/dm^3 Na$_2$SO$_4$ aq.sol.

is generated on the first oxide layer at -0.4 V.

Relatively new data obtained for gold plating on copper are shown in Fig. 8.5.[13]   The
PA signal amplitude gradually increases progressively with the plating, especially for a
current density of 2 mA/cm^2.   Next we observed the surface plated under a current density
of 2 mA/cm^2 at various cathodic charges (0.5, 1 and 4 C/cm^2) using a scanning electron
microscope (SEM).   The SEM photographs showed that the roughness of the plated
surface gradually increases progressively with increase in plating coverage.   The increase in
surface roughness makes the PA signal amplitude larger.   SEM photographs taken under
different current densities at 4 C/cm^2 showed that as the roughness of the plated surface
increased the steady value of the PA signal amplitude became larger.   In addition, we tried
to estimate the thickness by measuring the phase difference between the reference signal
from a chopper and the PA signal obtained from a piezoelectric transducer attached to the
rear of the electrode.   The results obtained are shown in Fig. 8.6.[13]   The phase delay of the
generated PA signal gradually increased monotonically as plating progressed.   So we
concluded that the phase delay of the generated PA signal increased in accordance with the
thickness of the plated layer.

As a result we can successfully estimate the *in situ* roughness of a plated gold layer from
the PA signal amplitude as well as estimate the *in situ* thickness of the plated layer from the
phase difference of the PA signal.   This method is quite new and useful with regard to
control plating.

We also applied the photoacoustic technique to nickel plating with scanning laser beam
to obtain an *in situ* two-dimensional PA signal image.[14]

Recently we have tried to apply this photoacoustic technique to "Ni-B electroless"
plating.[15]   Fig. 8.7(c) shows the comparison of deposition rate at pH 8 and 10; the slopes
of these straight line represent the deposition rates.   In Fig. 8.7(a) deposition rate is shown
as a function of pH.   These figures suggest that the covering rate at pH 10 is much larger
than that at pH 8.   Fig. 8.7(b) shows the initial PA signal decay.   Considering the above

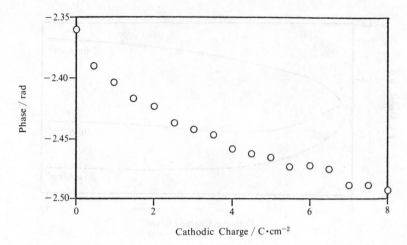

Fig. 8.6 PA signal (phase) − cathodic charge plot, current density 0.5 mA/cm² [gold plating on copper], electrolyte; 3×10^{-2} mol/dm³ Na₃Au(SO₃)₂ + 1.4×10^{-1} mol/dm³ EDTA + 3.3×10^{-1} mol/dm³ Na₂SO₄ aq.sol.

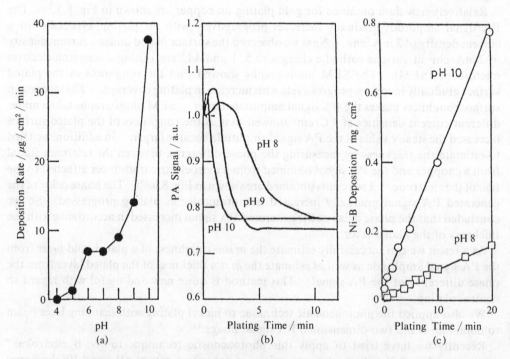

Fig. 8.7 (a) Dependence of pH on the Ni–B deposition rate, (b) Time dependence of PA signal amplitude at pH = 8, 9 and 10 (c). Time dependence of the amount of Ni–B deposition at pH = 8 and 10.

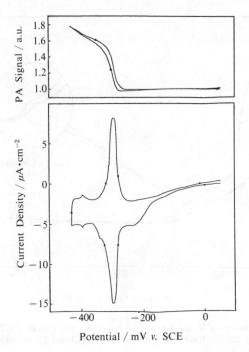

Fig. 8.8 Cyclic voltammogram and PA signal-potential curve for the system Ab/Pb^{2+}; scan rate 1 mV/s, modulation frequency 125 Hz, Electrolyte; 0.1 mol/dm^3 NaClO$_4$+0.01 mol/dm^3 Pb(ClO$_4$)$_2$, +0.005 mol/dm^3 HClO$_4$.

discussions it is thought that this decay curve represents the covering rate of the electroless plating process, that is, the PA signal decay is then differentiated to give covering rate. Other information concerning electroless plating, e.g. decomposition of the plating solution, evolution of H$_2$ gas, can also be detected using PAS.

Our most recent research on PAS is shown in Fig. 8.8.[9] We have succeeded in detecting the underpotential deposition of Pb from Pb(ClO$_4$)$_2$ aqueous solution onto a Ag substrate.[16] The current-potential curve shows clearly the peaks associated with Pb underpotential deposition at about −300 mV (deposition or dissolution) vs. SCE as reported by previous workers. On the other hand, the PA signal-potential curve shows a slight increase or decrease at the potential mentioned above. This increase or decrease is thought to be caused by Pb UPD. We also succeeded in detecting the slow transformation phenomena of Pb adsorbates on Ag electrode surfaces. This phenomenon was detected as a slight fluctuation of the PA signal as shown in Fig. 8.9.[9]

8.4.2 *In situ* Investigation of Semiconductor Electrode Surface

Our earlier work in applying this technique to semiconductor electrodes is shown in Fig. 8.10.[17] The working electrode was a CdS single crystal. Under cathodic polarization (−2.0 V vs. SCE) in 1 M KCl, CdS decomposes as follows

$$CdS + 2e^- \longrightarrow Cd + S^{2-}.$$

Eventually Cd metal is deposited on the surface of the electrode. As shown in Fig. 8.10,

174

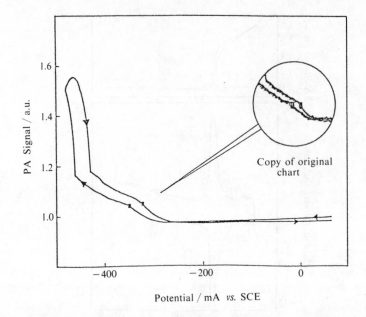

Fig. 8.9 Cyclic voltammogram and PA signal-potential curve for the system Ab/Pb²⁺; scan rate 0.5 mV/s, modulation frequency 125 Hz, Electrolyte; 0.5 mol/dm³ NaClO₄ + 5 × 10⁻³ mol/dm³ Pb(ClO₄)₂, pH 3.55 (controlled by aq. HClO₄).

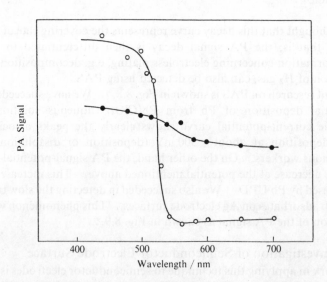

Fig. 8.10 Photoacoustic spectrum for CdS electrode, before (○) and after (●) cathodic polarization (deposition of Cd), Electrolyte; 1 M KCl, Sample thickness; 0.3 mm, Modulation frequency; 30 Hz.

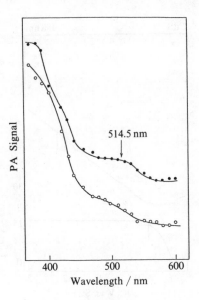

Fig. 8.11 Photoacoustic spectrum for ZnO electrode, before (○) and after (●) deposition of PbO₂, Electrolyte; 0.2 M KNO₃ + 0.01 M Pb²⁺ sol., Anodic charge; 25 mC/cm² (1.5 V/sce).

after cathodic polarization, PA signal amplitude increases in the region of longer wavelengths.   This is due to the absorption of deposited Cd.   Thus through this technique, electrochemical decomposition of semiconductor electrode in the dark can be estimated *in situ*.

Similarly photoelectrochemical reactions can be estimated using PAS.   A typical example is shown in Fig. 8.11.[18]   ZnO was used as the working electrode in electrolyte involving Pb^{2+} ion.   Under photoanodic polarization, the photogenerated hole in ZnO reacts with Pb^{2+} in the electrolyte as follows.

$$Pb^{2+} + 2h^+ + 2ZnO \longrightarrow PbO_2 + 2Zn^{2+}$$

As a result, the darkbrown colored PbO_2 is deposited on the white colored ZnO electrode.   As shown in Fig. 8.11, after photoanodic polarization, the PA signal amplitude increases in the visible region of wavelength.   This example demonstrates the ability of PAS to detect a photoelectrochemical reaction.

A relatively recent example of PAS application to photoelectrochemical reaction is shown in Fig. 8.12.[19]   The working electrodes used were n-TiO₂, n-CdS and n-ZnO.   The equation developed from PTS (Photothermal spectroscopy)[20] can also be applied to PAS, since both methods involve essentially the measurement of heat signals and the theoretical considerations are the same.   For PAS, the equation becomes

$$E(\Delta P/\Delta P_o) = (Q_{sc} + T\Delta S)/(It) + e\eta_q(V - V_{fb})$$

where E is the energy of the incident monochromatic light (eV/photon), I the average absorbed intensity of light (photon/s), t the illumination time (s), Q_{sc} the heat evolved in the semiconductor via recombination and other radiationless processes, $T\Delta S$ the heat evolved in term of an entropy change for the whole cell reaction (Electrochemical Peltier Heat), and

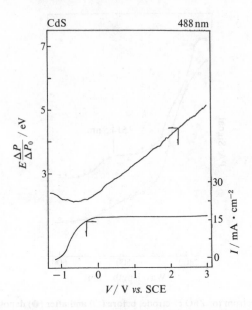

Fig. 8.12 Dependence of I (photocurrent) and $E(\Delta P/\Delta P_0)$ on V (applied potential) n-CdS photoelectrode in 0.2 mol/dm³ Na₂SO₄, 1 mol/dm³ NaSO₃ aq. (chopping frequency 110 Hz).

e the elementary electric charge. η_q is the quantum efficiency of the photooxidation, ΔP and ΔP_0 are the PA signal amplitudes from the PZT at applied potential V and in the open circuit respectively, and V_{fb} is the flatband potential.

Therefore, under constant illumination conditions (i.e., EIt is held constant), a plot of $E(\Delta P/\Delta P_0)$ versus $(V-V_{fb})$ yields the quantum efficiency, η_q, from the slope of the plot.

Figure 8.12 shows the dependence of the photocurrent and the relative change in the PA signal $(\Delta P/\Delta P_0)$ multiplied by the photon energy (E) on the electrode potential (V) for the CdS/Na₂SO₃, Na₂SO₄ aq. system.   The PA signal amplitude is proportional to the electrode potential in the saturated photocurrent region.   Taking the slope equal to the quantum efficiency, we find that the values measured by PAS in this study are in good agreement with those obtained by PTS (see Tables 8.1 and 8.2).[20-23]   It has been reported that the quantum efficiency obtained by PTS coincides with the one obtained by actinometry.[20-23]

We have also applied PAS to obtain *in situ* quantum efficiency for a photoelectrochemical reaction at p-type InP.[24]

Similar applications have been done by other groups.   For example, Rappich *et al.* reported that at an n-TiO₂ (rutile) thin-film electrode made by flame-oxidation of Ti foil, the internal quantum efficiency of the photocurrent, the Peltier heat, and the energy conversion efficiency for photoanodic water oxidation have been determined from the photoacoustic measurement without having to calibrate the intensity of the light source.[25]

TABLE 8.1 Measured Quantum Efficiencies for n-TiO$_2$, n-CdS, and n-ZnO by Photoacoustic Spectroscopy

	Saturation current[†1] mA cm^{-2}	Quantum efficiency η
n-TiO$_2$[†2]	5.44 (6.24)	0.8±0.05 (1.0±0.05)
n-CdS	16.4 (28.0)	0.9±0.01 (1.5±0.01)
n-ZnO	2.72 (5.36)	0.8±0.1 (1.5±0.1)

†1 For TiO$_2$ and ZnO relatively low powder He–Cd laser (325 nm) and for CdS high power Ar-ion laser (488 nm) were used.
†2 TiO$_2$ electrode was prepared by thermal oxidation of Ti metal plate.
     Figures in parentheses indicate the value in the case of current doubling reaction.

TABLE 8.2 Measured Quantum Efficiencies for n-TiO$_2$, n-CdS, and n-ZnO by Photothermal Spectroscopy

	Saturation current mA cm^{-2}	Quantum efficiency η
n-TiO$_2$[†]	1.63 (2.15)	0.6 (0.7)
n-CdS	0.85 (1.43)	1.0 (1.7)
n-ZnO	1.23 (2.25)	0.9 (1.8)

† Single crystal TiO$_2$.
   Figures in parentheses indicate the value in the case of current doubling reaction.

8.5 The Future of Photoacoustic and Photothermal Application Series

Today there are many *in situ* surface analysis methods.   One of the most demonstrative is the Scanning Tunneling Microscope (STM), invented by Binnig and Rohrer.[26]   One of the advantages of STM is its ability to resolve individual atoms.   Another advantage is that it can work in a solution,[27] enabling the investigation of electrode surfaces *in situ*.

The PAS method described in this article uses light as the probe, so the spatial resolution is not comparable to that of STM.   But photoacoustic technique has its particular advantage in that it is simple and suited for automative inspection in the factory.   As shown in Fig. 8.9, even relatively fast transient phenomena can be detected through this method.   At present, STM is not suited for observing such fast surface changes.

Now we are studying UPD using the Mirage method.   This is similar to the PAS method.   The general setup for this method is shown in Fig. 8.13.   A laser beam for activation passes through a liquid electrolyte first and is then absorbed at the solid/liquid interface.   The laser beam probe grazes the surface of the solid and is deflected by the gradient in the liquid.   This method is widely used as a valuable spectroscopic tool for

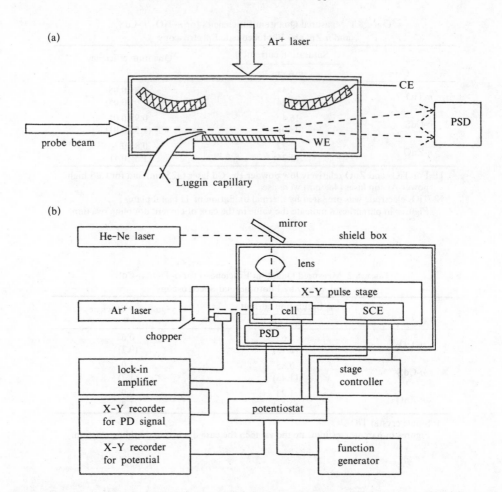

Fig. 8.13 Schematic illustration of the experimental apparatus (a) and arrangement (b) for Mirage method.

examining surfaces and interfaces.[28-38]   It has been reported that this method may provide higher resolution for microchemical analysis than PAS.[39] Using this method, the dynamics of UPD phenomena may be clarified in the future.

REFERENCES

1. A. G. Bell, *Am. J. Sci.*, **20**, 305 (1880).
2. M. L. Viengerov, *Dokl. Akad. Nauk. SSSR*, **19**, 687 (1938).
3. Y.-H. Pao, Ed: *Optoacoustic Spectroscopy and Detection*, Academic Press, Inc., New York, 1977.
4. A. Rosencwaig, *Analytical Chemistry*, **47**, 592A (1975).
5. L.-G. Rosengren, *Appl. Opt.*, **14**, 1960 (1975).
6. R. Gerlach and N. M. Amer, *Appl. Phys.*, **23**, 319 (1980).
7. M. S. Shumate, R. T. Menzies, J. S. Margolis, L.-G. Rosengren and *Appl. Opt.*, **15**, 2480 (1980).
8. A. Rosengwaig, in: *Photoacoustics and Photoacostic Spectroscopy*, p. 137, John Wiley & Sons, New York, 1980.
9. S. Yoshihara, R. Takahashi, M. Okamoto, E. Sato and A. Fujishima, *Electrochim. Acta*, **36**, 1959 (1991).
10. A. Fujishima, H. Masuda and K. Honda, *Bull. Chem. Soc. Jpn*, **53**, 1542 (1980).
11. A. Fujishima, H. Masuda and K. Honda, *Chem. Lett.*, **1979**, 1063.
12. K. Ogura, A. Fujishima, Y. Nagae and K. Honda, *J. Electroanal. Chem.*, **162**, 241 (1984).
13. S. Yoshihara, R. Takahashi, M. Odaka, I. Miura, E. Sato and A. Fujishima, *J. Electroanal. Chem.*, **278**, 409 (1990).
14. S. Yoshihara, E. Sato and A. Fujishima, *Ber. Bunsenges. Phys. Chem.*, **94**, 603 (1990).
15. K. Irie, Y. Takebayashi, I. Miura, S. Yoshihara and E. Sato, *J. Surf. Fin. Soc. Jpn*, **42**, 1044 (1991).
16. S. Yoshihara, R. Takahashi, M. Okamoto and E. Sato, *J. Surf. Fin. Soc. Jpn*, **42**, 1044 (1991).
17. H. Masuda, A. Fujishima and K. Honda, *Chem. Lett.*, **1980**, 1153.
18. H. Masuda, S. Morishita, A. Fujishima and K. Honda, *J. Electroanal. Chem.*, **121**, 363 (1981).
19. S. Yoshihara, A. Aruchamy and A. Fujishima, *Bull. Chem. Soc. Jpn*, **61**, 1017 (1988).
20. A. Fujishima, Y. Maeda, G. H. Brilmyer and A. J. Bard, *J. Electrochem. Soc.*, **127**, 840 (1980).
21. Y. Maeda, A. Fujishima and K. Honda, *Chem. Lett.*, **1980**, 271.
22. A. Fujishima, Y. Maeda and K. Honda, *Bull. Chem. Soc. Jpn*, **53**, 2735 (1980).
23. Y. Maeda, A. Fujishima and K. Honda, *J. Electrochem. Soc.*, **128**, 1731 (1981).
24. S. Yoshihara and A. Fujishima, *Mat. Res. Bull.*, **23**, 759 (1988).
25. J. Rappich and J. K. Dohrmann, *Ber. Bunsenges. Phys. Chem.*, **92**, 1342 (1988).
26. G. Binning and H. Rohrer, *IBM J. Res. Develop.*, **30**, 355 (1986).
27. J. Scneir, R. Sonnenfeld, P. K. Hansma and J. Tersoff, *Phy. Rev B*, **34**, 4979 (1986).
28. B. S. H. Royce, F. Sanchez-Sinencio, R. Goldstein, R. Muratore, R. Williams and W. M. Yim, *J. Electrochem. Soc.*, **129**, 2393 (1982).
29. W. B. Jackson, N. M. Amer, A. C. Boccara and D. Fournier, *Applied Optics*, **20**, 1333 (1981).
30. T. Hata, H. Hatsuda, M. Kawakami and Y. Sato, *Jpn. J. Appl. Phys.*, **24**, Suppl. 24-1, 204 (1985).
31. K. Yatabe, H. Ohta, M. Yamaguchi and K. Morigaki, *Philosophical Magazine B*, **60**, 73 (1989).
32. L. Chahed, A. Gheorghiv, M. L. Theye, I. Ardelean, C. Senemaud and C. Godet, *J. Non-Crystalline Solid*, **114**, 471 (1989).
33. J. Pawliszyn, M. F. Weber, M. J. Dignam, A. Mandelis, R. D. Venter and S-M. Park, *Anal. Chem.*, **58**, 236 (1986).
34. J. Pawliszyn, M. F. Weber, M. J. Dignam, A. Mandelis, R. D. Venter and S-M. Park, *ibid*, **58**, 236 (1986).
35. J. Pawliszyn, *ibid*, **58**, 243 (1986).
36. S. Kalem, *Phys. Rev. B*, **37**, 8827 (1988).
37. P. G. Varlashkin and M. J. D. Low, *Applied Spectroscopy*, **40**, 1170 (1986).
38. M. J. Smith and R. A. Palmer, *ibid*, **41**, 1106 (1987).
39. N. Terasaki and M. Tanaka, *Bunko Kenkyu*, **32**, 117 (1983) (in Japanese).

9

In-situ Scanning Tunneling Microscopy of Electrode/Solution Interfaces

Kingo ITAYA

Department of Engineering Science, Faculty of Engineering, Tohoku University, Sendai 980, Japan

9.1 Introduction

Several recent investigations have demonstrated scanning tunneling microscopy/microscope (STM) to be a powerful new technique for electrode surface characterization with atomic resolution *in situ* at surfaces under potentiostatic control.[1,2] It is already well estabished in surface physics that the technique is unique in its ability to determine both the structural and the local electronic properties of surfaces of metals and semiconductors in ultra-high vacuum (UHV).[3,4]

Understanding the electrochemical reactivity of noble metals such as platinum (Pt) and gold (Au) is very important in modern electrochemistry.[5-9] Although many structure sensitive methods on an atomic scale such as low-energy-electron diffraction (LEED) have been used to characterize electrochemically treated electrodes under UHV conditions,[5-9] it is always necessary to transfer the electrode from the electrolyte solution to the UHV environment.   This *ex-situ* experiment may involve structural surface changes during the transfer of the electrode.

Semiconductor/liquid interfaces are also interesting and important systems for characterization in the field of photoelectrochemistry.[10,11] Althouh tremendous efforts have been made during the last twenty years to obtain a better understanding of photoelectrochemical reactions, there is not much information available about structures and electric properties of semiconductor electrodes with atomic resolution in electrochemical environments.

Since Hansma and co-workers first demonstrated that STM can operate in electrolyte solutions[12], much progress has been made in exploring the possibilities of STM for characterizing the solid/liquid interface with atomic resolution.   The objective of this chapter is to briefly highlight some of the recent progress from this laboratory and others on *in-situ* STM with atomic resolution.   It is not possible to review all of the published accounts of *in-situ* STM results in this format.   The reader is referred to more comprehensive reviews published elsewhere.[1,2]

9.2 *In-situ* Electrochemical STM

The first STM used for the solid/liquid interface was based on a two-electrode configuration, where a tunneling voltage was simply applied between the tip and the substrate.[12] In other words, the potentials of both the substrate and the tip were not

controlled with respect to a reference electrode.   In most electrochemical measurements
with a two-electrode cell, the working electrode (substrate) must be coupled with a
reversible reference electrode to control the true potential.   It is almost impossible to
control the electrode potentials of the tip and substrate for STM measurements with a two-
electrode configuration.   However, a new system called the electrochemical STM (ESTM)
has been introduced by the present author.[13]   In this system with a four-electrode
configuration, the electrode potentials of the substrate and the tip can be independently
controlled relative to a reference electrode.   The apparatus offers new possibilities for
complete *in-situ* observation of electrochemical reactions under potential control.   The
tunneling and faradaic currents should be expected to flow between the substrate and the
tip, and the substrate and the counter electrode, respectively.   It is desirable for STM
observation in electrolyte solutions that the tip potential be kept at certain regions to
minimize the faradaic processes at the tip/solution interface.   It has been found that the tip
can be continuously scanned over the surface even while electrochemical reactions are
occurring at the working electrode, although a screening effect of the tip for the diffusion of
reactants must be taken into account.   Similar apparatus have been described by several
groups.[14-16]

9.3   Metal Electrodes

Electrochemical reactivities of noble metals such as platinum (Pt), gold (Au), rhodium
(Rh), palladium (Pd), and others have long been discussed by many investigators, using
single crystals with different orientations as well as polycrystals.   Although classical
electrochemical methods such as cyclic voltammetry have provided a remarkable sensitivity
to characterize submonolayer processes occurring at electrode/solution interfaces, until
recently there were few *in-situ* methods available to determine the structure of electrode
surfaces on the atomic scale.   Many spectroscopic techniques such as infrared
adsorption,[17,18] second harmonic generation,[19] and x-ray spectroscopies[20,21] have recently
been applied to solid/liquid interfaces to obtain structural information.   Nevertheless,
ESTM seems to be a direct method for the surface characterization of metal electrodes on
an atomic scale in electrolyte solutions, and the information obtained greatly complements
that obtained from the purely conventional surface spectroscopies.

Several groups have attempted to establish this technique as an electrochemical tool
having atomic resolution, since the *in-situ* imaging capability was demonstrated by Hansma
et al., as described above.   Wiechers *et al.* first demonstrated that single atomic steps of
Au(111) can be imaged in an electrolyte solution using an ESTM.[22]   Since the atomic layer
resolution of metals was achieved on Au(111), various metal electrodes including thin films
of Au,[23-26] Pt,[27] Rh,[28] Pd,[28] and Ag[29,30] have been investigated with atomic layer
resolution.   It is important to realize that atomically flat and clean surfaces must be
prepared in order to obtain atomic information about the surface structure with
STM.   Achieving atomic resolution is very difficult or almost impossible on rough
surfaces.

It is known that atomically flat surfaces of metals can be prepared by two methods.   One
is essentially based on epitaxial growth in vacuum.   Au(111) films have been prepared on
substrates such as cleaved mica and examined by STM.[23,31]   However, a critical question
which must be addressed is whether the surface can be transferred from the vacuum to the

electrolyte solution without chemical change or contamination.   Holland-Moritz *et al.* observed an unstable behavior in the motion of atomic steps of Au(111) films on mica due to contamination during the preparation process.[31]

The second method is to use bulk single crystals.[22,24-30]   Great efforts have been made in the last decade to characterize the role of surface structure in electrocatalysis using single crystal electrodes.[5-9]   The hydrogen adsorption-desorption reaction has been intensively examined on single crystal Pt electrodes.   Clavilier *et al.* have demonstrated the so-called flame annealing-quenching technique to prepare bulk single crystal-electrodes.[32]   In this method, the Pt electrode was annealed in a flame, then quickly brought into contact with pure water.   It is well-known that the hydrogen adsorption-desorption peaks observed on the Pt surfaces prepared by Clavilier's method can be explained by assuming atomically controlled step-terrace structures.[33-35]   Clavilier's work and that of Motoo and Furuya encouraged us to apply the above method in our STM investigations.   We have applied this technique exclusively to prepare atomically flat and clean surfaces of Au(111) and Au(100), Pt(111), Rh(111), and Pd(111), as described in our previous reports.[24,26-28,46,48,49]

Figure 9.1 shows typical STM images of Pt(111) and Pt(100) obtained in an aqueous sulfuric acid solution.[27,28]   STM images of Au(111) and Au(100) in a perchloric acid solution are shown in Fig. 9.2   In the images of the Au(111) surface, monatomic step heights of *ca.*2.4 Å are observed and the orientations of the steps differ by 60° as expected for a surface with the three-fold symmetry of the Au(111) surface.   Monatomic step lines observed on Au(100) were not straight as shown in Fig. 9.2(b).   In addition to a monatomic step lying in a long twisting curve, many islands of monatomic height (*ca.* 2.0 Å) in the shape of a rounded square are observed on the Au(100) surface.   Similar islands can also be seen on Pt(100), as shown in Fig. 9.1(b).   The terraces observed on these surfaces seem to be absolutely flat.   Observation of the absolutely flat terraces and the orientation of the steps suggest that the surfaces of Pt and Au have (1×1) structures in the present conditions.

9.4   Structural Changes

Reconstruction of surfaces is well known in UHV.[36]   Similar reconstructions have also long been discussed on Au electrodes in aqueous solutions.[5,6,37]   Very recently, surface reconstructions have been revealed by *in-situ* STM studies.[38-40]   For example, the Au(110)-(1×1) structure is transformed to a (1×2) structure in the double layer region by lowering the electrode potential to −0.3 V *vs.* SCE in a HClO$_4$ solution.[40]   It is very important to compare the structures of reconstructed surfaces in UHV and in electrochemical interfaces to fully understand the electronic properties of the electrode surface.

The electrochemical oxidation-reduction reactions of noble metals are also important when considering structural changes at electrode surfaces.   Island formation has been described for an atomically flat Pt(111) surface after applying potential cycles.[27,28]   For Au electrodes, Trevor *et al.* reported roughening, annealing, and dissolution accompanying the oxidation-reduction of the Au(111) surface.[23]   A large protruding feature in the shape of steps and the disappearance of islands have been reported on an Au(100) surface even in potential cycles limited to the double layer region.[25]   Unexpected roughening has also been reported on Au(111) films on mica in aqueous solutions.[41]   However, we did not see

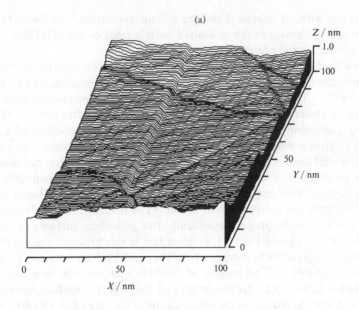

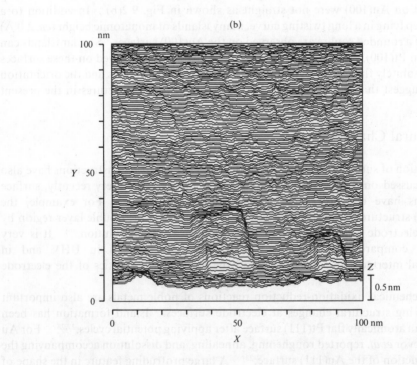

Fig. 9.1 STM images of Pt(111) (a) and Pt(100) (b) surfaces obtained in 0.05 M H_2SO_4.[27]

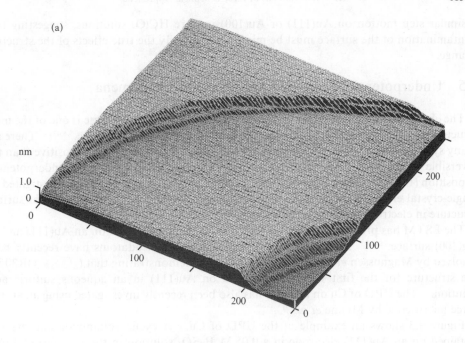

(a)

nm

1.0
0

(b)

nm

0.5
0

Fig. 9.2 STM images of Au(111) (a) and Au(100) (b) surfaces obtained in 0.1 M HClO$_4$.[24,26]

a similar step motion on Au(111) or Au(100) in pure HClO₄ solutions, suggesting that contamination of the surface must be minimized to study the true effects of the structure change.

9.5   Underpotential Deposition and Related Phenomena

The electrochemical deposition of metals on a foreign metal substrate is one of the most structure-sensitive reactions, occurring at the electrode/solution interface.[5,6,42]   There are many systems where the first monolayer is deposited at potentials more positive than the reversible Nernst potential of the respective bulk phase, the so-called underpotential deposition (UPD).   The UPD of metals as well as hydrogen has long been investigated on single-crystal electrodes with different orientations in order to reveal the role of surface structure in electrochemical reactions.

The ESTM has previously been applied to study the UPD of Pb on an Au(111) and an Ag(100) surface.[29,43]   Atomic images of individual copper adatoms have recently been resolved by Magnussen et al.,[44,45] and our group,[46] demonstrating that $(\sqrt{3}\times\sqrt{3})R30°$ is the structure for the first UPD layer of Cu on Au(111) in an aqueous sulfuric acid solution.   The UPD of Cu on Au(111) has also been recently investigated using an atomic force microscope by Manne et al.[47]

Figure 9.3 shows an example of the UPD of Cu.   A cyclic voltammogram (cv) was obtained on an Au(111) electrode in a 0.05 M H₂SO₄ solution in the present of 1 mM

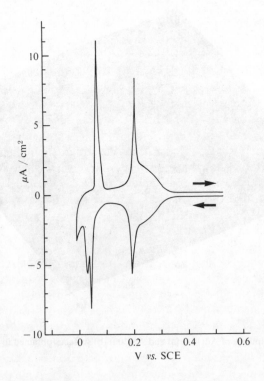

Fig. 9.3 Cyclic voltammogram for a Au(111) electrode in a 0.05 M H₂SO₄+1 mM CuSO₄ solution.[46]

$CuSO_4$.[46]   It is clear that two different waves for UPD of Cu can be seen at potentials between 0.35 V and 0 V *vs.* SCE before starting the bulk deposition.   Fig. 9.4(a) shows our observation of atomic corrugation of the Au(111) aquired at 0.4 V *vs.* SCE, where no Cu UPD has occurred.   This atomic resolution image indicates that the Au(111) surface has a (1×1) structure in this condition.   The electrode potential was then scanned in the cathodic direction and was held at 0.15 V between two UPD peaks.   A very clear STM image of the initial Cu deposition was observed with corrugation heights of *ca.* 0.5–0.7 Å as shown in Fig. 9.4(b).   The distance of the nearest neighbors of Cu atoms is *ca.* 4.8 Å.   The atomic rows of Cu are at an angle of 30° relative to the underlying Au lattice.   These observations make it possible to draw the conclusion that the structure of the first Cu adlayer is $(\sqrt{3} \times \sqrt{3})R30°$.   However, interesting phase boundaries are often observed in images acquired on larger scan areas as shown in Fig. 9.5.[46]   It can be seen in this image that there are at least two different types of phase boundary as indicated by the white arrows. Fig. 9.6 depicts the boundary marked by arrow (b) in Fig. 9.5.   In this case, two $(\sqrt{3} \times \sqrt{3})R30°$ domains are simply shifted by a half position, suggesting that the adsorption of Cu occurs almost equally on three-fold hollow sites on Au(111).   Note that there are two non-equivalent three-fold hollow sites on the (111) surface of fcc-metals.   Therefore, two domains observed in Fig. 9.5 seem to have the fcc-type stacking (ABC) and the hcp-type stacking (ABA), respectively.

We have found the exact same structure, $(\sqrt{3} \times \sqrt{3})R30°$, for the UPD of Cu on Pt(111)[48] and for the UPD of Ag on Au(111)[49] in aqueous sulfuric acid solutions.   It is reasonable to assume that the appearance of the widely spaced structure of $(\sqrt{3} \times \sqrt{3})R30°$ is due to the presence of anions such as SO_4^{2-} and HSO_4^- on the surface.   Recent *in-situ* infrared spectroscopic studies have clearly shown that these anions are strongly adsorbed on Pt surfaces.[17,18]   The adsorbed anions are thought to stabilize the $(\sqrt{3} \times \sqrt{3})R30°$ structure on the (111) surfaces.   Elucidating the role of the coadsorbed anions is important in understanding the UPD processes.

Chemisorbed molecular species on metal electrodes are also important for electrochemistry.[9]   Although STM studies have been reported for iodine on Pt(111)[50,51] and Au(111),[52] benzene on Rh(111),[53] sulfur on Re(001)[54] and liquid crystal monolayers on graphite,[55] not many reports demonstrate the structures of chemisorbed species with atomic resolution at the solid/liquid interface.   Nevertheless, recent STM images of CO adlayers on Rh(111)[56] and Pt(100)[57] acquired at the electrochemical interface will stimulate further investigations to resolve chemisorbed molecular species on electrode surfaces.

9.6 Semiconductor Electrodes

The *in-situ* STM technique can be used as an appraisal method to characterize the surface structure of semiconductor electrodes in solutions as well.   Surfaces of GaAs have been imaged in a KOH solution.[58]   A photoelectrochemical etching of GaAs has been demonstrated using an STM.[59]   However, we have shown that the ESTM can more importantly be applied for the determination of electronic properties of semiconductor/ solution interface.[60–62]

Figure 9.7(a) shows a typical current-potential curve of a TiO_2 electrode observed under chopped illumination in a 0.1 M KCl solution (pH=4.0).[60]   A photoanodic current begins to flow at *ca.*−0.2 V *vs.* Ag/AgCl.   Mott-Schottky plots showed straight lines with an

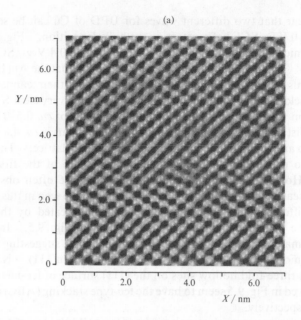

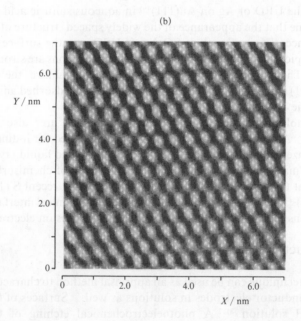

Fig. 9.4 STM images obtained at 0.4 V (a) and 0.15 V (b).[46]

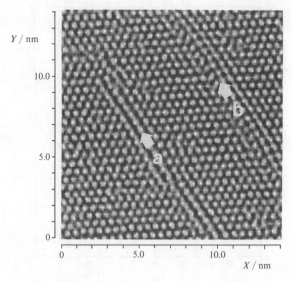

Fig. 9.5 STM image of a 14×14 nm² area of a copper adlayer.[46)]

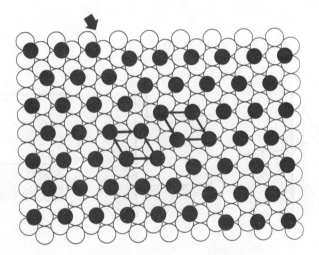

Fig. 9.6 Model structure of the copper adlayer and boundary.[46)]

intercept of −0.2 V indicating that the flat band potential is located near this value.

A well-known interfacial energetics diagram for an n-type semiconductor/liquid interface is shown in Fig. 9.8 to understand the electron tunneling processes at the n-type semiconductor/liquid/metal junction.[10,11,60–62)]   Fig. 9.8(a) shows a situation where the electrode potential of the semiconductor is positive with respect to the flat band potential (E_{FB}).   In this situation, a space charged layer is formed near the surface, but diminished at the flat band condition where the electrode potential is equal to E_{FB}, as shown in

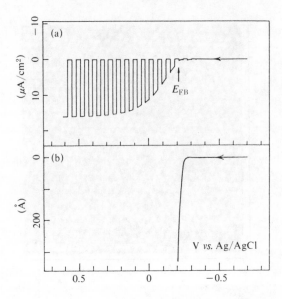

Fig. 9.7 Current-potential curve of TiO₂ (a) and displacement of z-piezoelectric tube (b).[60]

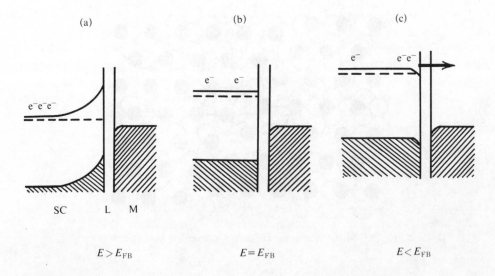

Fig. 9.8 Interface energetics for n-type semiconductor/liquid/metal junction.[60,61]

Fig. 9.8(b).   The surface is degenerated by applying further negative potentials and is expected to behave as a metal electrode, as shown in Fig. 9.8(c).   On the basis of the energetics of the n-type semiconductor/liquid interface, the electrode potential of the tip electrode is assumed to be more positive than the flat band potential, as indicated in

Fig. 9.8.   Under this situation, the electron tunneling from the conduction band in the semiconductor to the vacant levels in the tip electrode is thought to be possible only when the electrode potential of the semiconductor is more negative than E_{FB} because of a blockade of the electron tunneling due to the space charge layer.

In order to examine the above criterion, the voltage applied to the z-piezoelectric tube of the tip scanner was recorded changing the electrode potential of the semiconductor. Fig. 9.7(b) shows dependence of the voltage on the electrode potential.[60]   Very stable tunneling currents were observed as long as the electrode potential was set at negative values with respect to the E_{FB}.   Eventually, the change in the z-voltage is quite small in this potential region.   However, the electron tunneling is totally inhibited when the electrode potential is more positive than E_{FB}, resulting in the tip being plunged into the semiconductor, as expected from Fig. 9.7(a).   It is obvious that the electron tunneling probability from the conduction band in the semiconductor is sharply decreased by the formation of the space charge layer.

These results strongly suggest that ESTM has a remarkable capability to examine the electric properties of the semiconductor/liquid interface as well as the surface topography of semiconductors in solutions.   ESTM has been applied to n-ZnO,[61] GaAs,[63] Ge,[64] Si,[62,65,66] and other semiconductors.[67]   Finally, it is noteworthly that the chemical wet etching of semiconductors, particularly Si, is becoming more important for LSI technology.   Atomic resolution has recently been achieved in UHV on a Si(111) surface prepared by a chemical etching.[68]   We have recently resolved the first atomic STM image of the Si(111)(1×1) surface treated with a NH_4F solution in an aqueous sulfuric acid solution.[69]   An atomic image has also been acquired in air on a Si(111) surface using AFM.[70]   The above success ensures that the wet chemical etching of Si will be revealed at the atomic level in the near future.

Finally, it should be noted that carbon electrodes are also very important not only for an academic viewpoint but also with regard to practical applications, including fuel cells.   Although an anodic oxidation of a graphite surface has been investigated with an *in-situ* STM,[71] further work is needed to elucidate the reactivities of carbon atoms on graphite with atomic resolution.

Acknowledgment

The author wishes to thank Prof. N.Furuya at Yamanashi University, Dr. K.Sashikata and all collaborators for carrying out experiments at our laboratory.

References

1. R. Sonnenfeld, J. Schneir and P. K. Hansma, in: *Modern Aspects of Electrochemistry* (R. E. White, J. O'M. Bockris and B. E. Conway, eds.), Vol. 21, Plenum Press, New York, 1990, pp. 1–28.
2. T. R. I. Cataldi, I. G. Blackham, G. Andrew, D. Briggs, J. B. Pethica and H. A. O. Hill, *J. Electroanal. Chem.*, **290**, 1 (1990).
3. Proceedings of the 5th International Conference on STM, *J. Vac. Sci. Technol.*, **B9**, 401 (1991).
4. Proceedings of the 6th International Conference on STM, *Ultramicroscopy* Vol. 42–44 (1992).
5. D. M. Kolb, in: *Advances in Electrochemistry and Electrochemical Engineering* (H. Gerischer and C. W. Tobias, eds.), Vol. 11, John Wiley and Sons, New York, 1978, pp. 125–271.

6. D. M. Kolb, *Ber. Bunsengesn. Phys. Chem.,* **92**, 1175 (1988).
7. A. Hamelin, in: *Modern Aspects of Electrochemistry* (B. E. Conway, R. E. White and J. O'M.Bockris, eds.), Vol. 16, Plenum Press, New York, 1985, pp. 1–101.
8. P. N. Ross and F. T. Wagner, in: *Advances in Electrochemistry and Electrochemical Engineering* (H. Gerischer and C. W. Tobias, eds.), Vol. 13, John Wiley and Sons, New York, 1984, pp. 69-112.
9. A. T. Hubbard, *Langmuir,* **6**, 97 (1990).
10. H. Gerischer, *Electrochemica Acta,* **35**, 1677 (1990).
11. R. Memming, in: *Electroanalytical Chemistry* (A. J. Bard, eds.), Vol. 11, Marcel Dekker, New York, 1979, pp. 1–84.
12. R. Sonnenfeld and P. K. Hansma, *Science,* **232**, 211 (1986).
13. K. Itaya and E. Tomita, *Surf. Sci.,* **201**, L507 (1988).
14. P. Lustenberger, H. Rohrer, R. Christph and H. Siegenthaler, *J. Electroanal. Chem.,* **243**, 225 (1988).
15. T. Twomey, J. Wiechers, D. M. Kolb and R. J. Behm, *J. Microsc.,* **152**, 537 (1988).
16. K. Uosaki and H. Kita, *J. Electroanal. Chem,* **259**, 301 (1989).
17. N. Furuya, S. Motoo and K. Kunimatsu, *J. Electroanal. Chem.,* **239**, 347 (1988).
18. P. W. Faguy, N. Markovic, R. R. Adzic, C. A. Fierro and E. B. Yeager, *J. Electroanal. Chem.,* **289**, 245 (1990).
19. M. L. Lynch, B. J. Barner and R. M. Corn, *J. Electroanal. Chem.,* **300**, 447 (1991).
20. G. Tourillon, D. Guay and A. Tadjeddine, *J. Electroanal. Chem.,* **289**, 263 (1990).
21. G. Materlik, M. Schmäh, J. Zegenhagen and W. Uelhoff, *Ber. Bunsenges. Phys. Chem.,* **91**, 292 (1987).
22. J. Wiechers, T. Twomey, D. M. Kolb and R. J. Behm, *J. Electroanal. Chem.,* **248**, 451 (1988).
23. D. J. Trevor, C. E. D. Chidsey and D. N. Loiacono, *Phys. Rev. Lett.,* **62**, 929 (1989).
24. H. Honbo, S. Sugawara and K. Itaya, *Anal. Chem.,* **62**, 2424 (1990).
25. R. J. Nichols, O. M. Magnussen, J. Hotlos, T. Twomey, R. J. Behm and D. M. Kolb, *J. Electroanal. Chem.,* **290**, 21 (1990).
26. H. Honbo and K. Itaya, *J. Chim. Phys.,* **88**, 1477 (1991).
27. K. Itaya, S. Sugawara, K. Sashikata and N. Furuya, *J. Vac. Sci. Technol.,* **A8**, 515 (1990).
28. K. Sashikata, N. Furuya and K. Itaya, *J. Vac. Sci. Technol.,* **B9**, 457 (1991).
29. R. Christoph, H. Siegenthaler, H. Rohrer and H. Wiese, *Electrochimica Acta,* **34**, 1011 (1989).
30. M. Höpfner, W. Obretenov, K. Jüttnev, W. J. Lorenz, G. Staikov, V. Bostanov and E. Budevski, *Surf. Sci.,* **248**, 225 (1991).
31. E. Holland-Moritz, J. Gordon II, G. Borges and R. Sonnenfeld, *Langmuir,* **7**, 301 (1991).
32. J. Clavilier, *J. Electroanal. Chem.,* **107**, 211 (1980).
33. J. Clavilier, K. El Achi and A. Rodes, *Chem. Phys.,* **141**, 1, (1990).
34. A. Rodes, K. El Achi, M. A. Zamakhchari and J. Clavilier, *J. Electroanal. Chem.,* **284**, 245 (1990).
35. S. Motoo and N. Furuya, *Ber. Bunsenges. Phys. Chem.,* **91**, 457 (1987).
36. H. Ohtani, C. -T. Kao, M. A. Van Hove and G. A. Somorjai, *Prog. Surf. Sci.,* **23**, 155 (1986).
37. D. M. Kolb and J. Schneider, *Electrochimica Acta,* **31**, 929 (1986).
38. X. Gao, A. Hamelin and M. J. Weaver, *J. Chem. Phys.,* **95**, 6993 (1991).
39. X. Gao, A. Hamelin and M. J. Weaver, *Phys. Rev. Lett.,* **67**, 618 (1991).
40. X. Gao, A. Hamelin and M. J. Weaver, *Phys. Rev. B,* **44**, 10983 (1991).
41. E. Holland-Moritz, J. Gordon 2, K. Kanazawa and R. Sonnenfeld, *Langmuir,* **7**, 1981 (1991).
42. B. E. Conway, *Prog. Surf. Sci.,* **16**, 1 (1984).
43. M. P. Green, K. J. Hanson, R. Carr and I. Lindau, *J. Electrochem. Soc.,* **137**, 3493 (1990).
44. O. M. Magnussen, J. Hotlos, R. J. Nichols, D. M. Kolb and R. J. Behm, *Phys. Rev. Lett.,* **64**, 2929 (1990).
45. O. M. Magnussen, J. Hotlos, G. Beitel, D. M. Kolb and R. J. Behm, *J. Vac. Sci. Technol.,* **B9**, 969 (1991).
46. T. Hachiya, H. Honbo and K. Itaya, *J. Electroanal. Chem.,* **315**, 275 (1991).
47. S. Manne, P. K. Hansma, J. Massie, V. B. Elings and A. A. Gewirth, *Science,* **251**, 183 (1991).
48. K. Sashikata, N. Furuya and K. Itaya, *J. Electroanal. Chem.,* **316**, 361 (1991).
49. T. Hachiya and K. Itaya, *Ultramicroscopy,* **42–44**, 445 (1992).
50. B. C. Schardt, S. -L. Yau and F. Rinaldi, *Science,* **243**, 1050 (1989).
51. S.- C. Chang, S. -L. Yau, B. C. Schardt and M. J. Weaver, *J. Phys. Chem.,* **95**, 4787 (1991).
52. R. L. McCarley and A. J. Bard, *J. Phys. Chem.,* **95**, 9618 (1991).
53. H. Ohtani, R. J. Wilson, S. Chiang and C. M. Mate, *Phys. Rev. Lett.,* **60**, 2398 (1988).
54. D. F. Ogletree, C. Ocal, B. Marchon, G. A. Somorjai, M. Salmeron, T. Beebe and W. Wiekhaus, *J. Vac. Sci. Technol.,* **A8**, 297 (1990).
55. D. P. E. Smith, H.Hörber, Ch. Gerber and G. Binnig, *Science,* **245**, 43 (1989).
56. S.-L. Yau, X. Gao, S.-C. Chang, B. C. Schardt and M. J. Weaver, *J. Am. Chem. Soc.,* **113**, 6049 (1991).
57. C. M. Vitus, S.-C. Chang, B. C. Schardt and M. J. Weaver, *J. Phys. Chem.,* **95**, 7559 (1991).
58. R. Sonnenfeld, J. Schneir, B. Drake, P. K. Hansma and D. E. Aspnes, *Appl. Phys. Lett.,* **50**, 1742 (1987).
59. C. W. Lin, F.-R. F. Fan and A. J. Bard, *J. Electrochem. Soc.,* **134**, 1038 (1987).
60. K. Itaya and E. Tomita, *Chem Lett.,* **1989**, 285.

61. K. Itaya and E. Tomita, *Surf. Sci.,* **219**, L515 (1989).
62. E. Tomita, N. Matsuda and K. Itaya, *J. Vac. Sci. Technol.,* **A8**, 534 (1990).
63. P. Carlsson, B. Holmstrom, H. Kita and K. Uosaki, *J. Electroanal. Chem.,* **283**, 425 (1990).
64. T. Thundat, L. A. Nagahara and S. M. Lindsay, *J. Vac. Sci. Technol.,* **A8**, 539 (1990).
65. M. Szklarczyk, A. Gonzalez-Martin, O. Velev and J. O'M. Bockris, *Surf. Sci.,* **237**, 305 (1990).
66. R. Houbertz, U. Memment and R. J. Behm, *Appl. Phys. Lett.,* **58**, 1027 (1991).
67. K. Hinokuma, K. Sakamaki and A. Fujishima, *Bull. Chem. Soc. Jpn.,* **63**, 2713 (1990).
68. G. S. Higashi, R. S. Becker, Y. J. Chabal and A. J. Becker, *Appl. Phys. Lett.,* **58**, 1656 (1991).
69. K. Itaya, R. Sugawara, Y. Morita and H. Tokumoto, *Appl. Phys. Lett.,* **60**, 2534 (1992).
70. Y. Kim and C. M. Lieber, *J. Am. Chem. Soc.,* **113**, 2333 (1991).
71. A. A. Gewirth and A. J. Bard, *J. Phys. Chem.,* **92**, 5563 (1988).

10

Microtopography of Electrochemical Surface Layers

Rolf H. Muller

Materials Sciences Division, Lawrence Berkeley Laboratory and Department of Chemical Engineering, University of California, Berkeley, CA 94720, U.S.A.

10.1 Introduction

The microtopography of surfaces is of interest for purposes of visual appearance and the control of optical properties needed in electro-optic applications.   In addition, the topography of materials is often indicative of the underlying microstructure which, in turn, is related to many of its physical and chemical properties.   For metal films, these properties include conductivity, porosity, reactivity, corrosion and wear resistance.   The development of microtopography during the formation of surface layers also allows one to infer mechanisms of the electrochemical formation of solid phases (electrosolidification or electrocrystallization processes).   Of particular interest here are the control of nucleation and growth of anodic and cathodic layers.

Since very thin layers, encountered in the early stages of film formation, are often not stable outside the electrolytic environment, the use of *in situ* experimental techniques is important for studies on the formation of electrochemical surface layers.   Some of the principal techniques used are described briefly in the following section.

10.2 Experimental Techniques

10.2.1 Spectroscopic Ellipsometry

In ellipsometry, changes in the state of polarization, caused by the reflection of polarized light on the specimen surface, are measured.   These measurements can be sensitive to changes in surface topography on the atomic scale, as they are to the formation of surface layers.   In spectroscopic ellipsometry, measurements are conducted over a broad spectral range, thus greatly enhancing the information available for the interpretation of measurements in terms of physical quantities.   The principles of ellipsometry, instrumentation and applications have been reviewed previously.[1,2]

The ellipsometer used in this work is illustrated in Fig. 10.1.[3]   It has been upgraded in different ways since it was originally described.[4]   It is of the compensating type that provides the greatest accuracy.   The light beam propagates from the lower left to the upper right of the figure.   It emanates from a Xe high-pressure white source.   A narrow spectral band is selected by a rotating, continuously variable interference filter.   A full spectral scan over the visible can be obtained in three sec.   Telescopes are used to collimate and collect the beam.   Faraday cells are located in the optical path before and after reflection on the

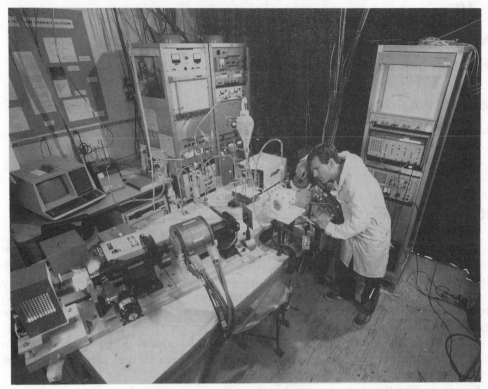

Fig. 10.1 Self-compensating spectroscopic ellipsometer with white light source, rotating continuously variable
         interference filter, collimator with polarizer, first Faraday cell, achromatic compensator, specimen,
         second Faraday cell and (not visible) telescope with analyzer and photomultiplier.

specimen for modulation at 10 kHz and measurement by automatic compensation within
about 1 ms.   A Fresnel rhomb serves as achromatic compensator.   The specimen is
contained in the electrochemical cell shown in the center.   The large amount of data
generated during experiments is collected by a microcomputer.

Optical models are used for the interpretation of ellipsometer measurements.   A large
number of models has been investigated for their applicability to different electrochemical
surface layers[5,6]; a few are illustrated in Fig. 10.2[3]:   In the simplest model, a layer is
represented by a continuous, compact film on a smooth substrate.   For known optical
constants of film material and substrate, this model is defined by one parameter, the film
thickness.   The description of a single porous film of known composition requires two
parameters, thickness and volume faction (porosity).   Microroughness can often be
represented by an equivalent porous layer.   A new level of complexity is added to optical
models by discontinuous or island films.[7,8]   For known optical properties of film and
substrate materials such a model contains two unknown parameters, thickness and
coverage.   Multiple-layer models involve combinations of different types of single
films.   A model of this type that has been found applicable to silver oxide layers[9] employs
islands of porous oxide (characterized by coverage, volume fraction and thickness) on top
of a nonporous oxide (characterized by thickness) and requires four parameters for its

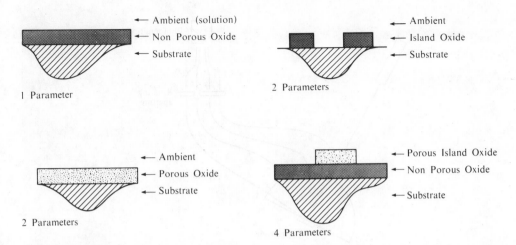

Fig. 10.2 Optical film models for the interpretation of spectroscopic ellipsometer measurements.   For known
         optical constants of substrate and film materials, the number of unknown parameters increases with the
         complexity of the model from 1 to 4.

characterization.   Inhomogeneous layers, in which optical properties change continuously
with thickness e.g., due to gradual changes in composition or porosity, can be represented
by multiple layers; the results converge with increasing numbers of layers.   This model
requires only two parameters, the overall thickness and the functional dependence of
the film properties on thickness.   Linear and parabolic porosity profiles have been
used.[10]   Inhomogeneous films can also be used to represent surface roughness.[11]

   Optical models are selected under consideration of different experimental information,
but primarily on the basis of their ability to predict ellipsometer measurements.   In an
optimization process, which usually requires a significant computational effort, the
independent parameters of the model are systematically varied to achieve best agreement
with measurements by minimizing the sum of squares difference between measured and
predicted ellipsometer parameters.[12]   With spectroscopic ellipsometer measurements,
five-dimensional optimizations have been conducted.[9]   Thus, five model parameters have
been derived from the two ellipsometer parameters measured over the visible spectrum.

10.2.2 Elastic Light Scattering

   The measurement of light scattered in different directions from an electrode surface at the
incident wavelength (elastic scattering) has been used to obtain information on surface
topography.[13]   From the scattered intensity, one can derive the number of scattering sites,
and from the angular distribution, their size.   The equipment built for this purpose is shown
schematically in Fig. 10.3.   A laser beam is incident normal (zero angle of incidence) on the
electrode surface.   The scattered light is collected over one quadrant by fiber optic probes
from 5° to 85° in one degree increments.   The fibers are selected sequentially by a rotating
aperture and their light is directed to a photomultiplier.

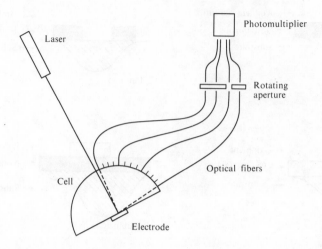

Fig. 10.3 Schematic of scatterometer for the *in situ* measurement of elastically scattered light from an electrode
surface as a function of scattering angle.   The scattered light is collected in 1° increments by optical
fibers (4 only shown for clarity) that are selected by a rotating aperture for sequential readout.

10.2.3 Scanning Tunneling Microscopy

Scanning tunneling microscopy can provide surface topographic information with
atomic resolution.   A commercial instrument[14] has been used in this work in the constant
tunneling-current (e.g., 2nA) mode of operation in which the probe tip is moved over the
specimen surface with a constant tip-to-surface separation (e.g. 10 nm).   For the observation of an immersed electrode, it has been found important to apply an insulating coating
to the probe wire[15] in order to reduce the background current to values below the tunneling
current (0.2 nA at 100 mV have been obtained).   The probe tip is moved in three directions
by a tube-shaped piezoelectric positioner.   Depending on the cell design used, reference
and counterelectrodes are located in the cell or connected to it by electrolyte-filled tubes.

The topographic (height) information obtained by scanning tunneling microscopy is
collected in digital form and can be displayed in different ways.   Four display modes used
are illustrated in Fig.10.4 for the same Cu deposit.   The conventional line plot (upper left)
shows a 600×450 mm area with 100 nm peak-to-valley distance.   Contour lines with 18 nm
increments are given in the upper right.   The half-tone image on the lower left employs a
height-coded gray scale with high regions being brighter than low regions.   The image in
the lower right employs a height-derivative coded gray scale.   This display mode provides
an image that is richest in surface detail.

10.2.4 Raman Spectroscopy

Raman spectroscopy has been used to provide vibrational spectra which are characteristic of the composition of electrode surfaces.[16,17]   A highly efficient light collection
system consisted of a single monochromator, used in conjunction with sharp band-pass
interference filters for removing elastically scattered light and plasma lines from the
laser.   Also, the entire spectrum is observed simultaneously with a 1024 element intensified

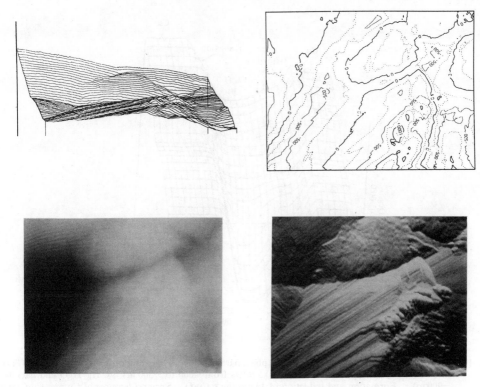

Fig. 10.4 Display modes for STM topographic information. Cu deposit from 10 mM Cu(ClO₄)₂, 0.5 M
NaClO₄, pH 2, 60 sec at −25 mV, after 30 sec at −500 mV.   600 × 450 nm area; line plot (110 nm peak-
to-valley), contour lines (18 nm increments), height-coded gray scale, height-derivative coded gray
scale.

photodiode array connected to an optical multichannel analyzer.   The electrochemical cell
was equipped with windows for optimum angles of incidence (70° from the surface normal)
and collection (60° from the surface normal and in the plane perpendicular to the plane of
incidence).

The information obtained by use of the different techniques will be illustrated by results
from two anodic and two cathodic systems.

10.3 Anodic Films

10.3.1 Oxidation of Copper

Spectroscopic ellipsometer measurements of the anodic formation of Cu_2O on Cu(111) in
1 M KOH during a potential sweep are illustrated in Fig. 10.5, where the measured phase
parameter delta is shown as a function of potential and wavelength.[13]   The potential sweep
in the anodic direction extends from −600 mV to −300 mV and is followed by a cathodic
sweep from −300 mV to −900 mV.   The data show the oxidation and reduction of the
surface, with a maximum Cu_2O thickness (140 Å) being obtained at about
−460 mV.   Reversal of the potential sweep at −300 mV results in a small shelf in the

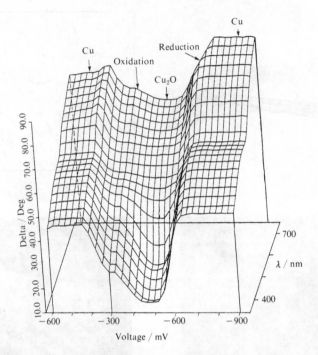

Fig. 10.5 Spectroscopic ellipsometer measurement (phase parameter delta) of oxidation and reduction of Cu(111) in 1 M KOH during potential sweep at 0.5 mV/s from −600 to −300 mV *vs.* Hg/HgO and back to −900 mV. Formation and reduction of 14 nm thick Cu_2O. Spectral features of Cu and Cu_2O are visible.

plot. The wavelength-dependence of the data shows the spectral features of Cu and Cu_2O.

The cyclic voltammogram[13] corresponding to the optical measurements in Fig. 10.5 is given in Fig. 10.6. The anodic peak at −365 mV corresponds to the formation of Cu_2O.[16] The film thickness for the same specimen, also shown in Fig. 10.5, has been derived from the spectroscopic ellipsometer measurements. The thickness increases in the anodic region (even after reversal of the potential sweep direction) and decreases in the cathodic current region. The fastest decrease in thickness coincides with the cathodic current peak. The apparent negative thickness given below −700 mV is an artifact of the optical model used, which was that of a homogeneous single film and did not consider the roughening of the surface. The amount of oxide derived from the film thickness agrees with that expected from the charge passed.

The elastic light scattering during anodic oxidation of copper is illustrated in Fig. 10.7 for a larger range of potentials.[13] The scattering intensity increases with increasing anodic potential (−500 to −100 mV) in two steps which correspond to the formation of Cu_2O and $Cu(OH)_2$. The increase in scattering intensity is indicative of an increase in the number of scattering centers (roughness elements). The scattered light is distributed over all angles with an approximately $\cos^2$ dependence, which is characteristic for scattering from small particles. The light scattering results are in agreement with results obtained by ellipsometry, scanning electron microscopy (SEM) and Raman spectroscopy.

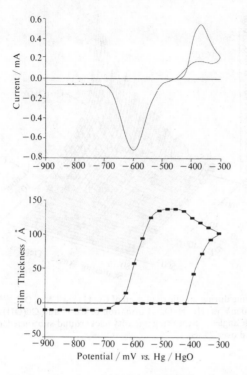

Fig. 10.6 Formation and reduction of Cu_2O on Cu(111) in 1 M KOH.   Current and thickness during potential
sweep at 0.5 mV/s.   Film thickness derived from spectroscopic ellipsometer measurements (delta
shown in Fig. 10.5) by use of a single-film optical model with adjustable, wavelength-dependent optical
constants; negative thickness due to roughening.   Small persistent cathodic current due to oxygen
reduction.

From the spectral power density of the scattering[13] and an assumed initial roughness
(100 Å), the RMS roughness of the copper electrode during oxidation has been derived
from the light scattering measurements (Fig. 10.8).   A small increase in roughness (about
200 Å) is observed during Cu_2O formation, supporting a solid-state transformation
mechanism.   The larger increase in roughness during $Cu(OH)_2$ formation at more anodic
potentials agrees with a precipitation reaction for this product.   Needles of precipitated
hydroxide with about 600 Å diameter are shown in the SEM pictures of Fig. 10.9,[13]
confirming the small dimensions derived from the scattering.   The Cu_2O surface was found
featureless by SEM.

Oxidation products on copper have been identified by Raman spectroscopy.   Fig. 10.10
illustrates how, with increasing anodic (positive) potential, Cu_2O (633 cm^{-1}) is formed first,
followed by $Cu(OH)_2$ (488 cm^{-1}).[16]   Since CuO is a weak Raman scatterer, its formation
is not seen on the spectra.   Its presence has been identified by modulated photoelectrochemical measurements.[17]   Upon reversal of the potential sweep, the two Raman peaks
disappear in reverse order.

202

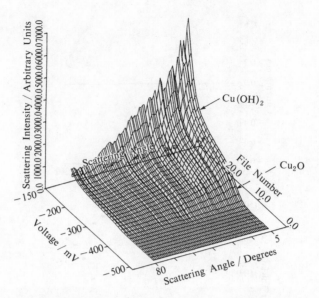

Fig. 10.7 Elastic light scattering during anodic oxidation of Cu(111) in 1 M KOH.   Potential sweep at 0.5 mV/s from −500 to −150 mV *vs.* Hg/HgO.   Formation of Cu₂O and Cu(OH)₂.   Small particles result in scattering over large angles.   Scattering intensity background-subtracted, each angular scan is average of 30 scans acquired over 25 sec.

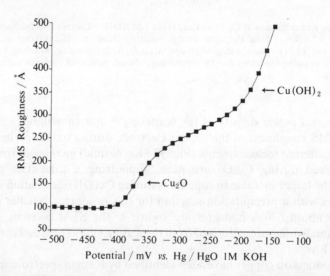

Fig. 10.8 Surface roughness during anodic oxidation of Cu derived from elastic light scattering at 0.5 mV/s shown in Fig. 10.7.   Onset of Cu₂O formation at −400 mV, small nuclei; onset of Cu(OH)₂ formation at −200 mV, needles of 60 nm diameter.

Fig. 10.9 Scanning electron micrograph of anodic Cu(OH)$_2$ layer formed at 100 mV *vs.* Hg/HgO in 1 M KOH
         showing precipitate needles of 60 nm diameter.   Magnification shown holds for picture on left, scale
         bar 6450 nm; magnification 10 times higher at right, scale bar 645 nm.

10.3.2 Oxidation of Silver

The optical model that was found to best represent ellipsometer measurements of Ag$_2$O
formation is shown in Fig. 10.11.[9]   It is a two-layer island film model that consists of a
primary comapct (nonporous), homogeneous oxide layer and a layer of porous secondary
oxide crystals, represented by an island film.   With the optical constants of Ag$_2$O being
known, this model requires four parameters for its description: the thickness of the primary
(compact) film and the porosity, thickness and coverage of the secondary (island)
film. The two thickness parameters, derived from spectroscopic ellipsometer
measurements for film growth at constant potential (above the nucleation potential) are
given in Fig. 10.12.[9]   The primary layer is seen to grow initially from underpotential and
monolayer to multilayer dimensions.   Its thickness decreases greatly when the secondary
crystals are nucleated (50 sec) and gradually recovers afterwards.   The nucleation of the
secondary crystals is not immediate, although the applied potential is sufficient for
nucleation.   The induction time indicates the need for a critical primary layer thickness
before nucleation.   Such behavior is not expected on the basis of a dissolution-
precipitation mechanism.   The surface coverage by the secondary (island) film derived

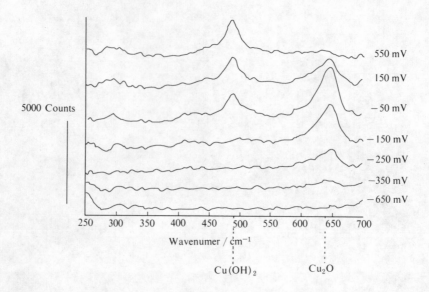

Fig. 10.10 Raman spectroscopy of Cu oxidation in 1 M KOH. Anodic potential sweep at 0.5 mV/s. Spectra shown at selected potentials *vs.* Hg/HgO, offset for readability. Peaks at 488 cm⁻¹ and 633 cm⁻¹ for Cu(OH)₂ and Cu₂O, respectively. Detector exposure time 100 s/scan.

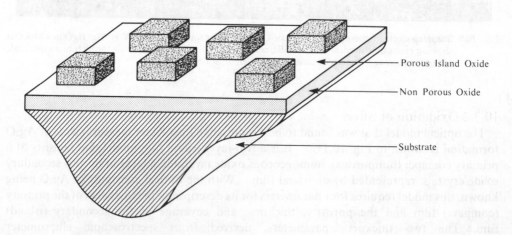

Fig. 10.11 Two-layer island-film optical model for anodic Ag₂O formed on Ag(111) in 1 M KOH. Nonporous homogeneous (primary) layer and porous (secondary) oxide crystals, represented by island film. Free parameters of model: thickness of nonporous layer and thickness, porosity and coverage of island layer.

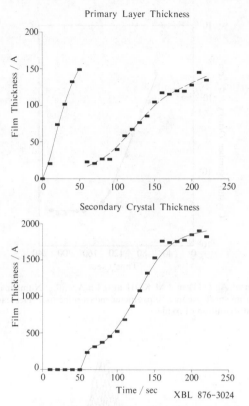

Fig. 10.12 Thickness of nonporous (primary) and porous island (secondary) oxide layers derived from spectroscopic ellipsometer measurements. Anodic oxidation of Ag(111) in 1 M KOH at 200 mV vs. Ag/AgCl, 4 M KCl. Decrease of nonporous layer thickness at onset of island film growth.

from the ellipsometer measurements, surprisingly, is found to decrease after nucleation. From thickness and coverage of the secondary layer, the number density of growing crystals has been derived (under the assumption of hemispherical shapes). This number density is found to decrease by several orders of magnitude during the early stages of film growth. For the galvanostatic conditions shown in Fig. 10.13, the number density decreases from 2×10^{10} cm^{-2} to 3×10^8 cm^{-2} between 60 sec and 160 sec of film growth.[9]

Light scattering measurements during Ag$_2$O formation are in agreement with the ellipsometer interpretation. As shown in Fig. 10.14, the angular distribution of scattered light changes during film growth from one over large angles from the incident (normal) direction, characteristic of small particles, to one over near angles, characteristic of large particles.[13] This change supports a redistribution of material between growth centers after nucleation of the secondary layer (at approximately 50 sec).

Scanning tunneling microscopy (STM) further confirms this redistribution: Fig. 10.15 shows a surface element of 2.3×3.6 μm is size.[13] The original substrate surface (A) is found to roughen gradually as the underpotential oxide layer grows to the primary multilayer (B). Nucleation of the secondary layer results in a sharp increase in roughness

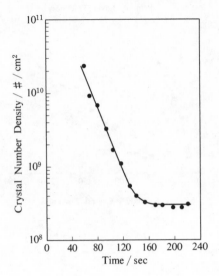

Fig. 10.13 Anodic oxidation of Ag (111) in 1 M KOH at 0.1 mA/cm². Number density of secondary oxide crystals derived from spectroscopic ellipsometer measurements. Decrease during early film growth stage indicates redistribution of oxide.

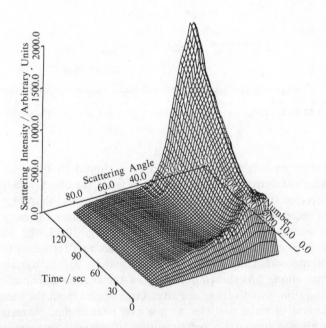

Fig. 10.14 Elastic light scattering during anodic oxidation of Ag (111) in 1 M KOH at 200 mV vs. Hg/HgO. Formation of Ag₂O. Initial formation of many small particles results in scattering over large angles. Later redistribution of oxide to fewer large particles accounts for brief decrease in scattering intensity and scattering primarily over near angles. Scattering intensity background-subtracted, each angular scan is average of 4 scans acquired over 3.9 sec.

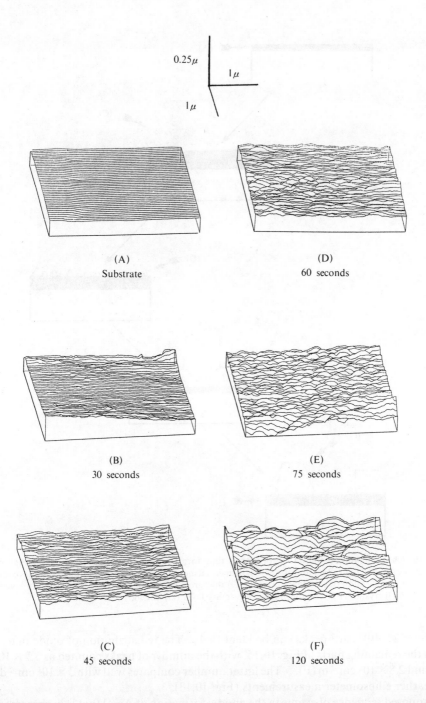

0.25μ

1μ

1μ

(A)
Substrate

(D)
60 seconds

(B)
30 seconds

(E)
75 seconds

(C)
45 seconds

(F)
120 seconds

Fig. 10.15 Scanning tunneling micrographs of the anodic oxidation of sputtered Ag in 1 M KOH at 290 mV *vs.* Hg/HgO. After nucleation of secondary crystals in C, the number density of peaks decreases as their size increases.

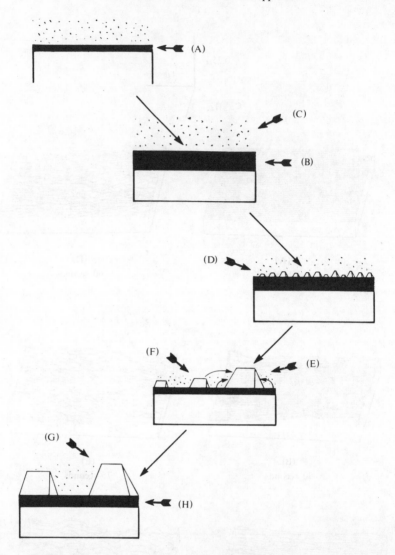

Fig. 10.16 Schematic representation of proposed film formation mechanism for Ag_2O on Ag in KOH.
Formation of primary multilayer (B) from initial monolayer (A) and formation of soluble oxide species
(C); nucleation of secondary crystals (D) that grow by transfer of oxide from primary layer (E) and
small crystals (F); reestablishment of primary layer (H) at end.

(C); about 2×10^{10} cm^{-2} peaks can be identified.   The redistribution of oxide materials is
seen in the remaining parts of Fig. 10.15, with the number of peaks counted as 5.7×10^9 cm^{-2}
in (E) and 2.8×10^8 cm^{-2} in (F).   The latter number compares well with 3×10^8 cm^{-2} derived
from earlier ellipsometer measurements (Fig. 10.13).

A proposed sequence of events in the anodic formation of Ag_2O that is in agreement with
the different experimental observations is illustrated in Fig. 10.16:[9]   An initial monolayer
(A), formed by adsorpotion and precipitation of dissolution products (C), grows to the

primary multilayer (B).   Nucleation of the secondary crystal layer (D) occurs after the primary layer reaches a critical thickness (approximately 150 Å).   The secondary crystals initially grow by the transfer of oxide from the primary layer (E), resulting in a decreased thickness of the latter. A further redistribution of oxide from small to large secondary crystals (F) results in a large decrease in the number density of secondary crystals.   After the secondary crystals reach a diameter of about 1000 Å, their solubility does not depend greatly on size anymore and they continue to grow independently (G) in constant numbers.   Also, the primary layer is reestablished (H).

10.4 Cathodic Films

10.4.1 Deposition of Lead

  The initial stages in the potentiostatic deposition of lead from a solution of 5 mM lead acetate and 1 M sodium acetate on silver with a Pt counter electrode and a Ag/AgCl reference electrode have been investigated by scanning tunneling microscopy (STM) with 3 nA tunneling current and 300 mV tunneling bias.[18]   Formation of a lead UPD layer was observed around 150 mV anodic of bulk lead deposition with no obvious changes in surface topography.   The STM line scans in Fig. 10.17 show the initial roughening of the originally smooth (RMS roughness 5 nm), evaporated silver substrate by the formation of lead nuclei (A).   Upon further deposition, the short-range roughness decreases (B).   Subsequently,

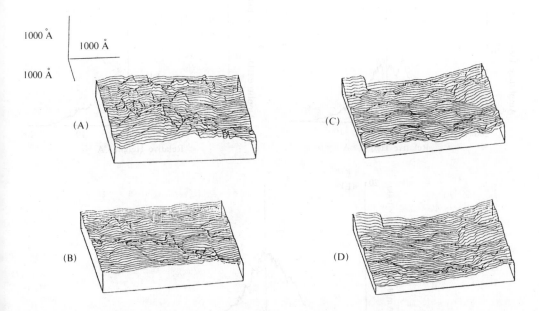

Fig. 10.17 Scanning tunneling micrographs of different stages in the electrodeposition of Pb on Ag at −650 mV
        vs. Ag/AgCl from 5 mM PbAc, 1 M NaAc.   Substrate surface featureless.   (A) After 100 sec, bulk
        deposition with large number of small (5–10 nm) growth centers.   (B) After 300 sec, reduction of
        short-range roughness by growth.   (C) After 1000 sec, increase in roughness by nucleation in surface
        recesses.   (D) After 1200 sec, reduction of roughness.

the deposit passes through several roughening (C) and smoothing (D) cycles which result from the increasing size of nuclei, followed by renucleation in recessed regions.

For the quantitative characterization of the surface topography of STM measurements, the amplitude density functions of the surfaces shown in Fig. 10.17 have been determined.[13,18]   They are given in Fig. 10.18 and represent the probability of the presence

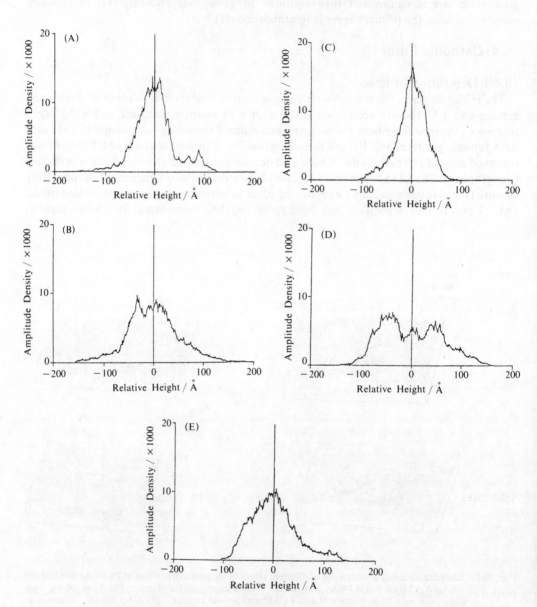

Fig. 10.18. Amplitude density function for Ag substrate surface (A) and Pb deposits (B–D) shown in Fig. 10.17. Successive roughening and smoothing cycles shown by broadening and narrowing of distribution.

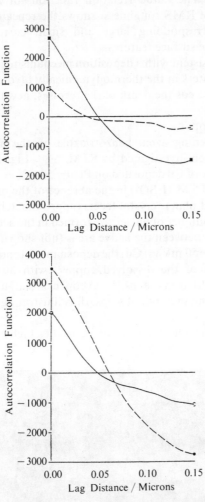

Fig. 10.19 Autocorrelation function for Pb deposits shown in Fig. 10.17.   ■ 100 sec, □ 300 sec, ● 1000 sec, ○ 1200 sec.   Successive roughening and smoothing cycles shown by value of autocorrelation function at zero lag distance (square of RMS roughness).

of any height below (negative) or above (positive) the mean electrode surface.   The original substrate (A) shows a narrow distribution of heights characteristic of smooth surfaces.   The wide distribution given in Fig. 10.18(B) demonstrates the roughening seen in the corresponding Fig. 10.17(A).   The peak of the original distribution has been shifted to about −40 Å by the nuclei which appear as protrusions and cause the broad peak on the positive side of the distribution in Fig. 10.18(B).   The repeated smoothing and roughening cycles are well visible in Figs. 10.18(C) to (E), that correspond to Figs. 10.17(B) to (D).   The dual-mode distribution in Fig. 10.18(D) shows the recesses on the negative side of the distribution and the protrusions on the positive side.

As another evaluation of surface profiles, autocorrelation functions for the same surfaces, are given in Fig.10.19.[18] The autocorrelation function for zero lag distance, which represents the square of the RMS roughness, shows the repeated changes fom rough to smooth surfaces with corresponding large and small correlation distances, which correspond to the size of the surface features.

The observations are consistent with a deposition mechanism that involves the successive re-nucleation of growth centers in the thermodynamically favored recessed regions of the surface. As the growth exceeds the depth of the recesses, new roughness is generated.

10.4.2 Deposition of Copper

The effect of the brightening agent benzotriazole on the microtopography of electrodeposited copper has been investigated by STM.[19,20] Fig. 10.20 shows a derivative-coded gray scale STM image of Cu deposited on Pt at -50 mV vs. Cu from an acidic sulfate electrolyte (0.5 M $CuSO_4$, 0.5 M H_2SO_4) in the absence of the brightening agent. Large crystals with well-developed planar crystal facets (approximately 200 nm wide), resulting from the growth of a small number of nuclei, are formed in the active areas of the electrode, with large electrode regions between the active areas (not shown) remaining bare.

Under potential control (-50 mV vs. Cu) the deposit microtopography has been found to be stable after exhaustion of the dissolved copper, with atomically smooth regions separated by single- and multiatomic steps.[15] At open circuit, however, rapid dissolution started immediately, resulting in a loss of steps, thus illustrating the importance of *in situ* observation.

In the presence of benzotriazole,[19] deposition occurs at a higher overpotential and results

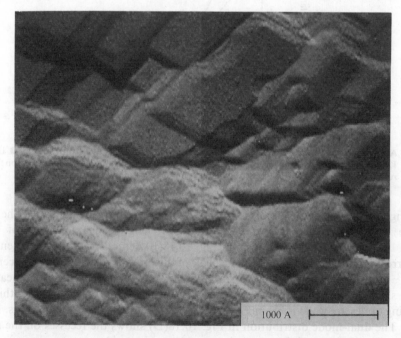

1000 A

Fig. 10.20 Derivative-coded gray scale STM image of Cu deposited on Pt from 0.5 M $CuSO_4$, 0.5 M H_2SO_4 at -50 mV vs. Cu. Small number of large crystals with planar facets.

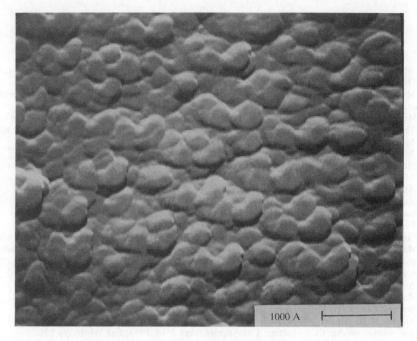

Fig. 10.21 Derivative-coded gray scale STM image of Cu deposited on Pt from 0.5 M CuSO₄, 0.5 M H₂SO₄, 0.1 mM BTA.   Large number of small growth centers.

in a large number (approximately 9×10^{10} cm^{-2}) of uniformly distributed growth centers, which are considerably smaller (approximately 30 nm) than the wavelength of light (approximately 550 nm) (Fig. 10.21).   Brightening is therefore achieved by the high nucleation density that results in small surface features.

10.5 Conclusions

The combination of different experimental techniques has been found useful for the study of electrochemical film formation.   Physical mechanisms of film formation have been derived from the observed microtopographies.   Similarities have been found in the nucleation and growth of anodic and cathodic surface layers.   Approaches to the control of film properties can be based on the mechanisms of electrochemical phase formation (electrosolidification).

ACKNOWLEDGMENTS

This work was supported by the Assistant Secretary for Conservation and Renewable Energy, Office of Transportation Technologies, Electric and Hybrid Propulsion Division of the U.S. Department of Energy under Contract No. DE-AC03-76SF00098.

REFERENCES

1. R.H. Muller, in: *Advances in Electrochemistry and Electrochemical Engineering,* Vol. 9, (R.H. Muller, ed.) pp. 167–226, John Wiley & Sons, New York, 1973.
2. R.H. Muller, in: *Techniques for Characterization of Electrodes and Electrochemical Processes,* (R. Varma and J.R. Selman, eds.) pp. 31–125 John Wiley & Sons, New York, 1991.
3. S.T. Mayer, An Ellipsometric Spectroscopy Study of Anodically Formed Silver (I) Oxide Films on Silver, M.S. Thesis, University of California, Berkeley, Department of Chem. Engr. (Dec. 1985), Report LBL-20503.
4. R.H. Muller and J.C. Farmer, *Rev. Sci. Instrum.,* **55**, 371 (1984).
5. R.H. Muller and C.G. Smith, *Surf. Sci.,* **96**, 375 (1980).
6. J.C. Farmer and R.H. Muller, *J. Electrochem. Soc.,* **132**, 313 (1985).
7. R.H. Muller and J.C. Farmer, *Surf. Sci.,* **135**, 521 (1983).
8. M.J. Armstrong and R.H. Muller, *J. Appl. Phys.,* **65**, 3056 (1989).
9. S.T. Mayer and R.H. Muller, *J. Electrochem. Soc.,* **135**, 2133 (1988).
10. F. Schwager, Y. Geronov and R.H. Muller, *J. Electrochem. Soc.,* **132**, 285 (1985).
11. C.A. Fenstermaker and F.L. McCrackin, *Surf. Sci.,* **16**, 85 (1969).
12. J.C. Farmer and R.H. Muller, *J. Electrochem. Soc.,* **132**, 39 (1985).
13. S.T. Mayer, An *In Situ* Study of the Anodic Film Formation of Cu, Ag, and Zn in Alkaline Media, Ph.D. Dissertation, University of California, Berkeley, Dept. of Chem. Engr., (Dec. 1989), Report LBL-28085.
14. Nanoscope I, Digital Instruments Inc., Goleta, CA 93117, U.S.A.
15. M.J. Armstrong and R.H. Muller, *J. Electrochem. Soc.,* **136**, 584 (1989).
16. S.T. Mayer and R.H. Muller, *J. Electrochem. Soc.,* **139**, 426 (1992).
17. D.T. Schwartz and R.H. Muller, *Surf. Sci.,* **248**, 349 (1991).
18. S.T. Mayer, R.H. Muller and P.N. Ross, *In Situ* Scanning Tunneling Microscopy of Multilayer Pb Electrodeposition on Ag, ECS Meeting, Los Angeles, May 7–14, 1989, Ext. Abstr. No.521.
19. M.J. Armstrong and R.H. Muller, *J. Electrochem. Soc.,* **138**, 2303 (1991).
20. M.J. Armstrong, The Role of Inhibitors during Electrodeposition of Thin Metallic Films, Ph.D. dissertation, University of California, Berkeley, Dept. of Chem. Engr. (1990), Report LBL-28972.

11

Laser Interferometry as an *in-situ* Technique to Characterize Electrochemical Processes

Y. Fukunaka, F. McLarnon* and Z. Asaki

Dept. of Metallurgy, Kyoto University, Kyoto, 606 Japan
*Energy & Environment Division, Lawrence Berkeley Laboratory, University of California, Berkeley, California 94720, U. S. A.

11.1   Introduction

Numerous studies have been carried out on the ionic mass transfer associated with laminar natural convection and on the resultant distribution of current density along a plane vertical cathode installed in unstirred electrolyte.   The interferometric technique has been introduced to better understand the concept of concentration polarization and to provide direct visualization of the concentration profile in the immediate vicinity of the electrode.   The historical development of this line of inquiry is briefly summarized here.

Nernst[1] introduced the concept of concentration overpotential in 1904.   Haring and Blum[2] proposed the concept of primary and secondary distribution of current density in 1923, and in 1931, Glasstone[3] introduced a procedure for calculating the limiting current density of noble metal ion based on the assumption of constant thickness of a diffusion layer.   These classical investigations provided the basis for modern concepts of rate processes at the electrode/electrolyte interface.   Samarcev[4] applied Schlieren interferometry in 1934, followed by Read and Graham's studies,[5] which first demonstrated experimetally with the pinhole method that the cathodic diffusion layer developed with electrode height.   Based on these observations, Brenner[6] tried to measure the concentration distribution of electrolyte by using the freezing method.   During the same period, Kasper[7] applied potential theory to calculate the distribution of primary current density.

Wagner[8] introduced boundary layer theory to analyze the limiting current density distribution along a vertical plane copper cathode in $CuSO_4$ solution in 1949.   He properly recognized the analogy between natural convection due to heat transfer and that due to ionic mass transfer caused by electrodeposition.   He then supplemented Kasper's method and introduced the concept of a polarization parameter assuming a linear polarization curve.[9]   A few years later, Wilke *et al.*[10] experimentally confirmed the analogy between natural convection due to heat transfer and that due to electrodeposition at the limiting current density.

In 1954, Ibl and coworkers[11-13] introduced Jamin interferometry and measured the concentration profile of Cu^{2+} ion in the cathodic concentration boundary layer.   They also measured the electrolyte velocity distribution due to natural convection.[13]   Electrochemical phenomena such as corrosion were qualitatively observed using Schlieren methods by

215

Cooper,[14] Stephenson and Bartlett[15] and Yeager *et al.*[16] in the 1950's.   In the 1960's, O'Brien employed Fizeau-type fringe interferometry to image concentration profiles,[17] and Asada *et al.*[18] presented a method of calculating current density distribution by taking account of the concentration distribution.

In the 1970's, the application of interferometry to this field became prevalent, stimulated by the invention of the laser.[19-29]   The Berkeley group[20] pointed out that the incident light beam is deflected toward the direction of higher refractive index in the electrolyte and presented a correcting method to account for the beam deflection.   Their series of papers illustrates how to interpret interferograms, and demonstrates quantitative measurement of electrochemical phenomena by interferometry.[21-25]   This series of papers signaled the start of modern interferometric measurements in electrochemical engineering.   At the same time, holographic interferometry, in which the optical preparatory and alignment procedures are far less critical than those of classical techniques, was introduced to observe the anodic dissolution of iron in sulfuric acid and the electrodeposition and dissolution of copper in copper sulfate solution by Knox *et al.*[26] and Srinivasan.[27]   Clifton and Sanchez[28] discussed the optical errors encountered in using holographic interferometry, and Awakura and Kondo[29] also applied this technique to measure the concentration profile of Cu^{2+} ions along a cathode surface.

As described above, many successes have been reported on the measurement of concentration profiles using laser interferometry.   However, because only the refractive index profile can be observed by interferometry, there are limitations to the conversion of refractive index distributions into the concentration profiles for multicomponent electrolytes.   In order to elevate the ionic conductivity of the electrolyte and to attain a uniform distribution of current density, an excess amount of supporting electrolyte is usually added to industrial electrolytes.   From this point of view, the effect of H_2SO_4 as a supporting electrolyte[30-32] has been discussed in recent communications.[33,34]

Ibl and Braun's study tried to estimate the interfacial concentration of Cu^{2+} and H^+ ions when the boundary condition at the cathode is specified.[30]   This is along the same line of investigation Brenner conducted by freezing the electrolyte to estimate surface pH in alloy plating approximately half a century ago.[6]   Although Selman and Newman[31] pointed out the possibility that H^+ ion is accumulated near the cathode surface and the upward natural convection is depressed, the concentration profile of H^+ ion near the cathode has not yet been successfully measured.

A comprehensive review of interferometry in electrochemical research has been published by Muller.[20]   However, his review does not address recent applications of holographic interferometry.   The present review primarily addresses the measurement of concentration profiles in $CuSO_4$–H_2SO_4 solutions as a model system.   An experimental technique employing an image sensor[33] is first described, followed by a summary of two-wavelength holographic interferometry (TWHI).[34]   Some applications of laser interferometry in electrochemical systems are also outlined.

11.2   Optical Techniques to Measure Concentration Profiles

11.2.1   Image Sensors[33]

The peak of the absorption spectrum of Cu^{2+} ion is located at about 800 nm, whereas the absorption peak of H^+ ion is at about 200 nm.[35]   Because the absorption peaks of ions are widely separated, Beer-Lambert's law can be applied to measure the concentration profile of Cu^{2+} in $CuSO_4$-H_2SO_4 solution.   By measuring the distribution of absorbance with an image sensor, such as a Multi-Channel Photo-Detector (MCPD), together with an appropriate interference filter, the concentration profile of Cu^{2+} ion near the electrode is obtained.

The optical arrangement is illustrated in Fig. 11.1.   The cathode rod was rotated to a position where its enlarged silhouette recedes farthest in the monitoring scope to assure the parallelness of the cathode surface to the incident beam.   However, a diffraction pattern was observed near the electrode surface,[36] as seen in Fig. 11.1(B). I_A and I_B in this figure correspond to the absorbance distribution measured during steady state electrolysis and before electrolysis.   This pattern was found to be significantly influenced by the distance between the focal plane and the knife edge, indicating that significant light deflection effects are distorting the pattern.   Because the diffraction pattern near the cathode surface was fairly similar to those for an ideal slit, it was concluded that the observed diffraction pattern was caused by a partial coherency due to the incident beam's trajectory parallel to the cathode surface.   Therefore, the geometrical position of the cathode surface could be determined by applying the Frenel diffraction theory (Fig. 11.1(c)).[37]

The measured absorbance curve in the boundary layer was extrapolated toward the cathode surface (*i.e.* the surface location derived from diffraction theory), over a distance of 50 to 80 micrometers, and the distribution of absorbance was determined.   The agreement between the concentration profiles of Cu^{2+} ion in aqueous 0.05 M $CuSO_4$ solution measured by the absorbance technique and by conventional holographic interferometry[29,38] was fairly good.

11.2.2   Two-wavelength Holographic Interferometry[34,38]

A. Introduction

The above-described measurements with MCPD were performed on an electrode that was designed to be wide enough for the induced natural convection not to be influenced by the existence of cell wall.   Therefore, significant noise due to light diffraction was sometimes superimposed on the output signal of light absorbance.   The surface concentration of H^+ ion was calculated by subtracting the refractive-index increment corresponding to the light absorbance due to Cu^{2+} ion from the refractive index of solution, which is a function of both Cu^{2+} and H^+ ion concentrations.   The solution refractive index was independently measured by holographic interferometry.   Due to the optical complexity of this procedure, the resultant measuring error of H^+ ion concentration was fairly large.   It was therefore decided to carry out simultaneous measurement of concentration profiles of both ions by using two-wavelength holographic interferometry.

Ross *et al.*[39] tried to apply the principle of two-wavelength interferometry in 1960. Much later, Panknin and Mayinger[40,41] succeeded in measuring simultaneously the temperature and concentration distributions in the boundary layer formed by the sublimation of naphthalene by using two-wavelength holographic interferometry.

The principle of two-wavelength holographic interferometry (TWHI) in electrochemical systems is shown schematically in Fig. 11.2.   These regression equations for the concentration dependence of refractive index of electrolyte were obtained in orthogonal experiments with TWHI.[38]   The profiles of refractive index in the cathodic boundary layer are measured simultaneously at two different wavelengths, and the phase differences S_i

218

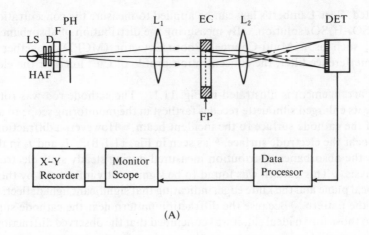

X-Y Recorder	Monitor Scope	Data Processor

(A)

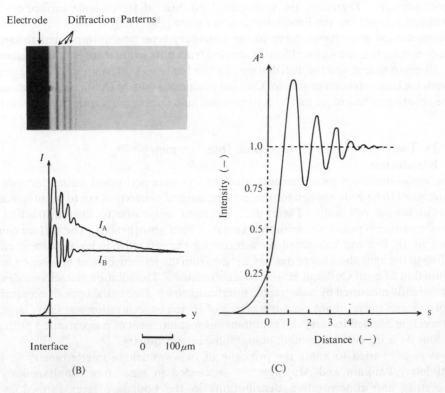

Fig. 11.1 Optical arrangement for measurement of absorbance distribution near electrode with image sensor.
(a) Optical arrangement
LS: light source, HAF: heat absorbance filter, D: diffuser, F: interference filter, DET: detector.
(b) Absorbance distribution and diffraction pattern
I_A: during electrolysis, I_B: before electrolysis.
(c) Fresnel diffraction pattern

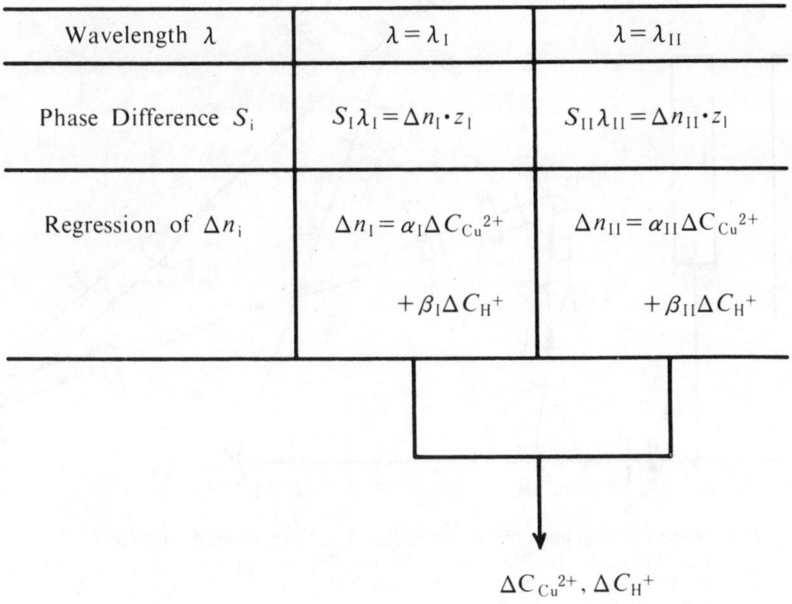

Wavelength λ	$\lambda = \lambda_I$	$\lambda = \lambda_{II}$
Phase Difference S_i	$S_I \lambda_I = \Delta n_I \cdot z_I$	$S_{II} \lambda_{II} = \Delta n_{II} \cdot z_I$
Regression of Δn_i	$\Delta n_I = \alpha_I \Delta C_{Cu}{}^{2+}$ $+ \beta_I \Delta C_H{}^+$	$\Delta n_{II} = \alpha_{II} \Delta C_{Cu}{}^{2+}$ $+ \beta_{II} \Delta C_H{}^+$

$$\Delta C_{Cu}{}^{2+}, \Delta C_H{}^+$$

Fig. 11.2   Principle of two-wavelength holographic interferometer in an electrochemical system.
$\Delta n_1 = 0.023718 \, \Delta C_{Cu^{2+}} - 0.010912 \, \Delta C_{H^+}$ ($\lambda_1 = 488$ nm)
$\Delta n_2 = 0.023257 \, \Delta C_{Cu^{2+}} - 0.010118 \, \Delta C_{H^+}$ ($\lambda_2 = 633$ nm)

($i = 1$, 2) at a given horizontal distance y from the cathode surface are calculated by regression.

B. Experimental Arrangement

The optical arrangement of TWHI is schematically illustrated in Fig. 11.3.   An argon gas laser emitter and a helium-neon gas laser emitter were used as the light sources.   The laser beams were mixed at a half-mirror B_1 to produce a single beam with a single optical axis.   The mixed beam was split into two beams by another half-mirror B_2 after it passed through a half-wavelength plate $\lambda/2$ and a shutter S.   The objective beam was collimated to a diameter of 1.2 cm by an objective lens E_1 (magnification: $\times 10$) and another lens LE_1 ($f = 200$ mm).   After passing through the vicinity of the cathode suface in the electrolytic cell C, the beam was projected onto a holographic plate H on which the image of the cathode surface was recorded.   The center line of the cathode surface was focused on the holographic plate by a lens LE_2 ($f = 135$ mm) which removes the chromatic aberration caused by the different colors of the laser beams.   The reference beam was also collimated to a diameter of 50 mm by lens E_2 (magnification: $\times 40$) and lens LE_3 ($f = 200$ mm).   Then the reference beam was superimposed with the objective beam on the same holographic plate.   The reconstructed interferograms were recorded with a camera CA.

C. Interpretation of Interferograms

When a light beam passes through a medium wherein there exists a distribution of refractive index, the incident beam is deflected toward the optically denser direction.   The corrections based on Svenson's method[42)] were made for the thermal boundary layer by

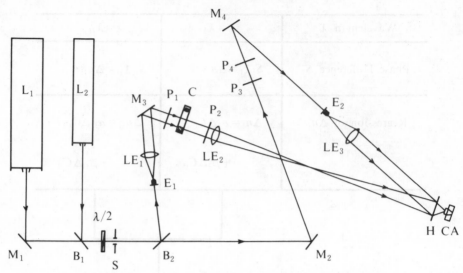

Fig. 11.3 Optical arrangement of two-wavelength holographic interferometer.
L_1: Ar laser, L_2: He–Ne laser, M: Mirror, B: Beam splitter, E: Expander, LE: Lens,
P: Polarizer, S: Shutter, C: Electrolytic cell, H: Hologram, CA: Camera,
$\lambda/2$: Half-wavelength plate.

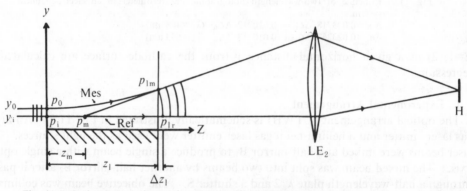

Fig. 11.4 Optical beam trajectory in cathodic diffusion layer.
LE_2: Lens, H: Hologram, p_o, p_i: Points of beam entrance at test section, p_m: Object
point in test section, p_{lm}, p_{lr}: Points where beams leave test section (m: objective beam,
r: reference beam), z_m: correct focusing plane, z_l: geometrical path length of reference
beam.

Hauf and Grigull.[43]   A similar correcting method should be established in the present
work by setting up the interferometer equation.

The beam trajectory in a cathodic diffusion layer is shown schematically in Fig. 11.4.
The curve P_0P_{lm} represents the trajectory of the objective beam which enters the electrolyte
at $y = y_0$ and deflects due to the gradient of refractive index.   The shift of interference
fringes is caused by the difference in the optical path length between the reference and
objective beams.

The experimental arragement assures that the reference beam entering at a point P_1 and
the objective beam entering at P_0 are focused on the hologram.   Presuming that the lens

LE$_2$ is optically ideal, the optical path length of the reference beam between P_{lr} and the hologram is equal to that of objective beam between P_{lm} and the hologram, because points P_{lr} and P_{lm} are on the same wave front.   Therefore, the difference in the optical path length between the beams is equal to the difference between P_iP_{lr} and P_0P_{lm}.   It follows that

$$S\lambda = n_\infty \overline{P_iP_{lr}} - n(y) \cdot \widehat{P_oP_{lm}} \tag{11.1}$$

$$= n_\infty \left[z_m + (z_1 - z_m)\sqrt{1+(\frac{dy}{dz})_1^2} \right] - \int_0^{z_1} n(z)\sqrt{1+(\frac{dy}{dz})^2}\, dz \tag{11.2}$$

Eqation (11.2) is called the "interferometer equation."

The distribution of the refractive index in the cathodic boundary layer is often assumed to be a linear function of the horizontal distance from the cathode surface[20,43]

$$n(y) = n_0 + (\frac{dn}{dy})_{y_0} \cdot (y - y_0) \tag{11.3}$$

The trajectory of the transmitted beam through a linear concentration boundary layer is represented according to Fermat's principle[37] by

$$y - y_0 = \frac{1}{2n_0}(\frac{dn}{dy})_{y_0} \cdot z^2 \tag{11.4}$$

When the focal plane of lens LE$_2$ is set at the center line of the cathode, $z_m = (1/2)z_1$, the image of the cathode surface remains unchanged from its position at the start of electrolysis.   The final interferometer equation can then described as

$$S\lambda = (n_\infty - n_i)z_1 - \frac{1}{12n_0}(\frac{dn}{dy})_{y_0}^2 \cdot z_1^3 \tag{11.5}$$

The first term on the right-hand side of Eq.(11.5) represents the simple interferometer equation, and the second term shows the effect of the light deflection S.   Introducing a notation, ε_{z1}, which is defined as $\tan \varepsilon_z = (dy/dz)_{z1}$, the relationship between the distance between interference fringes b and ε_z is given by Grigull[44] as

$$\sin\frac{\varepsilon_{z1}}{2} = \frac{\lambda}{2b} \tag{11.6}$$

where

$$(\frac{dy}{dz})_{z_1} = \frac{\lambda}{b} \tag{11.7}$$

Thus the correction term in the more precise interferometer equation is expressed by

$$\Delta S \cdot \lambda = \frac{n_0}{12}(\frac{\lambda}{b})^2 \cdot z_1 \tag{11.8}$$

The true phase difference is calculated by adding the correcion term of Eq. (11.8) to the observed phase difference.   The reader interested in a more detailed analysis is referred to publications by the Berkeley group.[20-25]   The Berkeley group has developed a method to derive concetration profiles (of arbitrary functional form) from experimental interferograms that may be significantly distorted by light-deflection effects.

D. Experimental Results and Discussion

A few examples of the interferograms obtained by two-wavelength holographic interferometry are shown in Fig. 11.5.   Electrolysis was carried out at a cathodic current density of $i = 0.946$ mA/cm^2 in aqueous 0.05 M CuSO$_4$–1.85 M H$_2$SO$_4$ solution.   Fig. 11.5(A) is the holographic interferogram regenerated simultaneously by combined laser beams of Ar and He–Ne at wavelengths of 488 nm (Ar) and 632.8 nm (He–Ne),

Cathode   0   0.5   1 mm

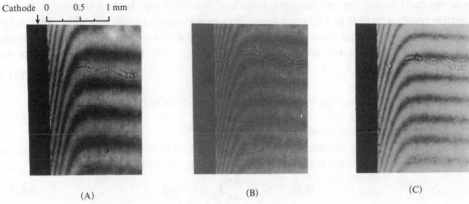

(A)   (B)   (C)

Fig. 11.5 Interferogram obtained by two-wavelength holographic interferometer at
$i = 0.946$ mA/cm^2 in 0.05 MCuSO$_4$–1.85 MH$_2$SO$_4$ solution.
(A) regenerated by both Ar laser and He–Ne laser, (B) regenerated by Ar laser,
(C) regenerated by He–Ne laser.

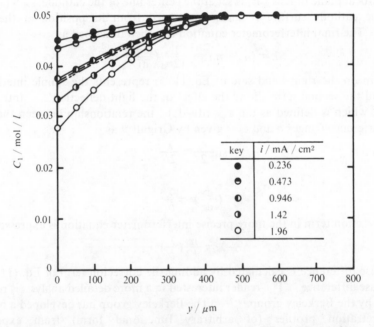

key	i / mA / cm^2
●	0.236
◐	0.473
◑	0.946
◕	1.42
○	1.96

Fig. 11.6 Concentration profiles of Cu^{2+} ion at $x = 4$ cm in 0.05 M CuSO$_4$ solution.

respectively.   Fig. 11.5(B) and (C) are the interferograms separately regenerated by Ar and
He–Ne laser, respectively.

The apparent phase differences S in the cathodic boundary layer in these interferograms
were measured.   Then the true phase differences were calculated for both wavelengths
according to the above-described correcting procedure.   The concentration profiles of
Cu^{2+} ion and H$^+$ ion in the cathodic boundary layer were then obtained by combing the ideal

interferometer equation with the regression equations of refractive indices of electrolyte at the two wavelengths.

A few examples of the concentration profiles of Cu^{2+} ion at the location $x = 4$ cm from the lower edge of cathode in 0.05 M $CuSO_4$ solution, for various current densities, are shown in Fig. 11.6.   Fig. 11.6 also shows the concentration profiles of Cu^{2+} ion at a current density of 0.946 mA/cm² measured by three different methods: conventional holographic interferometry (dashed line),[29] image sensor (dashed and dotted line)[33] and two-wavelength holographic interferometry (solid line).[34,38]   The agreement is satisfactory.

The concentration profiles of Cu^{2+} ion in aqueous 0.05 M $CuSO_4$–1.85 M H_2SO_4 solution are shown in Fig. 11.7.   It is seen that the concentration difference between the cathode surface and the bulk electrolyte, and the concentration gradient at the cathode surface, in aqueous 0.05 M $CuSO_4$–1.85 M H_2SO_4 solution are considerably larger than those in aqueous 0.05 M $CuSO_4$ solution at the same current density.   The different contributions of ionic migration to the species mass transfer rates in solutions may cause such an effect.   At the same time, hydrogen ions accumulate near the cathode surface (under the present electrolytic condition of no hydrogen gas evolution), and a concentration profile of H^+ ion is formed to balance the fluxes of migration, diffusion and convection and satisfy the electroneutrality requirement (Fig. 11.8).

The observed concentration profiles in both solutions are similar to each other, and can be plotted in dimensionless form are illustrated in Fig. 11.9.   The data obtained from the absorbance distribution measured with MCPD are also included in this figure.   The agreement between the theoretical correlation and the experimental results is satisfactory.

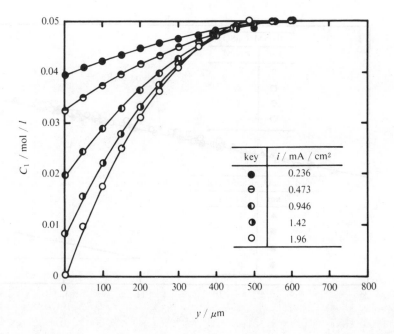

Fig. 11.7 Concentration profiles of Cu^{2+} ion at $x = 4$ cm in 0.05 M$CuSO_4$–1.85 MH_2SO_4 solution.

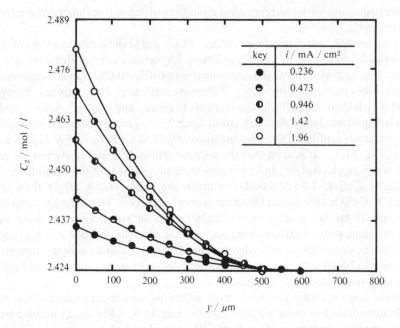

Fig. 11.8 Concentration profile of H$^+$ ion in 0.05 MCuSO$_4$–1.85 MH$_2$SO$_4$ solution.

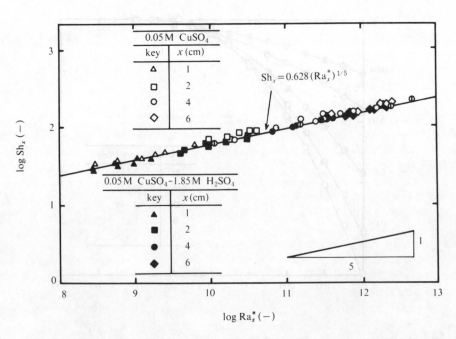

Fig. 11.9 Relationship between log(Sh$_x$) and log(Ra$_x$*) in both solutions (Ⓠ measured by absorbance distribution).

11.3   Applications in Electrochemical Research

Many papers describe the measurement of concentration profiles by interferometry. The concentration profiles can be quantitatively derived if the electrolyte is a single salt solution. However, conventional interferometry shows some limitations for multicomponent systems and only qualitative information can be derived. Most of these studies are related to the phenomenon of natural convection near a cathode induced by the electrodeposition of a metal. Some papers also deal with anodic processes and corrosion phenomena. Other investigations have addressed electrodeposition under forced convection, pulsed current, or in the presence of a magnetic field.

11.3.1   Horizontal Electrodes in the Cathode-Over-Anode Position

Metal ions are transferred to the cathode in the diffusional mode under such a configuration. O'Brien[17,45] prepared a cell which accomodated a wedge of electrolyte between electrodes and produced Fizeau-type fringes caused by the reflectance of the coatings on glass flats. This type of interferometer was originally proposed by Berg[46] to study crystal growth phenomena in aqueous solution.

McLarnon *et al.*[47] measured the transient refractive-index fields in stagnant $CuSO_4$ solutions during the galvanostatic deposition of copper. Camera F shown in Fig. 11.10, was positioned such that the plane of focus was located on the inside of the glass wall farthest from the camera. The transient interfacial concentrations for an experiment at $10 \ mA/cm^2$ are drawn in Fig. 11.11. The experimentally observed surface concentration agrees reasonably well with the theoretical prediction by a modified Sand equation which includes the effect of physical property variation of diffusivity and ionic transference number with electrolyte composition. The time variation of cell voltage $\Delta\phi$ is also plotted. The rapid increase in electrode potential is illustrated as the limiting transport conditions are approached.

Fringe patterns near horizontal electrodes in the position of anode over cathode were also observed by several groups.[48,49]

11.3.2   Vertical Plane Electrodes in Stagnant Electrolyte

Following the original measurements of the concentration profile of Cu^{2+} ion by Ibl's group,[11-13] many researchers[50-53] engaged in similar measurements. A series of papers from Berkeley[20-25] opened the door for quantitative measurements at steep concentration gradients in the electrochemical mass transfer boundary layer.

Awakura and Kondo[29] measured the steady state concentration profile of Cu^{2+} ion under the same condition as Ibl's group using holographic interferometry. They also measured the velocity profiles of natural convection[54] and the local current density distribution.[55]

The transient concentration profiles of Cu^{2+} ion after initiation of copper electrodeposition were measured at Kyoto University.[56,57] This electrochemical pocess can be described by analogy to Gebhart's theory of the development of natural convection caused by heat transfer.[58] When the non-dimensional duration time given by

$$T = Dt/\bar{\delta}^2 \tag{11.9}$$

(where $\bar{\delta}$ is the boundary layer thickness averaged over cathode height) is less than 0.1, the ionic mass transfer rate can be described by the diffusion mechanism. Steady state

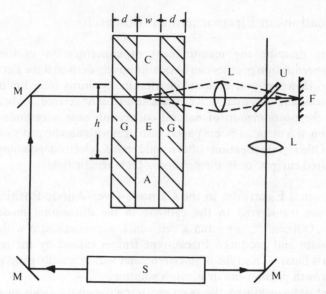

Fig. 11.10 Schematic diagram of interferometer and electrochemical cell (after McLarnon et al.[47]).
A: Copper anode, C: Copper cathode, E: 0.1 M CuSO$_4$ electrolyte, F: Film plane, G: Glass sidewalls, S: He–Ne laser, L: Lens (The test lens, focal length=87 mm, is 115 mm from the center of the cell. The focal length of the reference lens is 81 mm), U: Beam uniter, d=12.7 mm, h=2.54 mm, w=10 mm.

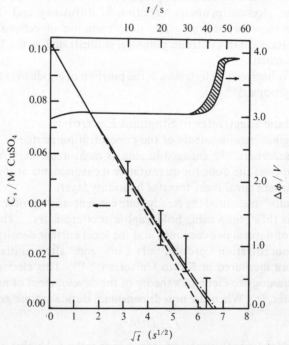

Fig. 11.11 Transient interfacial concentrations and cell voltage for horizontal electrode (i=10 mA/cm^2).

correlation equations are applicable for dimensionless times T greater than 0.4, as illustrated in Fig. 11.12.

When the direction of current density is reversed from cathodic to anodic,[57] an inflection point appears in the interference fringe pattern and downward anodic natural convection is initiated at the lower end of the electrode.   The anodic convection boundary layer grows upward with increasing time, and the remaining traces of the cathodic natural convetion boundary layer diminish.   This inverted flow of natural convection is observed experimentally.

Eklund *et al.*[59] and Alavyoon *et al.*[60] studied the stratification caused by the natural convection associated with electrodeposition of Cu^{2+} in $CuSO_4$ solution and that with the recharge and discharge cycling of the lead-acid battery.

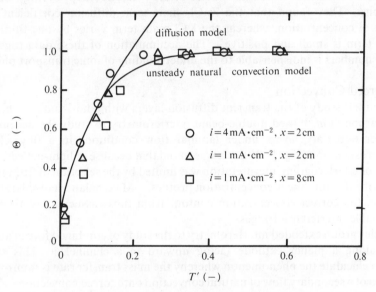

Fig. 11.12   Transient behavior of interfacial concentration of Cu^{2+} ion with development of unsteady natural convection along a vertical plane electrode.

11.3.3   Multicomponent Systems

Brenner[6] tried to measure the surface pH value along a cathode surface by a freezing method fifty years ago.   More recently, concentration profiles of aqueous nickel and cobalt chloride solutions have been measured during Ni–Co alloy deposition with microphotographic-colorimetry by Imanaga *et al.*[61,62]   Monochromatic wavelengths of 395 and 510 nm were selected spectrophotometrically, and horizontal electrodes in the cathode-over-anode position were used.   Current densities at which no evolution of hydrogen occurred were applied.

The refractive index change in $CuSO_4$–H_2SO_4 solution was measured by Tvarusko and Watkins[63] and Awakura *et al.*[64]   Matysik *et al.*[65] found that the interference pattern is significantly influenced by the diffusivity of supporting electrolyte and the dependence of refractive index on the concentration of each component.

Denpo *et. al.*[38] applied TWHI under galvanostatic conditions.   Based on similar measurements under potentiostatic electrolysis, the variation of surface overpotential with the total overpotential was compared to the same overpotential measured when the copper metal was electrodeposited from CuSO₄ solution.   It was found that the addition of excess amounts of H₂SO₄ significantly reduces the concentration overpotential and increases the surface overpotential.   The structure of the electrodeposited film was significantly changed.[66]

The importance of careful analysis of multicomponent diffusion cannot be over-emphasized.   The drastic simplifying assumptions made to facilitate analyses are frequently accepted owing to the almost universal absence of multicomponent diffusion data.   Miller et al.[67] measured the mutual diffusion coefficients for aqueous 0.5 M ZnCl₂ with KCl using a Rayleigh interferometer.   This electrolyte system corresponds to a fully charged zinc chlorine storage battery at various supporting electrolyte concentrations.   They found that the ZnCl₂ main-term diffusion coefficient is nearly independent of concentration, whereas the KCl main term varies by one-third and that ZnCl₂ cross term is small and positive.   The accumulation of these data together with transference numbers is indispensable to the understanding of ionic transport phenomena.

11.3.4   Forced Convection

Following their study of the transient diffusion layers with a horizontal cathode facing down, McLarnon et al.[68] used double-beam interferometry to study the development of mass transfer boundary layers under laminar flow conditions in a flow channel of rectangular cross section (Fig. 11.10).   It was found that because of light-deflection effects, the accuracy of interferogram interpretation was limited by the selection of fitting functions used to describe the non-linear concentration profiles.   Mass balance considerations were used to select the correct concentration contour from those associated with practically indistinguishable interference fringes.

The Berkeley group extended interferometry to the study of combined forced and natural convection along a planar cathode facing upward in a channel.[69]   This study was conducted to elucidate the phenomenon whereby the mass transfer rate is improved by the superposition of a secondary flow of natural convection onto forced convection.   The onset of natural convection effects occurred at a considerable distance downstream from the leading edge and was linked to the presence of a streaked deposit observed previously. This phenomenon was explained in terms of secondary laminar convective flows, i.e. roll cells.

The application of turbulent flow in electrochemical processes permits higher operating current densities.   McLarnon et al.[70] introduced flow obstacles into the electrolyte flow stream and employed interferometry to characterize this effect.   The effect of secondary flow induced by small flow obstacles at the cathode, indicated by a, b, c, d and e in Fig. 11.13(A), was compared to the effect of turbulent bulk flow produced by high electrolyte flow rates in an obstacle-free flow channel.   They recognized that the secondary flow induced by small flow obstacles significantly thins the local mass-transfer boundary layer only when the characteristic dimension of obstacles (the distance that the obstacles protrudes from the electrode surface into the electrolyte) is comparable to or exceeds the thickness of the local mass transfer boundary layer (Fig. 11.13(B)).

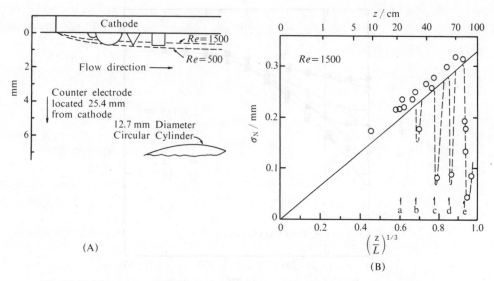

Fig. 11.13 Placement and size of obstacles in the flow channel (A) and Nernst boundary layer thickness at $Re = 1500$ (B).
The 0.28 mm semicircular cylinder is attached to the cathode surface at $z = 22$ cm, the 0.76 mm semicircular cylinder at 32 cm, 0.76 mm triangular parallelpiped at 47 cm, the 0.76 mm rectangular parallelpiped at 62 cm and the 12.7 mm diameter large circular cylinder is wedged between the two glass sidewalls at $z = 82$ cm.
Dotted line: Mass transfer boundary edge calculated as twice the Nernst boundary layer thickness

11.3.5   Pulsed Plating

The transient behavior of concentration profiles of Cu^{2+} ion under pulse plating at 0.1 to 50 Hz near a vertical plane copper cathode immersed in 0.05 M $CuSO_4$ solution was interferometrically measured (Fig. 11.14) at Kyoto University.[71,72]   The open symbols correspond to the concentration profile at the end of a pulse current period, whereas the hatched ones represent the start of each pulse period after quasi-steady state electrolysis is attained.   The duplex diffusion layer along a cathode in the quasi-steady state, which was conceptually proposed by Ibl in 1980,[73] was experimentally demonstrated by using an unusual pulse with a long period.   The concentration boundary layer thickness fluctuating in phase with the pulse current is roughly 100 micrometers thick, whereas the steady concentration boundary layer extends over 400 micrometers, as demonstrated in Fig. 11.14.   This research was followed by a study of silver electrodeposition from silver nitrate aqueous solution under pulsed current at a higher frequency of 5 to 500 Hz.[74]   By introducing the theory of ionic mass transfer rate associated with natural convection along a vertical plane cathode,[75] the important concept of a limiting current pulse was formulated.   The interaction between the nucleation caused by applied high overpotential and growth phenomena relating to the ionic mass transfer rate was also analyzed.

O'Brien and Santhanam[76] observed the interference fringe pattern associated with the galvanostatic deposition of polycarbazole by pulsing the current in the frequency range from 0.1 to 500 Hz.

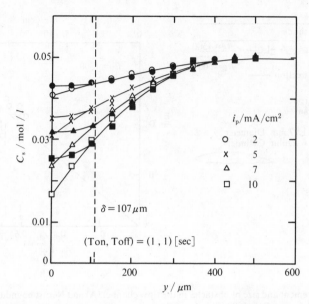

Fig. 11.14 Concentration profiles of Cu^{2+} ion under different pulsed current densities.

11.3.6 Effect of a Magnetic Field

The transient behavior of interference patterns during electrodeposition of copper from 0.1 M $CuSO_4$ solution was observed by O'Brien and Santhanam during a galvanostatic electrolysis in a magnetic field with variable strength of 0.1 to 0.6 T (tesla).   They observed that the enhancement of flow by a magnetic field is roughly proportional to the current density and the magnetic field strength.[77]   Also, the diffusion layer associated with electrodeposition of zinc from $ZnSO_4$ aqueous solution under the influence of magnetic field was observed.   The presence of a paramagnetic ion (Mn^{2+} or Cr^{2+}) in the electrolyte produced noticeable deviations in the concentration gradients.[78,79]

11.3.7 Organic Synthetic Materials

The electrochemical oxidation of Fe(II) in the presence of pyrrole, which is used to produce the conducting polypyrrole, was observed using laser interferometry by O'Brien and Santhanam.[80]   The growth of the diffusion layer during the electrodeposition of polypyrrole on a gold electrode in an acetonitrile bath containing 0.1 M $(C_4H_9)_4NClO_4$ and 60 mM freshly distilled pyrrole was also observed.[81]   They also studied the electrochemical oxidation of iodide, iodine, bromide and reduction of iodine and iodate in aqueous buffered solution at an electrodeposited polycarbazole electrode.[82]

11.3.8 Corrosion Phenomena and Anodic Dissolution

Cooper examined the anodic dissolution phenomena at Cu/HCl interface by the Schlieren method.[14]   Anodic dissolution of iron in sulfuric acid was observed by Knox *et al.* with holographic interferometry in 1967.[26]   O'Brien and Kolny observed interference patterns to evaluate the corrosion protection of epoxy primer and other coatings in the Zn/$ZnSO_4$/Zn system.[83]

Nakamura[84] studied the ionic mass transfer rate along a vertical plane copper anode immersed in $CuSO_4$–H_2SO_4 solution under the potentiostatic condition with TWHI.   He recognized that copper sulfate is precipitated at the anode when the Cu^{2+} concentration significantly exceeds its saturation value.

11.3.9   Measurement of Small Deformations of Electrodes

Pangarov and Kolarov[85] measured the small elastic deformation of a strip caused by a change in surface tension forces using holographic interferometry and obtained the electrocapillary curve of platinum in 0.05 M H_2SO_4 solution.   The measurement of strain in the film induced during the deposition process is of great practical importance.   Semiconductor electronic components are frequently connected with vapor-deposited alloy contact layers.   The interferometric technique was applied to measure the strain during electrodeposition of silver film applied as metallic heat sinks onto alloy contact layers by Begh *et al.*[86] and Read *et al.*[87]

The volume changes associated with the high-rate discharge of lithium/iodine batteries with pelletized cathodes has been measured by a holographic interferometry.[88,89]   This technique gives information on the changes in thickness of the hermetically sealed package, from which the uniformity of the volume change associated with high-rate discharge can be determined.   They found that the weight of polymer used in the cathode of lithium/iodine cells strongly influenced the volume change characteristics.[89]   *In-situ* laser interferometry at variable angles of incidence has also been used to determine the density of electrodeposited alpha- and beta- lead dioxide films as a function of plating current density.[90]

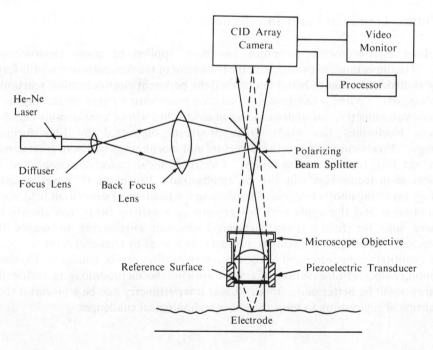

Fig. 11.15   Schematic diagram of a phase-detection interferometric microscope.

11.3.10   Topological Study of Surfaces

In order to investigate the leveling ability of electrolytic baths used in the bright plating processes, Nanev et al.[91] measured the refractive index profile in the electrolyte layer adjacent to a microprofiled cathode immersed in $CuSO_4$–H_2SO_4 solution.   They observed that the effect of the leveling additive on the diffusion coefficient of Cu^{2+} and the concentration boundary layer thickness are important characteristics of the electrochemical leveling mechanism,[92] which is contrary to the conclusion reached by others.   O'Brien and Saville[93] also tried to measure the two-dimensional refractive index profile formed near the edge of an electrode.

Kragt et al.[94,95] used phase-detection interferometric microscopy (Fig. 11.15), which was originally developed to measure the surface topography of lenses for photolithography[96] and magnetic tapes,[97] to obtain high-resolution surface images of a 100-micrometer diameter Fe disk exposed to 0.1 M H_2SO_4.   It was also applied to the in-situ measurement of Au electrode topography and variations in the refractive index of the solution during the oxidation of $K_4Fe(CN)_6$.[98]   This instrument, composed of a Fizeau interferometer attached beneath the objective of an optical microscope, is capable of measuring optical distances to within 4 nm with a horizontal resolution of 0.5 micrometer.   It detects the phase difference of laser light reflected from the test substrate relative to light reflected from an optical reference surface.[98]   The phase difference contains contributions from surface topography as well as variations in the refractive index of the solution surrounding the microelectrode.   This technique may also be applicable in identifying the electroactive sites on heterogeneous surfaces and fundamental studies of current and potential distribution around microelectrodes and microelectrode arrays.

11.4 Future Trends in Laser Interferometry

The laser interferometric technique has been applied to many electrochemical studies.   The importance of quantitative measurement of the concentration profile formed near the electrode in order to better understand the pertinent electrochemical reaction has been recognized.   When it can be combined with polarization curve measurements and with cyclic voltammetry, our understanding of electrodics will be considerably enriched.

Modern electronics has made great progress, supported by film formation technology.   Finely controlled surface structure and morphology will be in great demand, even in wet film formation technology.   Electrochemical processing associated with microfabrication technology will also be emphasized.   Furthermore, novel processing technology involving another degree of freedom in the reaction or deposition field, such as laser irradiation and the application of very strong magnetic fields, has already been introduced into the field of electrochemical reaction engineering to realize these requirements.   The required quality is, however, produced by trial-and-error.

If the quantitative measurement of concentration profiles can be conducted to relate to the phenomenological observation of crystal growth, the methodology to realize these requirements will be better understood.   Laser interferometry can be a powerful tool in electrochemical engineering to meet these new technological challenges.

ACKNOWLEDGMENTS

The authors wish to thank Profs. Y. Kondo, Y. Awakura (Kyoto University) and Dr. K. Denpo (Nippon Steel Corporation) for their valuable discussions.   Part of this work was carried out under the financial aid of The Institute of Space and Astronautical Science.

REFERENCES

1. W. Nernst, *Z. Phys. Chem.*, **47**, 52 (1904).
2. H. E. Haring and W. Blum, *Am. Electrochem. Soc.*, **43**, 313 (1923).
3. S. Glasstone, *J. Electrochem. Soc.*, **59**, 277 (1931).
4. A. G. Samarcev, *Z. Phys. Chem.*, **A168**, 45 (1934).
5. H. J. Read and A. K. Graham, *Trans. Electrochem. Soc.*, **78**, 279 (1940).
6. A. Brenner, *Proc. Am. Electroplaters' Soc.*, pp. 95–100 (1940).
7. C. Kasper, *Trans. Electrochem. Soc.*, **77**, 353; **78**, 131 (1940).
8. C. Wagner, *J. Electrochem. Soc.*, **95**, 161 (1949).
9. C. Wagner, *J. Electrochem. Soc.*, **98**, 116 (1951).
10. C. R. Wilke, M. Eisenberg, and C. W. Tobias, *J. Electrochem. Soc.*, **100**, 513 (1953).
11. N. Ibl, Y. Barrada and G. Trumpler, *Helvetica Chimica Acta*, **37**, 583 and 2251 (1954).
12. N. Ibl and R. H. Muller, *Z. Elektrochem.*, **59**, 671 (1955).
13. N. Ibl and R. H. Muller, *J. Electrochem. Soc.*, **6**, 346 (1958).
14. R. S. Cooper, *J. Electrochem. Soc.*, **105**, 506 (1958).
15. L. Stephenson and J. H. Bartlett, *J. Electrochem. Soc.*, **101**, 571 (1954).
16. W. R. Wolfe, N. Chessin, E. Yeager and F. Hovorka, *J. Electrochem. Soc.*, **105**, 590 (1954).
17. R. N. O'Brien and C. Rosenfield, *J. Phys. Chem.*, **67**, 643 (1963).
18. K. Asada, F. Hine, S. Yoshizawa and S. Okada, *J. Electrochem. Soc.*, **107**, 242 (1960).
19. A. Tvarusko and L. S. Watkins, *Electrochem. Acta*, **14**, 1109 (1969).
20. R. H. Muller, in: *Advances in Electrochemistry and Electrochemical Engineering*, vol.9, pp. 281–368, John Wiley & Sons Inc., New York, 1973.
21. K. W. Beach, R. H. Muller and C. W. Tobias, *J. Opt. Soc. Am.*, **63**, 559 (1973).
22. F. R. McLarnon, R. H. Muller and C. W. Tobias, *Appl. Optics*, **14**, 2468 (1975).
23. F. R. McLarnon, R. H. Muller and C. W. Tobias, *J. Electrochem. Soc.*, **122**, 59 (1975).
24. F. R. McLarnon, R. H. Muller and C. W. Tobias, *J. Opt. Soc. Am.*, **65**, 1011 (1975).
25. R. H. Muller, *Electrochim. Acta*, **22**, 951 (1977).
26. C. Knox, R. R. Sayano, E. T. Seo and H. P. Silverman, *J. Phys. Chem.*, **71**, 3102 (1967).
27. V. S. Srinivasan, in: *Advances in Electrochemistry and Electrochemical Engineering*, vol.9, p. 369–422, John Wiley & Sons Inc., New York, 1973.
28. M. Clifton and V. Sanchez, *Electrochim. Acta*, **24**, 445 (1979).
29. Y. Awakura and Y. Kondo, *J. Electrochem. Soc.*, **123**, 1184 (1976).
30. N. Ibl and U. Braun, *Chimica*, **21**, 395 (1967).
31. J. R. Selman and J. Newman, *J. Electrochem. Soc.*, **118**, 1070 (1971).
32. J. R. Selman and C. W. Tobias, *Advances in Chemical Engineering*, Vol. 10, pp. 211–318, Academic Press, New York, 1978.
33. Y. Fukunaka, K. Denpo, M. Iwata, K. Maruoka and Y. Kondo, *J. Electrochem. Soc.*, **130**, 2492 (1983).
34. K. Denpo, T. Okumura, Y. Fukunaka and Y. Kondo, *J. Electrochem. Soc.*, **132**, 1145 (1985).
35. J. Livingston, R. Morgan and R. H. Crist, *J. Am. Chem. Soc.*, **49**, 338 (1927).
36. M. Iwata, Masters thesis, Kyoto University, 1980.
37. M. Born and E. Wolf, *Principles of Optics*, 6th edition, p. 428, Pergamon Press, Oxford, 1980.
38. K. Denpo, Ph. D. dissertation, Kyoto University, 1983.
39. M. M. ElWakil and P. A. Ross, in: *Progress in Astronautics and Rocketry*, vol.2, p.265, Academic Press, New York, 1960.
40. F. Mayinger and W. Panknin, *Proc. 5th Int. Heat. Transfer Conf.*, Tokyo, 28–43 (1974).
41. F. Mayinger and W. Panknin, *J. Combust. Meas. Mod. Tech. Instrument*, 270 (1976).
42. H. Svenson, *Opt. Acta*, **1**, 25 (1954).
43. W. Hauf and U. Grigull, in: *Advances in Heat Transfer*, vol. 6, pp. 133–366, Academic Press, New York, 1970.
44. U. Grigull, *Int. J. Heat Mass Transfer*, **6**, 669 (1963).
45. R. N. O'Brien, *J. Electrochem. Soc.*, **111**, 1300 (1964) and **113**, 389 (1966).
46. W. F. Berg, *Proc. Roy. Soc.*, **A164**, 79, 1938.

47. F. R. McLarnon, R. H. Muller and C. W. Tobias, *Electrochim. Acta,* **21**, 101 (1976).
48. R. N. O'Brien, W. F. Yakymyshyn and J. Leja, *J. Electrochem. Soc.,* **110**, 820 (1963).
49. A. Abdelmassih and D. R. Sadoway, in: *Chloride Electrometallurgy* (ed. P.D.Parker), TMS/AIME, Warrendale, PA, 1982, pp. 43–57.
50. J. Auerbach, B. Gavish and S. Reich, *Nature,* **260**, 311 (1976).
51. R. N. O'Brien, *J. Electrochem. Soc.,* **122**, 589 (1972) and **124**, 96 (1974).
52. R. N. O'Brien, *Rev. Scient. Instrum.,* **35**, 803 (1964).
53. A. Eklund and R. N. O'Brien, *J. Electrochem. Soc.,* **138**, 2212 (1991).
54. Y. Awakura, K. Maruoka and Y. Kondo, *Denki Kagaku,* **4**, 207 (1977).
55. Y. Awakura, A. Ebata and Y. Kondo, *J. Electrochem. Soc.,* **126**, 23 (1979).
56. H. Urano and Y. Kondo, *Denki Kagaku,* **6**, 330 (1978).
57. Y. Fukunaka, T. Minegishi, N. Nishioka and Y. Kondo, *J. Electrochem. Soc.,* **128**, 1274 (1981).
58. Y. Fukunaka, K. Denpo, M. Iwata, K. Maruoka and Y. Kondo, *J. Electrochem. Soc.,* **130**, 2492 (1983).
59. A. Eklund, F. Alavyoon, D. Simonsson, R. I. Karlsson and F. H. Bark, *Electrochimica Acta,* **36**, 1345 (1991).
60. F. Alavyoon, Ph. D. dissertaion, The Royal Institute of Technology, Stockholm (1991).
61. H. Imanaga, K. Yoshino and H. Hattori, *Denki Kagaku,* **12**, 620 (1974).
62. H. Imanaga, K. Yoshino and H. Hattori, *Denki Kagaku,* **6**, 318 (1975).
63. A. Tvarusko and L. S. Watkins, *J. Electrochem. Soc.,* **118**, 580 (1971).
64. Y. Awakura, M. Okada and Y. Kondo, *J. Electrochem. Soc.,* **124**, 1050 (1977).
65. J. Matysik, J. Chmiel and A. Cieszczyk-Chmiel, *J. Electroanal. Chem.,* **195**, 39 (1985) and **200**, 375 (1986).
66. Y. Fukunaka, H. Doi and Y. Kondo, *J. Electrochem. Soc.,* **137**, 88 (1990).
67. D. G. Miller, A. W. Ting and J. A. Rard, *J. Electrochem. Soc.,* **135**, 896 (1988).
68. F. R. McLarnon, R. H. Muller and C. W. Tobias, *Ind. Eng. Chem. Fundam.,* **18**, 97 (1979).
69. F. R. McLarnon, R. H. Muller and C. W. Tobias, *J. Electrochem. Soc.,* **129**, 2201 (1982).
70. F. R. McLarnon, R. H. Muller and C. W. Tobias, *J. Electrochem. Soc.,* **132**, 1627 (1985).
71. M. Ogawa, Master's thesis, Kyoto University, 1985.
72. Y. Fukunaka and Y. Kondo, *Electrochim. Acta,* **26**, 1537 (1981).
73. N. Ibl, *Surf. Technol.,* **10**, 81 (1980).
74. Y. Fukunaka, T. Yamamoto and Y. Kondo, *Electrochim. Acta,* **34**, 1393 (1989).
75. Y. Fukunaka, T. Yamamoto and Y. Kondo, *J. Electrochem. Soc.,* **136**, 3278 (1989).
76. R. N. O'Brien and K. S. V. Santhanam, *J. Electrochem. Soc.,* **132**, 2613 (1985).
77. R. N. O'Brien and K. S. V. Santhanam, *J. Electrochem. Soc.,* **129**, 1266 (1982).
78. R. N. O'Brien and K. S. V. Santhanam, *Electrochim. Acta,* **12**, 1679 (1987).
79. R. N. O'Brien and K. S. V. Santhanam, *J. Appl. Electrochem.,* **20**, 427 and 781 (1990).
80. R. N. O'Brien and K. S. V. Santhanam, *Mol. Cryst. Liq. Cryst.,* **160**, 103 (1988).
81. R. N. O'Brien and K. S. V. Santhanam, *J. Electrochem. Soc.,* **130**, 1114 (1983).
82. R. N. O'Brien and K. S. V. Santhanam, *Electrochim. Acta,* **54**, 493 (1989).
83. R. N. O'Brien and H. Kolny, *Corrosion-Nace,* **34**, 262 and 354 (1978).
84. Y. Nakamura, Bachelor's thesis, Kyoto University, 1989.
85. N. Pangarov and G. Kolarov, *J. Electroanal. Chem.,* **91**, 281 (1978).
86. F. R. Begh, B. Scott, J. P. G. Farr, H. John, C. A. Loong and J. M. Keen, *J. Less-Common Metals,* **43**, 243 (1975).
87. A. G. Read, J. P. G. Farr and K. G. Sheppard, *Surf. Technol.,* **8**, 325 (1979).
88. L. C. Phillips, R. G. Kelly, J. W. Wagner and P. J. Moran, *J. Electrochem. Soc.,* **133**, 1 (1986).
89. C. C. Streinz, J. S. Steckenrider, J. W. Wagner and P. J. Moran, *J. Electrochem. Soc.,* **136**, 2811 (1989).
90. S. A. Campbell and L. M. Peter, *Electrochim. Acta,* **32**, 357 (1987).
91. CHR. Nanev, L. Mirkova, ST. Rashikov and R. Kaischev, *Electrodeposition Surf. Treat.,* **3**, 179 (1975).
92. CHR. Nanev, L. Mirkova, and K. Dicheva, *Surf. Coat. Technol.,* **34**, 483 (1988).
93. R. N. O'Brien and P. M. Saville, *J. Electrochem. Soc.,* **137**, 3797 (1990).
94. H. J. Kragt, D. J. Earl, J. D. Norton and H. S. White, *J. Electrochem. Soc.,* **136**, 1752 (1989).
95. J. F. Biegen and R. A. Smythe, *Proc. SPIE - Int. Soc. Opt. Eng.,* **897**, 207 (1988).
96. J. H. Bruning, D. R. Herriott, J. E. Gallagher, D. P. Rosenfeld, A. D. White and D. J. Brangaccio, *Appl. Optics,* **13**, 2693 (1974).
97. B. Bhushan, J. C. Wyant and C. L. Koliopoulos, *Appl. Optics,* **24**, 1489 (1985).
98. H. J. Kragt, C. P. Smith and H. S. White, *J. Electroanal. Chem.,* **278**, 403 (1990).

12

Photocurrent and Photopotential Transients of n- and p-GaAs and n- and p-InP

W. Plieth, G. Pfuhl and R. Matz*

Freie Universitaet Berlin, Takustrasse 3, 1000 Berlin 33 and
Siemens AG, München, Germany

12.1 Introduction

Photocurrent and photopotential transient measurements of n- and p-GaAs and n- and p-InP are described in this chapter. The decay of the photopotential follows a second order rate law. The potential dependence of the rate constant of the decay of the photopotential was determined and shows that the anodic shift of the onset of the photocurrent (with respect to the flatband potential) is caused by a large recombination rate in this potential region. A second result described in this chapter is the reversal of the photocurrent and its potential dependence. To explain this behavior a modified model of the band bending under high intensity laser illumination was suggested. Such a model should be considered when similar conditions of illumination are encountered, especially in the case of Raman spectroscopy.[1]

12.2 Experimentals

The experiments were carried out on polished single crystalline surfaces of (100) orientation. GaAs and InP crystallize in the cubic ZnS-structure.[2] The electrical data of the various wafers are summarized in Table 12.1.

The crystals were applied in squares, each having a surface area of $0.25 \ cm^2$ cleaved from a larger wafer. Back contact were made either by evaporation of gold or by use of an eutectic gallium-indium alloy. The ohmic nature of the back contacts was checked by the 4-point method. The electrodes were cleaned in an ultrasonic bath and generally pre-etched for 30 seconds in 2% bromine/methanol solution. After pre-etching, the electrodes were stored in tri-destilled water saturated with nitrogen.

The electrolyte was prepared from reagent grade chemicals using triply distilled water and was deaerated before insertion of the electrodes. A typical three-electrode electrochemical

TABLE 12.1 Properties of the semiconductor materials used in the investigation

	E_g/eV	Dopant	Carrier concentration $10^{18} \ cm^{-3}$	ε_r	$\rho/\Omega cm$
n-GaAs	1.42	Si	1.0	12.91	3×10^{-3}
p-GaAs	1.42	Zn	1.0	12.91	4×10^{-2}
n-InP	1.35	S	5.5–6.3	12.61	$(7.6–8.1) \times 10^{-4}$
p-InP	1.35	Zn	4.1–4.2	12.61	$(2.7–2.8) \times 10^{-2}$

cell was used for most of the experiments.   Reference electrodes were a mercury sulphate/ sulfuric acid electrode in acid electrolytes and a mercury oxide/sodium hydroxide electrode in alkaline electrolytes.   All potentials are given with reference to the normal hydrogen electrode.   A platinum electrode was used as the counter electrode.

12.2.1   Dark Current and Photocurrent Measurements

A potentiostat (Jaissle IMP 83) controlled by a computer (DEC, PDP 11/23) was used for the registration of the current-potential curves.   The potentiostat and the computer were connected by an analog-to-digital converter (Data Lock, PCI 6380 PMC).   All data were controlled by analog instruments.   For measurements of the capacitance and imped-ance, the lock-in amplifier technique was applied in an EG & G, a model 124 together with a 127; the modulation amplitude was 5 mV (RMS).   Potentioscans were also carried out, usually using a scan rate of 10 mV/s.

Photocurrent measurements were performed in two different illumination modes.   A 900 W plasma lamp combined with a monochromater (Zeiss grating monochromater, MB3) was used for wavelength dependence measurements.   When the quality of the light beam was important, this illumination system was substituted by a helium-neon laser ($\lambda = 633$ nm, 30 mW/cm^2).   Photocurrents could be measured continuously or with a chopper, com-bined with a lock-in amplifier.   The power of the light was controlled by a photometer (Photodyne, model 88XLC).

12.2.2   Photopotential- and Photocurrent-Transient Mearsurements

Photopotential- and photocurrent-transient measurements were carried out with an excimer laser (Lambda Physik, EMG 101), filled with XeCl and running at a wavelength of 308 nm, in combination with a dye-laser (Lambda Physik, FL 2000).   The photopulses were measured on a storage oscilloscope (Tektronix, model 7603) and averaged by adding typical 100 transients to a computer.

12.3   Dark Current and Photocurrent Measurements in the Visible Spectral Region

For comparison and orientation, the dark current and photocurrents of n-GaAs/p-GaAs and n-InP/p-InP in 0.05 and 0.1 mol/l H$_2$SO$_4$ are shown in Figs. 16.1–16.4.   The behavior of GaAs is well documented in the literature,[3-6] and the diagrams are in agreement with other findings.   The behavior of InP is not so well known.[7,8]   For n-InP, photoeffects are observed mainly in the anodic oxide layer region $E > 0.5$ V.   The anodic oxidation poten-tial is shifted only from 0.5 V to 0.4 V.   Similarly, the behavior of p-InP is remarkable, especially in the anodic region.   The photocurrent starts at approximately 0 V (similar to p-GaAs) but then develops "double peak" behavior with two pronounced maxima, espe-cially in the back scan of the potential.

The behavior of GaAs is usually interpreted by the band structure of the semiconductor.[3] Anodic or cathodic photocurrents are only observed in potential regions anodic of the flatband potential of n-GaAs (−0.8 V) or cathodic of the flatband potential of p-GaAs (0.6 V).   The photocurrent on n-GaAs does not occur immediately at the flatband potential, but the onset of the photocurrent is shifted to anodic potentials (−0.3 V).   This is also observed for the photocurrent on p-GaAs which is shifted from +0.6 V (E_{fb}) to

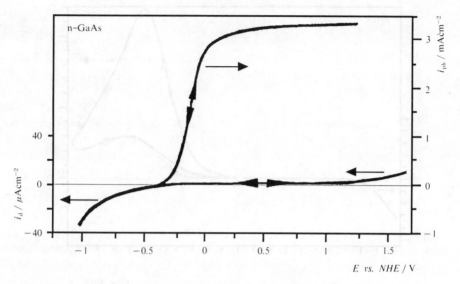

Fig. 12.1 Dark current-potential (i_d/E) and photocurrent-potential (i_{ph}/E) dependence of n-GaAs in 0.05 mol/l H_2SO_4; $\lambda = 632.8$ nm, $I = 30$ mW/cm²

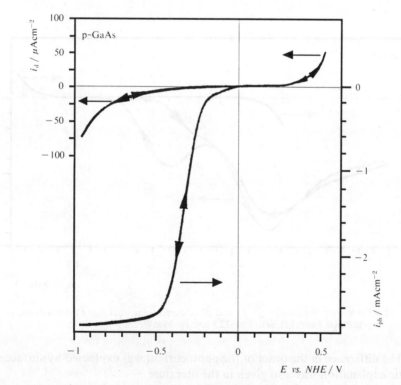

Fig. 12.2 Dark current-potential (i_d/E) and photocurrent-potential (i_{ph}/E) dependence of p-GaAs in 0.05 mol/l H_2SO_4; $\lambda = 632.8$ nm, $I = 30$ mW/cm².

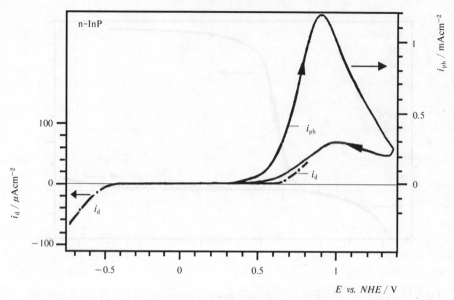

Fig. 12.3 Dark current-potential (i_d/E) and photocurrent-potential (i_{ph}/E) dependence of
n-InP in 0.1 mol/1 H_2SO_4; $\lambda = 632.8$ nm, $I = 30$ mW/cm^2.

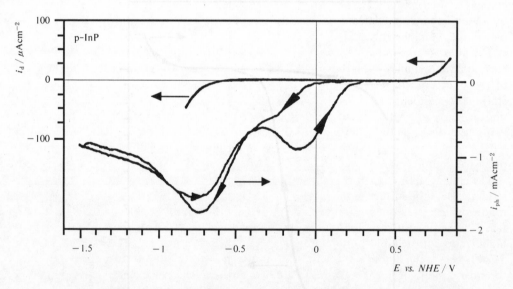

Fig. 12.4 Dark current-potential (i_d/E) and photocurrent-potential (i_{ph}/E) dependence of
p-InP in 0.1 mol/1 H_2SO_4; $\lambda = 632.8$ nm, $I = 30$ mW/cm^2.

−0.2 V.   The difference in the onset of the photocurrent was explained by surface states[9]
but a kinetic explanation was also given in the literature.[10]

The dark current of n- and p-InP can be explained (similar to GaAs) by the band structure
of the semiconductor with the flatband potentials of $E_{fb} = -0.4$ V for n- and $E_{fb} = +0.9$ V for

p-InP. However, the extreme shift of the onset of the photocurrent for n-InP from −0.4 V to +0.4 V was explained by a kinetic model assuming an oxide film on the surface blocking the photodissolution.[11,12] In the case of p-InP, the two-step reduction process may be connected with the reduction of the InP following the oxidation of water to hydrogen. The hydrogen evolution was recently described in the literature.[13,14]

12.4 Investigations in the Ultraviolet Spectral Region: Photocurrent and Photopotential Transients with Pulsed Lasers

In order to examine the kinetics after photoexcitation a pulsed excimer laser was used. The spectral region of these lasers is typically the ultraviolet, e.g. 308 nm with a XeCl gas filling. The pulse has a half width of 20 ns, typically.

12.4.1 Photocurrent Transients

Figs. 12.5 to 12.8 show the photocurrent transients after illumination with excimer laser pulses as a function of the potential. The photocharge/potential plots (Figs. 12.9 and 12.10) are obtained from these diagrams by integration.

Mostly anodic photocurrents are observed for n-GaAs and n-InP with the exception of n-InP at −0.4 V. The situaion for p-GaAs and p-InP is completely different, a pure cathodic photocurrent transient is observed only at the most cathodic potentials (−0.3 V for p-GaAs, −0.3 and 0.1 V for p-InP). With increasing anodic potentials the photocurrent changes from a cathodic into an anodic photocurrent, except in the case of p-GaAs whereby a pure anodic photocurrent transient is observed at +0.2 V while for p-InP, an almost constant cathodic part is achieved.

The photocharge potential plots (Figs. 12.9 and 12.10) differ from the stationary photocurrent potential ones. The onset of the photocharge for n-GaAs coincides with the onset of the photocurrent, but the photocharge for n-InP increases at a potential where the stationary photocurrent is still zero. For p-GaAs, one observes a linear change of the photocharge from cathodic to anodic values with no correlation to flatband potential. For p-InP the onset of the cathodic photocharge is shifted from the flatband potential to −0.2 V. The anodic photocharge increases anodically from the flatband potential but less intensive than for p-GaAs.

The change of the sign of the photocurrent transient may indicate a more complex band structure near the surface of the semiconductor than given by the simple space charge layer model which is frequently applied to describe the situation near cw-illuminated surfaces. The present situation is different for two reasons. Firstly, the optical energy is highly concentrated in short laser pulses. With an optical absorption coefficient of 5.7×10^5 cm^{-1}, the amount of 6×10^{22} photons/cm^3 is absorbed per laser pulse within the topmost atomic layers at 100 mJ/cm^2 (34% reflectivity). This strong excitation of electron-hole pairs is no longer covered by the independent electron approximation with a static band structure. Secondly, ultraviolet light has a weak penetration depth and excites electron-hole pairs with finite wave vectors well outside the center of the Brillouin zone. Therefore, holes, for example in p-material, are believed to reach the surface ballistically against the space charge electric field due to their initial kinetic energy.[5]

240

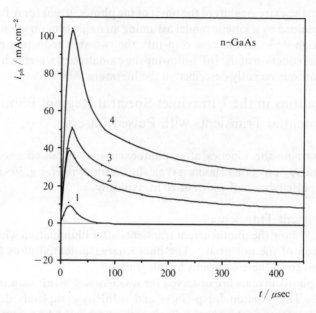

Fig. 12.5 Photocurrent transients (i_{ph}/t) of n-GaAs in 0.05 mol/1 H_2SO_4; excimer laser, $\lambda = 308$ nm, $I = 100$ mW/cm²; $E = -0.3$ V (1), $+0.3$ V (2), $+0.5$ V (3), $+0.7$ V (4).

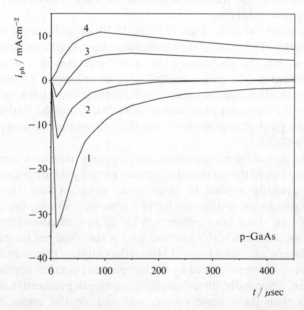

Fig. 12.6 Photocurrent transients (i_{ph}/t) of p-GaAs in 0.05 mol/1 H_2SO_4; excimer laser, $\lambda = 308$ nm, $I = 100$ mW/cm²; $E = -0.6$ V (1), -0.3 V (2), 0 V (3), $+0.2$ V (4).

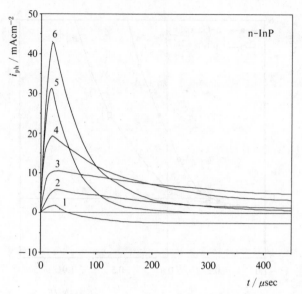

Fig. 12.7 Photocurrent transients (i_{ph}/t) of n-InP in 0.05 mol/1 H_2SO_4; excimer laser, $\lambda = 308$ nm, $I = 100$ mW/cm²; $E = -0.4$ V (1), -0.2 V (2), 0.0 V, (3), 0.2 V (4), 0.4 V (5), +0.6 V (6).

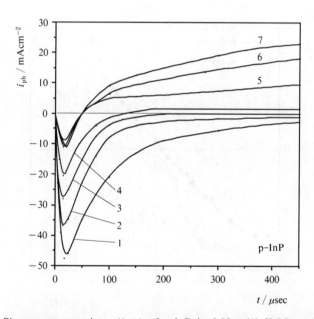

Fig. 12.8 Photocurrent transients (i_{ph}/t) of p-InP in 0.05 mol/1 H_2SO_4; excimer laser, $\lambda = 308$ nm, $I = 100$ mW/cm²; $E = -0.6$ V (1), -0.3 V (2), -0.1 V (3), +0.2 V, +0.65 (5), +1.0 (6), +1.5 (7).

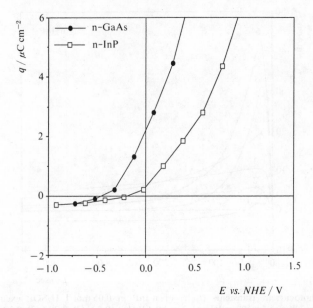

Fig. 12.9 Dependence of photocharge q of n-GaAs and n-InP on the potential E (integrated photocurrent transients of Figs. 12.5 and 12.7); 0.005 mol/l H_2SO_4; excimer laser, $\lambda = 308$ nm, $I = 100$ mW/cm².

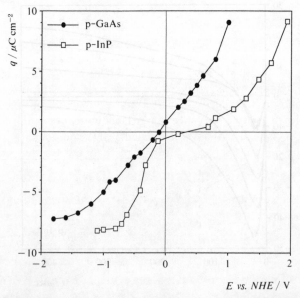

Fig. 12.10 Dependance of photocharge q of p-GaAs (1) and p-InP (2) on the potential E (integrated photocurrent transients of Figs. 12.6 and 12.8); 0.005 mol/l H_2SO_4; excimer laser, $\lambda = 308$ nm, $I = 100$ mW/cm².

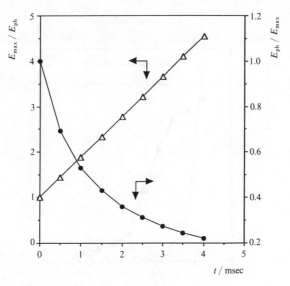

Fig. 12.11   Photopotential E_{ph} normalized with the maximum value E_{max} as a function of time; p-GaAs in 0.05 mol/1 H_2SO_4; excimer laser, $\lambda = 308$ nm.

12.4.2   Photopotential Transients

It is known that the decay of photopotentials of oxide films, observed with photopotential transient measurements with pulsed lasers, follows a second-order rate equation.[16]   The characteristic feature is the linear dependence of the reciprocal value of the photopotential on time.   Similar behavior was found for photopotential transients at GaAs and InP (Fig. 12.11).   The normalized reciprocal photopotential E_{max}/E_{ph} varies linearly with the illumination time (for ultraviolet wavelengths).   It is possible to formulate a law of time of second order for the kinetics of the recombination of the photogenerated electrons (e^-) and holes (h^+) within the space charge layer under open loop conditions.   The recombination rate constant k can then be calculated.   If the photocharge per unit area and the photopotential are designated by Q_{ph} and E_{ph}, respectively, the two are related by

$$Q_{ph} = CE_{ph}, \qquad (12.1)$$

i.e. C means a space charge capacitance per unit area.   The photopotential transients presented can then be described by assuming the following phenomenological decay law:

$$d[e^-]/dt = d[h^+]/dt = -k[e^-][h^+] \qquad (12.2)$$

$$\text{where } [e^-] = [h^+] = Q_{ph}/F \qquad (12.3)$$

meaning the number of photogenerated electrons and holes per unit area.   Integration of equation (12.2) after insertion of equations (12.1) and (12.3) and normalization of the photopotential with respect to its initial maximum E_{max} lead to

$$E_{max}/E_{ph} = 1 + kCE_{max}t/F. \qquad (12.4)$$

After obtaining C from the integrated photocurrent transients ($Q_{max} = CE_{max}$), relation

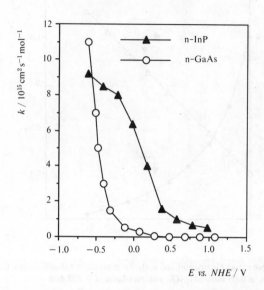

Fig. 12.12 Rate constant k of the recombination of photogenerated electrons (e⁻) and holes (h⁺) as a function of the potential E for n-GaAs and n-InP; 0.05 mol/1 H_2SO_4.

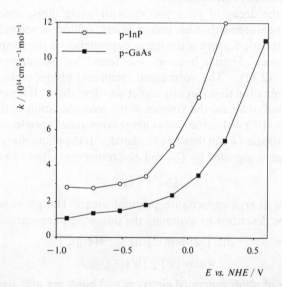

Fig. 12.13 Rate constant k of the recombination of photogenerated electrons (e⁻) and holes (h⁺) as a function of the potential E for n-GaAs and n-InP; 0.05 mol/1 H_2SO_4.

(12.4) permits the determination of the recombination rate constant from the slope in Fig. 12.11.

The recombination rate as a function of the potential is shown for n-GaAs and n-InP in Fig. 12.12 and for p-GaAs and p-InP in Fig. 12.13.   The recombination rate gives some explanation for the photocurrent/potential plots, shown in section 12.3.   For n-doped semiconductors, the recombination rate of n-GaAs is low for potentials anodic of −0.3 V and increases abruptly at more cathodic potentials.   This supports the recombination theory for the explanation of the gap between flatband potential and the beginning of the photocurrent at −0.35 V.   In the case of n-InP, the recombination rate increases at a much more positive potential ($E = 0.5$ V).   This supports the recombination theory in explaining the extreme shift of the onset of the photocurrent in the case of InP.

For p-InP, the potential dependence of the recombination rates changes its slope at approximately −0.3 V_{NHE}.   At the same potential the increase of the cathodic photocharge begins while the stationary photocurrent already starts at 0 V.

For p-GaAs, the recombination rate at cathodic potentials is still lower than for p-InP.   The increase in the slope of the potential dependence of the recombination rate begins at 0 V.   This coincides with the increase in the cathodic photopotential and with the behavior of the photocharge.

12.5   Discussion

The surprising behavior of the photocurrent pulses was in the reversal of the direction of the photocurrent especially for p-type GaAs and InP.   The motion of the different species in the space charge layer under illumination can be described as follows.   For n-III/V semiconductors, the photoholes move to the surface and oxidize the semiconductor if the potential is anodic of the decomposition potential.   No reversal of the current direction occurs.   For p-III/V semiconductors, the photoelectrons move to the surface, but if there are no reducible species in the electrolyte or if the potential is too anodic for the reduction of H^+-ions, no transfer into the electrolytic phase is possible.   Likewise, the reduction of Ga^{3+} or In^{3+} into the metallic state cannot occur because the potential is anodic of the reduction potential.   The photoelectrons remain in the surface area.   This leads to an increase in electron density at the surface and the build-up of a charge distribution with a tendency for reversal of the direction of the current.   A more detailed description of the potential distribution in the space charge region after illumination with laser pulses is given in Fig. 12.14[17]: a) describes the situation in the dark, b) the charge distribution after the laser pulse (schematic representation).   At high anodic potentials, the cathodic region of the photocurrent pulse should disappear as the electrode becomes quasi-metallic.   However, for p-InP, a cathodic current region is observed up to anodic potentials as high as +1.5 V.   This behavior may be explained by an oxide film changing the field gradient of the semiconductor in the surface region.

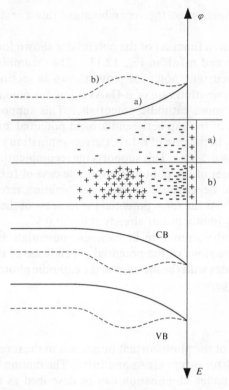

Fig. 12.14 Charge distribution in the space-charge layer of a p-type semiconductor after
illumination with a high intensity laser pulse (schematic description; the shift of the
flatband position under illumination has not been considered). a) space charge
layer in the dark, b) space charge layer after a laser pulse. Gradient of the electrical
potential: upper diagram; energy band bending of conduction band (CB) and
valence band (VB): lower diagram.

REFERENCES

1. W. Plieth, G. Pfuhl, A. Felske and W. Badawy, *Electrochimica Acta,* **34**, 1133 (1989).
2. S.M. Sze, *Phys. of Semicond. Dev.,* 2nd Ed. (1981).
3. W.A. Badawy, G. Pfuhl and W. Plieth, *J. Electrochem. Soc.,* **137**, 531 (1990).
4. R. Memming, *Prog. Surf. Sci.,* **17**, 37 (1984).
5. H. Gerischer, N. Muller and O. Haas, *J. Electroanal. Chem.,* **119**, 41 (1981).
6. W.H. Lafflere, F. Cardon and W.P. Gomes, *Surface Sci.,* **44**, 541 (1974).
7. A.A. Vervaet and W.P. Gomes, *J. Electroanal. Chem.,* **91**, 133 (1978).
8. S.Gröger, M. Handschuh and W. Lorenz, *J. Electroanal. Chem.,* **278**, 323 (1990).
9. J.J. Kelly and R. Memming, *J. Electrochem. Soc.,* **129**, 730 (1982).
10. M. Handschuh, W. Lorenz, C. Aegerter and T. Katterle, *J. Electroanal. Chem.,* **144**, 99 (1983).
11. A. Gagnaire, J. Joseph, A. Etcheberry and J. Goutron, *J. Electrochem. Soc.,* **132**, 1654 (1985).
12. D. Meisner, Ch. Sinn, R. Memming, P.H.L. Notten and J.J. Kelly, in: *Homogeneous and Heterogeneous
      Photocatalysis,* (E. Pelizetti and N. Serpone, eds.), D. Reidel, Dordrecht (1986), p. 317.
13. H.M. Kühne and J. Schefold, *Ber. Bunsenges. Phys. Chem.,* **92**, 1430 (1988).
14. J.M. Rosamil and B. Miller, *J. Electrochem. Soc.,* **135**, 1118 (1988).
15. D.V. Podlesnik, H.H. Gilgen and R.M. Osgood, *J. Appl. Phys. Lett.,* **45**, 563 (1984).
16. H.J. Rieger and W. Plieth, *Werkst. Korr.,* **39**, 603 (1988).
17. W. Plieth, *Ber. Bunsenges. Phys. Chem.,* in preparation.

13

Electrochemical Analysis of Electrode in Plasma and its Application

Satoshi ITO*, Haruo SHIMADA*[1], Wataru ITO*[2] and Muneyuki IMAFUKU*[1]

*   Steel Research Laboratories, Nippon Steel Corporation, 20-1 Shintomi, Futtsu, Chiba 299-12, Japan
*1 Advanced Materials & Technology Research Laboratories, Nippon Steel Corporation, 1618 Ida Nakahara-ku, Kawasaki 211, Japan
*2 Presently, Superconductivity Research Laboratories, 1-10-13 Shinonome, Kohtoh-ku, Tokyo 135, Japan

13.1 Introduction

Plasma processes such as plasma CVD, sputtering and ion plating have been widely used for fabricating semiconductor thin films and hard coatings. However, the reaction mechanism in plasma is not yet fully understood. This is particularly true for reactions occurring on the substrate surface.

In order to understand surface reaction, electrochemical concepts can be applied to the electrodes in processing plasma by the analogy of the one in aqueous solution as an electrode in conductive media. Very little systematic research on electrode reaction in plasma has been reported from this point of view. Some work employs techniques similar to those used in electrochemical reaction analysis in solution. Here we mainly review what we have investigated of the plasma process from the standpoint of electrochemistry together with related publications by a number of other authors.

First, an electrochemical analysis method was applied to the plasma system to discover whether the above idea would work, particularly with regard to oxygen behavior at the electrode surface. Second, oxidation of Cu metal electrode was investigated by plasma anodization from the analogy of the one in aqueous solution. Finally, the plasma oxidation phenomenon was applied to the fabrication of Yttorium Barium Copper Oxide (YBCO) superconducting thin film utilizing the multilayer technique.

3.1.1 Electrochemical Analysis of Electrode in Plasma[1]

Analogous to the electrochemical analysis of aqueous solution, plasma corresponds to the solution as the conductive medium. Plasma carries mainly cations, electrons and a few anions while solution has cations and anions. Electrodes immersed in solution act as a sort of Langmuir probe, or floating double probe usually used in plasma diagnostics.[2] However, electrochemical electrodes were generally considered *a priori* as a substrate for reactions such as oxidation, reduction, passivation or deposition, whereas probes are generally considered to be an electron conducting point for potential surveillance, free from reaction. Without any reaction product on the surface, the phenomenological potential-current relationship of probes in plasma strongly resembles the polarization curve in solution. Resarch on probe methods have been reported mainly in plasma of Ar, He or H_2, etc.,[3] very few in oxygen plasma,[4] particularly by the AC probe method. In contrast, AC impedance techniques have been used more and more for electrochemical reaction analysis of aqueous solution.[5] Therefore, AC impedance

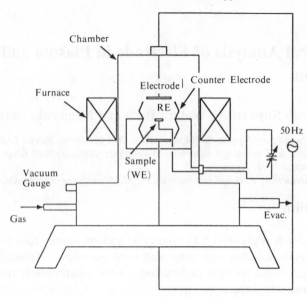

Fig. 13.1 Schematic drawing of experimental apparatus (vacuum chamber).

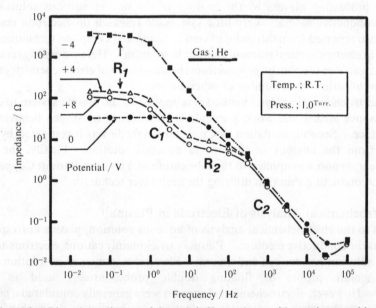

Fig. 13.2 AC impedance diagram of electrode in He gas plasma with negative to positive bias.

techniques were applied to analyze electrode surface reaction in plasma of He, He + H_2 and He + O_2 gas mixture.[1]

Experiments were conducted as follows. Platinum working electrode (WE), platinum counter electrode (CE) and reference electrode (RE) were installed in the usual electrochemical manner in the stable plasma area produced by the two other electrodes (normally excited by 50 Hz AC) in a Pyrex vacuum reactor, as shown in Fig. 13.1. The area ratio of CE to WE is comparably large in the different manner from probes used for the plasma analysis.   The infrared reflecting furnace surrounding the vacuum reactor was sometimes used when high temperature was necessary, as, for instance, in the case of YBCO film annealing with oxidation.

General procedure was as follows.   After the Pyrex reactor was evacuated to below 1×10^{-5} Torr using a turbo molecular pump, gases were introduced into the reactor through the mass flow controller at a given rate, keeping the rotary pump on.   Partial pressure of gases was measured using a Baratron.   An alternating current of 50 Hz was supplied between two discharge electrodes in the vacuum chamber at a power of 4 W to generate gas plasma.   A given direct current voltage was applied to the working electrode (sample) against reference electrode through a potentiostat as a bias voltage.

To investigate the characteristics of the electrode system, He gas, $He + H_2$ mixture gas and $He + O_2$ mixture gas were used with the total pressure 0.5–2.0 Torr.   Then electrochemical AC impedance was measured utilizing a potentiostat and a frequency response analyzer with a given bias voltage.

Typical resutls of He gas plasma are shown in Fig. 13.2, where positive or negative bias voltage referred to RE potential was applied to the WE.   The capacitive impedance at a frequency over 100 Hz remained almost unchanged irrespective of bias voltage, gas species, gas pressure and composition of gases.   With or without negative bias voltage, a resistance appeared at a frequency of 10 Hz or less.   This means that a pair of RC circuits connected parallel to each other can be fitted for the cases, although the values of the resistance were quite different respectively.   On the other hand, with positive bias voltage, two series of parallel connected RC circuits ($R_1 C_1$ and $R_2 C_2$) can be fitted.   This type of change with bias voltage in impedance diagram tended to be the same as that when $He + H_2$ mixture gas was utilized.   Generally speaking, electrons are repelled from a negatively biased electrode, making it difficult for electron current to flow into it.   In addition, cation transfer resistance which usually appears at much lower frequency than the measured range must be higher.   Therefore, R_1 may reflect the electron transfer resistance.   In contrast, a positively biased electrode attracts electrons not only to form an electron sheath, but also to facilitate ionization of neutral molecules at the electrode surface.   This resulted in the appearance of a larger capacitance C_1.   From this it can be said that the resistance R_2 represents the ionization reaction resistance of $He + e \rightarrow He^+ + e + e$ as, for instance, where electrons increase after the reaction.   Additionally, the capacitance C_2 will be the one between the electrode and the bulk region of the plasma because of no change by a variety of parameters.   These results can be depicted by an equivalent circuit across the interface, as shown in Fig. 13.3.

O_2 gas molecules can produce anion O_2^- and O^- [6,7] as well as cation O_2^+ often found in RF plasma.[8]   The introduction of O_2 molecules into He gas plasma makes the impedance diagram different from that of He and $He + H_2$ when the electrode is positively biased, as shown in Fig. 13.4.   That is to say, the capacitance C_1 did not appear clearly because of its small value and the resistance R_1 became much higher.   This is probably because oxygen anion such as O_2^-, O^- attracted to the electrode surface disturbs the formation of an electron sheath and moreover, retards electron transfer into the electrode.

As mentioned above, the plasma at the surface of the substrate can be analyzed by the electrochemical measurement method, considering the plasma and the substrate as a conductive medium and an electrode.

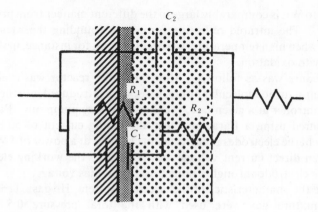

Fig. 13.3 A possible equivalent circuit at the interface between the electrode and plasma.

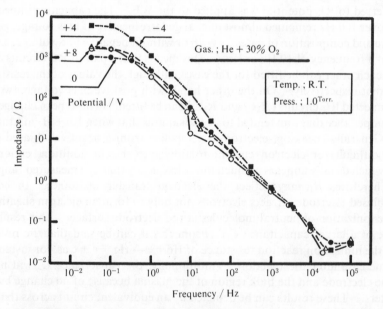

Fig. 13.4 AC impedance diagram of electrodes in He + O₂ gas plasma with bias voltage.

13.1.2   Plasma Oxidation under Bias Potential

A few reports on anodization in plasma have been published so far.   However, those dealt with mostly oxidation of Si.[9-11]   There is still debate regarding the presence of oxygen anions in the case of anodization.   Here, in order to understand and confirm the state of oxygen at the surface of the anodic electrode in a He + O₂ mixture gas plasma, the oxidation of Cu metal anode was investigated.   If the oxygen anion is present, Cu metal anode will react more readily to form Cu oxide under anodic bias voltage just as Cu anodization occurs in the electrolytic aqueous solution.

The vacuum chamber was heated to 450°C by the outer furnace in advance to facilitate

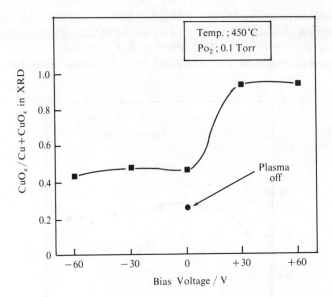

Fig. 13.5 Peak X-ray height ratio of Cu oxide formed under various bias voltages.

the reaction at the electrode surface.   The working electrode of 0.5 μm-thick Cu metal film made by sputtering on glass substrate was installed at the predetermined position in the chamber.   Then He + O₂ mixture gas was put into the chamber with plasma simultaneously.   Partial pressure of oxygen was varied from 0.1 to 0.3 Torr with a total pressure of 1.0 Torr.   After the Cu film electrode was exposed to plasma under bias voltage for 3 to 30 min, the chemical composition and the structure of the sample surface was investigated by X-ray diffraction and Auger analysis.

Peak height ratios of Cu oxide/(Cu metal + Cu oxide) by X-ray diffraction of the samples treated for 3 min are shown in Fig. 13.5.   The ratio of the Cu electrode surface exposed to the gas without plasma was about 0.2, indicating that some percentage of Cu metal was oxidized naturally in this medium.   On the other hand, with plasma, more of the Cu metal was oxidized, probably by surface bombardment of cations, anions or electrons.   Although negative bias voltage gives some activation to Cu metal oxidation, positive bias voltage exhibited much higher effect for oxidation, so-called anodization probably by oxygen anion bombardment.   With a bias higher than +30 V, anode surface was almost completely covered with the oxide, as shown in Fig. 13.5.   The compositional change of the oxidized Cu metal anode was analyzed along the depth by Auger analysis as shown in Fig. 13.6.   This shows that the O/Cu atomic ratio was around 0.5, meaning that mostly Cu₂O was formed under these conditions of plasma anodization.

From the results above, oxygen anions such as O₂⁻ and O⁻ anion may be formed to react with a metal surface to produce oxide much more effectively under positive bias than under negative bias voltage.

13.1.3 Application of Plasma Anodization of Cu to Fabrication of YBCO Superconducting Film[12]

Cu metal was found to be easily anodized particularly under positive bias voltage in

He + O_2 gas plasma as mentioned above.   This fact may be applied to fabrication of YBCO superconducting thin film, since the degree of oxidation of Cu in the perovskite structure of YBCO is essential for exhibiting superconducting characteristics.

YBCO superconducting film was fabricated by a two-stage procedure in which the

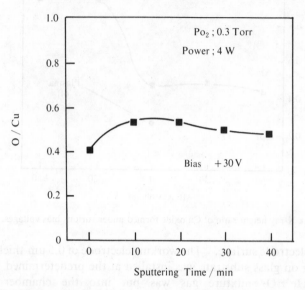

Fig. 13.6 O/Cu atomic ratio by Auger analysis along the depth of the oxide formed on the electrode surface.

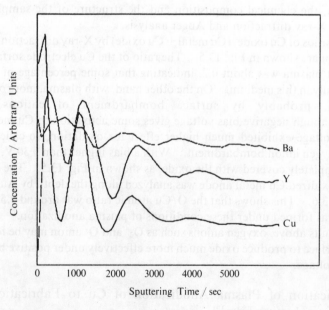

Fig. 13.7 Depth profile of the first five periods of the multilayered films from the top surface measured by SIMS.

preparation of multilayered film[13] from the starting material was followed by subsequent plasma anodization of Cu at the annealing temperatures.   Twenty layers of the unit multilayer structure Cu(177A)/Y$_2$O$_3$(170A)/Ba(625A) were deposited to about 2 μm thickness on the MgO single crystal substrate by the vacuum evaporation method.   This structure was used here since the simple calculation based on the assumption that each component has its own bulk density indicates the average stoichiometric composition of YBa$_2$Cu$_3$O$_{7-x}$.   The periodic structure of the obtained mutilayered films was examined by SIMS analysis.   Fig. 13.7 shows the depth profile of the first five periods of the multi-layered film from the top surface.   It can be seen that Y and Cu keep their periodic structure, but Ba was likely to diffuse into the other layers to some extent.

These multilayered films were transferred into the He + O$_2$ plasma processing chamber described above.   Plasma oxidation treatment, particularly of Cu, was carried out under a partial pressure of 1.9 Torr He and 1.0 Torr O$_2$, respectively, with the bias voltage −150 V to 150 V.   During the processing, the chamber was heated for simultaneous annealing to obtain an atomic rearrangement of the film to produce YBCO composition with the typical heat pattern as follows: heated up to 840°C at a rate of 7°C / min from room temperature, and after being kept at 840°C for 5 min, cooled down to room temperature at a rate of 100°C/h.

YBCO crystal structure usually has an orthorhombic structure where the C axis varies easily by the oxygen content.   In other words, the more it is oxidized, the shorter the C axis is.   Fig. 13.8 shows the effect of bias potential applied to the multilayered substrate on the lattice constant of the C axis of the fabricated YBCO crystals.   The positive bias potential gave the shorter C axis, meaning that the oxidation of Cu may be fully carried out under this bias potential.

The effect of the bias voltage on Tc was then measured as shown in Fig. 13.9.

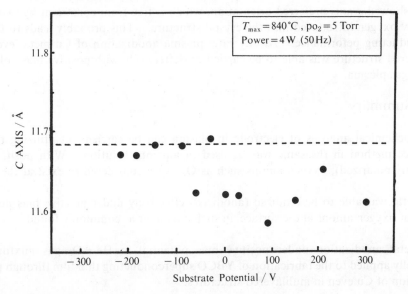

Fig. 13.8. The lattice constant of the C axis of YBCO crystal after oxidation treatment under various bias potentials.

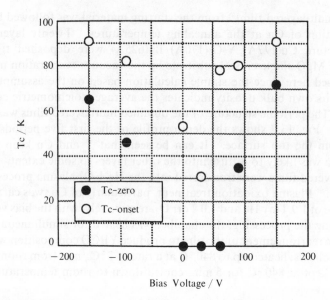

Fig. 13.9 Effect of the bias voltage in the plasma oxidation of YBCO material on *Tc*.

Superconducting thin films could not be obtained when the multilayered films were oxidized without plasma or in the plasma without any significant bias voltage. However, superconducting thin films could be successfully obtained not only under positive bias, but also under negative bias. Even though positively biased samples exhibited a more oxidized state, it had *a*- or *b*-axis preferred orientation, making it likely to be difficult to obtain a uniform crystal structure. On the contrary, negatively biased samples showed *c*-axis preferred orientation, which is free from constraint by expansion caused by oxygen introduced into the crystal structure. This probably leads to high *Tc* superconducting peformance. At any rate, plasma anodization of Cu metal even in a multilayered structure was able to be carried out effectively with positive bias voltage in He + O₂ gas plasma.

13.2   Summary

Electrochemical analysis of electrode in plasma can be carried out utilizing the AC impedance method in the same way as used in aqueous solution. With positive bias (anodically polarized), oxygen anions such as O_2^- were considered to exist at the anode surface.

Cu metal was able to be oxidized (anodized) effectively under positive bias potential because of oxygen anions at the surface, in such a manner as commonly found in aqueous solution.

Cu metal anodization under positive bias potential in He + O₂ gas mixture was successfully applied to the fabrication of YBCO superconducting thin film through plasma anodization of Cu even in mulilayered structures.

REFERENCES

1. H. Shimada and S. Ito, Proc. 56th Electrochem. Soc., Japan 1B31 (1989).
2. F.F. Chen, *Plasma Diagnostic Techniques*, Academic Press, NY, 1965.
3. J.L. Wilson, *J. Vac, Sci. Technol. A*, **7**, 972 (1989).
4. A. von Engel, *Electric Plasmas; Their Nature and Uses*, Taylor and Francis Inc., NY, 1983.
5. F. Mansfeld, *J. Electrochem. Soc.*, **36**, 301 (1981).
6. M. Bacal and H.J. Doucet, *Vacuum*, **24**, 5951 (1974).
7. J.B. Thompson, *Proc. Roy. Soc.*, **A262**, 503 (1961).
8. T. Sugano and Y. Mori, *J. Electrochem. Soc.*, **121**, 113 (1974).
9. J.R. Ligenza, *J. Appl. Phys.*, **36**, 2703 (1965).
10. J. Kraitchman, *J. Appl. Phys.*, **38**, 4323, (1967)
11. V. Qui Ho and T. Sugano, *Jpn. J. Appl. Phys.*, **19**, Suppl.19-1, 103 (1980).
12. W. Ito, H. Shimada and S. Ito, *Jpn. J. Appl. Phys.*, **29**, 2203 (1990).
13. C.X. Qui and I. Shin, *Appl. Phys. Lett.*, **52**, 587 (1988).

Index